FOUR DECADES
IN
Genesis

FR. THOMAS MATT

Fulton Books, Inc.
Meadville, PA

First originally published by Fulton Books 2017

ISBN 978-1-63338-403-3 (Paperback)
ISBN 978-1-63338-404-0 (Digital)

Printed in the United States of America

PART I

1967

CHAPTER 1

I was fifteen years old, in the throes of innocence, scooping ice cream at Baskin Robbins. Quickly, I became intimate with all thirty-one flavors. Not ingesting them all, mind you, but wearing them all on my sleeves.

I was in love with my coworker, the first love of my life. Maybe I didn't know what love was, but I called it "love" because I was experiencing physical discomforts that demanded explanation. I was constantly woozy and suffered some form of primordial fear that manifested itself verbally as stammers. Prior to love, I could speak. Not eloquently, but at least in complete sentences. Now I was seemingly incapable of mixing nouns, adjectives, and verbs into coherent statements. Her hair was sixteen and she was blonde years old. See what I mean? But what can you expect from a soon-to-be sophomore at a Jesuit prep school? She was gorgeous beyond belief, at least to a shy Catholic boy from a family of twelve children. My parents were strict adherents to the teachings of the church, especially regarding birth control. They were practitioners of the rhythm method. This method produced children with the predictable cadence of a metronome, resulting in a thundering herd of kids of which I'm the oldest son.

I was in love with Peggy. I wanted her to know. But I was scared shitless she'd find out. I guess it was the dilemma of my age. There's no life experience to fall back on. Prior to this, I was lost in sports, childhood chums, movies, and books. There was school, church, and everyday family life. Each was filled with routine, mundane activities which were ritualized and therefore easy to practice. Love was like living in a new dimension, qualitatively and quantitatively unique, scary, and intriguing.

Oh, I had seen the visible signs of love since childhood. Every Saturday matinee included at least one make-out scene. I was thoroughly disgusted, although now I don't know why. All of a sudden, and without any warning, girls (excepting only the most hideous physical specimens) have become objects of adoration. Disgust is gone. Not only do I want to kiss them, my hands, which apparently grew brains of their own last week, want to grope and touch them. I want to touch it all—their face, breasts, legs, and, especially, their underwear. Bras and panties are extremely titillating, and just the thought of either produces an immediate and sometimes embarrassing physical response. That's the catch for me. The mere thought of any significant part of a girl's anatomy (and I can't think of any insignificant parts), or of the things which are actually in contact with those parts, does the trick. I tested this response mechanism quite often while safely tucked under the desk in Fr. Sherman's freshman religion class. Sure enough, my uniform pants bulged at the zipper on every mental cue.

Amazing transformation, this love business. Who could ever prepare us for this reality? The Catholic church offers the old Jesuit approach but it comes out as clinical and antiseptic. Sexual intercourse and having an appendix surgically removed sounded remarkably similar. Obviously, my father can't help. He seemed just as befuddled with it as I was. What in the world does a father tell his kid to forewarn him of this coming? Timing is everything, and by the time a man is a father, he seems to have forgotten the suddenness and utter unpredictability of the transformation. One night, a boy falls asleep sorting out baseball cards, and the next morning, he wakes up with a raging hard-on. Girls, who yesterday were nuisances and pests, are today some kind of incredible intoxicant. Go figure.

I tried to speak to Peggy, but she's a light-year ahead of me. When you're my age, one year is a mind-boggling chasm to leap. I was about to begin my sophomore year in high school and she's going into her junior year. She's a promising cheerleader. I can't make the scout team. She has a driver's license. I have a learner's permit. She's been on dates. I can't date until next year. When the enormity of all these factors converged in my brain, I felt impotent. Being in this state makes me feel like Adam in the garden of Eden. After his snake got the better of him, he tried to slither out of God's view. I slithered back to the freezer and grabbed another tub of chocolate mint.

It was really no use fantasizing about Peggy. I didn't stand a chance. But then, as I came from the freezer and turned the corner, there she was, bending into the cooler to wrestle a scoop. The sight reinvigorated me and demanded that I stay in the ring and keep throwing punches. Why the hell not? She's killing me, anyway. While she was killing me, she intermittently spurred me on. The store was crowded and we flew from one cooler to the next attempting to fulfill our patrons' demands for a cool summer treat. The public we served could not make up their minds. I learned that four flavors of ice cream are the maximum a human brain can comprehend. Thirty-one simply produced paralysis of decisiveness.

As Peggy and I zigged and zagged along the narrow aisle behind the coolers, our bodies occasionally touched. Not collisions, mostly just brushes. A skimming of fabric upon fabric, exposed skin upon skin. She always looks unaffected when this occurred. Why is that with girls? Did they lack some essential wiring? When my body touched hers, all my circuits lit up and I craved for more. I got lucky, and my shoulder accidentally nudged her left breast. I was ecstatic and prayed to the saints for continued divine intervention. I only wish I could go around the counter and take a number like one of our customers. When Peggy shouts out the number I'm holding, I'll order her delicious breasts to go. "No, I don't need a cup or spoon, thank you. I'll just hold and fondle."

God, I'm going to hell with thoughts like these. Fr. Sherman warned us about craven images that bordered on the profane. He predicted that some of us would experience a twinge of sin that very summer.

"Peggy, ah…are you going home tonight? I mean…I know you're…ah…going home. I mean…ah…right after we close?"

"Yeah. Need a ride?"

"Oh, yeah…that…would be…ah…great."

Good God! This is it. This is how simply and quickly God performs miracles. A life is transformed in seconds. I have just obtained a ride in the love of my life's car. In an hour and a half, I would be breaking new territory on a landscape I was once convinced existed only in my dreams. Being in love apparently produces not only speech impediments and balloon pants, but also an amazing amount of adrenaline. It was now pumping into my system and overloading all the circuits. My customers were getting benefits in the forms of fast service and gargantuan scoops, but who cared about profit margins on a magical night like this?

When the owners locked the door, Peggy and I walked side by side to her car. I felt grown up. Sure, I was still a stammering, immature high school kid, but now there was a girl—no a woman, by my side. A bright, vibrant, voluptuous female who was older and more beautiful than I could imagine. She strolled with confidence and reached in her handbag for the keys. She gave her blue jeans and white cotton blouse justification for their very existence. They fit her body with grace and flair.

Her hair was golden blond and hung to her shoulders. Working with ice cream required wearing a hair net (an ordinance adopted no doubt by withered old men whose wives sport steel-wool hair). It did nothing to impair her beauty. She was slender, with perfectly sculpted hips dividing her five-and-a-half-foot frame. From my vantage point, Peggy possessed all the physical features that make men drool. Keeping my daytime saliva and nighttime emissions in check was a constant battle.

Her eyes were chestnut, and they melt my heart as she glanced in my direction. Fr. Sherman told us something about eyes being mirrors of the soul. It came up when we studied the writings of St. Augustine. Whatever old Augustine meant by this statement disappeared a nanosecond after the exam, but these eyes will never be forgotten. Ever. As she unlocked my door, I began to sense, without yet understanding, just why relationships are critical for human beings. Just being with her felt so, I didn't know, right, I guessed. This was a new emotion and I allowed it to flow freely within me. One taste of it was deliciously addictive. St. Augustine, I decided, must have been talking about something else entirely. The church would simply never sanction the way I felt. In spite of the church, I climbed into her car.

Volkswagen Beetles are built, I think, for the young. To me, the seating arrangement was comfortable yet intimately close. Sometimes being a teenager has its merits. We drove down Pacific Street and talked about the trivial issues of our lives.

"So what's it like having eleven brothers and sisters?"

"Noisy. And…no privacy."

"Well, this may sound crazy to you, but I'm envious. Being an only child is the complete opposite. Believe me, privacy and quiet have their drawbacks too."

"I guess so, but there are times…when it would be a welcome change."

"I think it'd be a blast having so many brothers and sisters."

"Yeah, well you'd love it till the first time you needed to…ah… use…you know…the bathroom. Then…believe me…you'd want out. Bathroom time is sacred in our house."

"God, I can't even imagine. It must be a zoo in the morning."

"Ah…it is."

"How do your parent's handle it? My mother is always telling me how much work I am. Your mother must be amazing."

"Mom…she's something. I don't have a clue how she does it. Dad…he's easier to figure. He gets out of the house as early as he can and works as long as he can. Guess he doesn't have the patience Mom has."

"Does your mom have maids to help cook and clean?"

"No, um, Dad's offered, but Mom says no."

"The older kids must help a lot. What stuff do you do?"

"The toughest job I ever had was in eighth grade. Mom made me move down to the nursery and take care of my baby sister."

"How old was she?"

"Just home from the hospital. She…was only days old."

"Wow. What did you do?"

"Everything…diapers, formula out of the bottle, burp—all of it."

"That's incredible. I love it."

"Well…sometimes it was great, but the hours sucked. She woke up at two or three in the morning. You get sick of that pretty quick."

"Yeah, but someday you'll be a great dad because of it."

For some reason, that last sentence caused me to blush, although she didn't seem to notice. As we pulled into my driveway, I wanted to tell her to just keep driving, the distance had been covered way too fast. I was beginning to get a little addicted to the discomfort I felt in her presence. Peggy spotted the swimming pool in our backyard.

"You have a swimming pool!"

"Yeah…it was put in when my parents built the house."

"Wow! Sometime you have to invite me for a swim."

"Sure…I …ah …definitely will. Uh…do you want to see it?"

"We won't disturb anyone at this hour, will we?"

This last was uttered with direct eye contact and, again I felt the blood rising to my face. Again, she seemed not to notice. Maybe moonlight didn't reflect well off pink.

As I guided her around the pool, I told her stupid and arcane swimming pool information. You know, junk about the board, the slide, the heater, and the lights. I could tell she really didn't care, but I kept right on talking because I didn't know what else to say, and she seemed content just to stare at the blue water. I sensed I was missing a moment there and I started to panic a little. My anxiety came out as more and more pool architecture. God, I couldn't stop. I was telling her about the difference between concrete pools and cinder block ones with vinyl liners. If someone didn't stop me, I was actually going to show her a bag of fungicide.

Peggy had heard enough and said she had to get home. I walked her to her car and thanked her for the ride. As she backed out of

10

the driveway, I knew I had botched it. Masterful in the beginning, clumsy in the middle, and god-awful in the end. God, why aren't there reference books you can buy to teach you the art and finesse of moments like these? My response to every new challenge seemed the same—plow ahead with the agility and subtlety of a bulldozer and hope for the best. I can only hope for another chance.

As I sulked through the garage door into the house, I was struck by how thoroughly my life had recently changed. Only months ago, I was a child growing up in a small Iowa town, bonded to boyhood friends playing baseball, sandlot football and golf. There were no real worries or cares to distract me, nothing earth-shattering to grab my attention. In other words, I was perfectly happy and content. Then, with no warning, my father uprooted my family from the quiet confines of Carroll, Iowa, and moved us to Omaha, Nebraska. I was simply bewildered by Omaha and scared. My father said that bigger cities had more business opportunities and more major attractions.

Peggy was my unchallenged no. 1 attraction then. I guess it will just take some time before I know how to act in her presence. After all, I just stepped out of my first experience with her alone. God, I hope she finds me half as interesting as I find her. At least she sounded intrigued by the size of my family and the fact we have a pool. The swimming pool could be the scene of future adventures, I was sure of that much. How to orchestrate getting the two of us in it remained a mystery.

Reality jumped up and bit me right between the eyes. My god, she only gave me a ride home. Here I am fantasizing about being in a relationship. The jump from a simple act of kindness to an involved courtship defied logic. It bordered on a quantum leap. Hell, maybe she's dating somebody else, and tonight was a simple work of mercy. Maybe she just decided on the spur of the moment to give a poor schmuck a ride home. She knew I normally walked home, and she never offered before. Oh shit, reality sucks. I went to bed wracking my brain for any hint she may have given about another boy in her life. I couldn't think of one, so my depressed state began to lift. I turned to the only resource I could think of.

"God, I have a small request for you. Could I please have another chance with Peggy? I will pay more attention in religion class. Thank you. Good night."

Yes, I really did believe that prayers illumine the heavens and resound through the celestial court. I knew a lot of older people didn't believe that, but I did and I always will. I fell asleep confident that God had heard my prayer.

Sure enough, my invitation came the very next evening. For the ride home, we pilfered two root-beer floats from work. Peggy suggested we stop and enjoy them on the grassy knoll overlooking Westside High School's football field. I felt a little guilty for the petty theft because clearly this moment was divinely granted, but it was short-lived. On a hot and humid evening, we engaged in conversation while I desperately prayed for the wisdom I so clearly lacked the night before.

"Tom, you know, for a buck an hour we sure dish out a lot of ice cream."

"Yeah…I wish they wouldn't keep the freezers so cold. The stuff is rock hard."

I immediately regret the term "rock hard." Peggy seems oblivious to the irony.

"You're forgetting something."

"What?"

"We're peons, high school kids desperate to make a few bucks. We'll put up with anything. Working conditions are not negotiable for kids our age."

"So…we got root-beer floats to even the score."

"Silly not to."

"I like when you say that…I never heard it before you. Where did you hear it?"

"I don't remember. I've been using it for years, and I forgot where it came from."

"Stay with it…it fits you."

"Thanks. So what's it like going to an all boy's school?"

"Well…it's a bit strange in some ways."

"In what way?"

"We don't compete to impress girls...obviously. We just try to fit in."

"God, it would be great not to have to spend all the time I do trying to get the right look. I make a pledge every night to stop this nonsense of looking right. But in the end, I always get sucked in. It would be nice to sometime say what the heck, I don't care."

"Peggy...I bet you look great without any effort."

"Wow. That's...so...nice. You...ah...kind of floored me with that...I don't know what to say."

"Well...it's the truth."

"So...you've never been on a date."

"I don't have a driver's license...just a permit."

"Gosh, I'm sorry. I keep forgetting you're fifteen."

"That really sounds awful...doesn't it?"

"No. Your birthday is in November, right?"

"Yeah."

"Mine's in March. I'm only what...eight months older. What's eight months? It's no big deal. I don't care."

"You've been on dates...ah, haven't you?"

"A couple times."

"Guys from Burke High?"

"Two guys. Just two."

"Sorry. I didn't mean it...any other way."

"Oh, I know you didn't. One guy was okay, but he never called back. The other one was a jerk and guess what?"

"Did he call again?"

"You got it."

"If the other guy...ah...called back...you know, would you—"

"Go out with him?"

"Yeah."

"Depends."

"On....what?"

"Oh....I'm not telling just yet."

"Okay...fair enough. I was hoping you weren't going to say you're...famous line."

"Which one, 'Silly not to' ?"

"Yeah, that one."

"Nope. I didn't use it, did I?"

We continued to talk and laugh about the adventures in our lives. None of them were heroic or newsworthy. They were just typical adolescent experiences. Some were products of the job we shared while others were from school. It is reassuring because it provided a link with each other. My greatest unspoken fear was being alone. I could sense it scared her just as much as me. My eyes were locked on the beauty of this girl beside me. From my point of view, there were no flaws or shortcomings. I could only see beauty.

*****

Fr. Sherman guided us freshmen through the book of Genesis in the Bible. It was the first book, and I fell in love with it from the first chapter. We used St. Augustine's book *The City of God* as a commentary to Genesis. Fr. Sherman said it was an exegesis. No one in class had any idea what that meant until he told us that it was a critical explanation or analysis of a text. *The City of God* would make the book of Genesis come alive in our lives. I bought into this hook, line, and sinker.

In the Genesis account of Adam and Eve, before the fall, they looked at each other and saw only the work of art God had sculpted. Adam wasn't taking mental notes about the shape of Eve's legs or the size of her breasts, and Eve didn't shoot critical glances toward Adam's nose or gut. "God created man in the image of himself, in the image of God he created him, male and female he created them" (Gen. 1:27). In other words, they were comfortable being human, delighted to share in each other. All good relationships begin like the Genesis story. Being enthralled in the beauty of another is the starting point. It's also kind of nice that the story was set in a garden. Enthrallment deserves an elegant setting. Who knows, the original garden may have looked a lot like a grass-covered hillside on a beautiful early-summer evening.

The fall from grace changed Adam and Eve's perspective. They looked at themselves and each other and were alarmed. For the first time since creation, humans felt less than, not whole, and insignif-icant. They felt the need to be "fixed" because shame had entered their lives. Unfortunately, they had no idea how to fix themselves. Cosmetic surgery, dermatology, psychiatry, designer clothing, and a host of other disciplines and trades all trace their beginnings to that first bite of fruit.

> Now the snake was the most subtle of all the wild animals that Yahweh God had made. It asked the woman, "Did God really say you were not to eat from any of the trees in the Garden?" The woman answered the snake, "We may eat the fruit of the trees in the Garden. But the fruit of the tree in the middle of the Garden God said, 'You must not eat it, nor touch it, under the pain of death.'" Then the snake said to the woman, "No, You will not die! God knows in fact that the day you eat it your eyes will be opened and you will be like gods, knowing good from evil." The woman saw that the tree was good to eat and pleasing to the eye, and that it was enticing for the wisdom that it could give. So she took some of its fruit and ate it. She also gave some to her husband who was with her, and he ate it. Then the eyes of both of them were opened and they realized that they were naked. So they sewed fig-leaves together to make themselves loincloths. (Gen. 3:1–7)

Eventually, most relationships acknowledge the fall from grace. Given enough time, the saga of Adam and Eve too often becomes our story too. Get to know someone long enough, well enough, and you'll start seeing shortcomings and character defects. You'll begin to wonder what happened to the person who aroused all those emotions inside of you. Where did she go? Who is this stranger next to me? You may even think it's time to high tail it out of here, to run for dear life.

The snake was ingenious. It tempted by making other things and other people appear enticing. The enticement was especially clever because it always masked a lie with a snippet of truth. The snake was honest when it told Adam and Eve they wouldn't die. They ate the fruit and lived to tell about it. The snake lied like a dog when it told them they would be like God. Once they took the bite, they ran for cover. Their resemblance was not to God, but to the snake, as they slithered from God's view. The death God referred to was an extinction of the covenant. After ingesting the fruit, the covenant was despoiled to the point where the elegant setting simply disappeared. Paradise was lost as toil, pain, and despair came into view. What a horrendous consequence for such a shitty little sin. Folklore has depicted the fruit as an apple, but it does not say in the text. I thought it must have been a fig because it would fit the area it was written in. How unfortunate to get royally screwed for eating a fig. Disobedience can certainly be a bitch.

*****

As I sat next to the love of my life, I privately wanted to get screwed too. Even though I held the thought, I also knew it is grandiose and unattainable. Peggy and I were only in the first days of our relationship. There were so many days yet to encounter. But I do share a glimpse of God as I gaze at her. Just like God viewing creation, I see her and she is good. Very good.

Time vanished from the football field and disappeared into some black hole. The vacuum it plunged into turned hours into minutes. Suddenly, she glanced at her wristwatch and startled me with her jump. We beat it to the car, and she sped me home. Fortunately, with so many brothers and sisters under one roof, I could enter my house past curfew and go unnoticed.

One of the parental commandments etched in stone is no dating until sixteen years of age. Since I was just fifteen, I was a long ways from that privilege. Time is apparently not the same for all human beings. To a teenager, the days move swiftly but the years are tediously slow. According to adults, days often drag while years slip by

with ever accelerating speed. Anyway, I was stuck in li/
the living girl of my dreams and the lifeless practice of
dience. I really didn't want to deceive my parents but ι ..
Peggy. I needed a compromise, and I needed it quickly.

Telling my parents straight out about Peggy would have been
a disaster since she had opened the door to my desire and passion
and I was opting to keep that door ajar. This new moral dilemma
demanded immediate attention. As a product of Catholic education,
I decided to investigate church teaching to find an answer.

The *Baltimore Catechism* was the source of my elementary religious education. I memorized and regurgitated it line by line. One
beauty of Catholicism is its long history. The church has been in
business for centuries, so it's encountered nearly every moral issue. I
was taught that an informed conscience is our best response to moral
dilemmas. Reading the wisdom compiled by past moralists is the way
to become informed. They critically examined the issues from every
conceivable angle. The fruits of their labor provide the church with
teachable doctrine. The *Baltimore Catechism* represented the compilation of their collected knowledge. The answer to my dilemma
had to be in there somewhere. Even as a rookie, I knew morality is
a complicated maze difficult to traverse. What I really needed was a
loophole. Some logical rationalization to mitigate guilt.

Regarding Peggy, the answer came like a thunderbolt from
heaven. I hearken back to the church's teaching on lies. Lies are
measured in degrees and variances. White lies are the most harmless
because their consequences are slight. As the consequences increase
and the severity of harm rises, the lie becomes an occasion for serious
sin. Serious sin severs our relationship with God, so it speaks of acts
that are ungodly. My association with Peggy is far from ungodly. In
fact, I have concluded it was divinely inspired. These facts and lessons prompt me to pursue a course of benign, yes even moral, parental deception. Lying also assured future dates with Peggy and, most
of all, satisfied my hormonal desires. A teenager and his hormones
are daunting competition for parents and other moralists. Moralists
and parents should probably just wait out the teenager's growth and
the hormones' decline.

My first kiss loomed in the near future. All the signs were present. The joint eagerness to touch, the slightly prolonged gaze when eye contact occurred—in short, the silent invitation emitted by two people who enjoy being together. The football field became our after-hours sanctuary. We set up shop there every evening to unwind from work and journey into the mystery of a relationship. Naturally, it was to be the site of our first kiss.

My arm around her shoulder was the first physical move I attempted. It took incredible courage just to initiate that simple action. Once done, I was baffled by the stupidity of my former terror. My arm rested on her shoulder like a natural appendage, and our conversation went on as if nothing had changed. In reality, everything had changed, and suddenly, the moment mysteriously appeared. Our faces turned to one another as if our necks were meshed gears and we fell simultaneously silent. I moved my face closer to her, closed my eyes, and miraculously touched my lips to hers. Gentleness was my primary concern as the divine linkage was made. After some indefinable period of time, I pulled back and asked her, "Did I do that right?"

I wasn't sure whether it was the question or the impish look on my face, but she let out a burst of laughter that embarrassed me. My face swelled crimson red, and my eyes sunk to the ground. When she saw this, she said, "I'm sorry. I didn't mean to embarrass you. It's just that it was so cute and innocent of you to ask."

What came next was worth my embarrassment. She took me in her arms and positioned herself so I was pressed against her wonderful chest. Her breasts seemed to melt against my torso as I embraced her. I could, or imagined I could, feel the tiny, button-hard nipples through her clothes and mine. I wanted to keep them there forever. Then she took further initiative and placed her hands on the back of my head and kissed me with force and abandon. Her tongue made a slight inroad into my mouth as every synapse in my body oscillated with electric chemical activity. With every movement she made, additional areas of my body announced their presence.

Now she gently guided me onto the grass and moved her hands over my head and shoulders. My task was simply to follow. I had no intention of disrupting that moment. We kissed and moved our hands across the sides of our shirts. Caution, fear, and training restrained any movement into areas that might offend her. When she pulled away, our eyes met. Her lips opened, and she formed the words "Thank you," then whispered them into my ear. That was all, just "Thank you." I responded, "Thanks for helping me."

Amazingly, this statement was spoken without a stammer. Somehow, I was able to speak in a complete sentence. This was an epiphany moment, and I already instinctively knew it would be treasured for a lifetime.

She drove me home, I kissed her gently on the lips, walked into the house and went to bed. I was different now, and I knew it. The core of my soul was connected, significant, and whole. Like a warm embrace enveloping my spirit, colorful and elegant threads of recent memory wound through the tapestry of my soul. They were precious gifts presented by another person who wanted to share them with me. Receiving them was easy. Hopefully, I gave something in return. The thought of being selfish at that moment sounded like an abomination before God.

CHAPTER 2

Occasionally, my parents went on trips without the kids. Recently, it became noticeable that their periodic respites from parenting usually produced another child. Now they were going to Las Vegas, and the departure date was next week. This left us and our St. Bernard, Taurus, in the hands of a "young married couple."

I began scheming immediately. Somehow, I would convince the young married couple to allow Peggy and me the therapeutic benefit of our swimming pool after a night in ice cream. My intentions being what they were—I needed a time late at night when all the urchins were fast asleep. Romantic moods would be sabotaged by little eyes and faint giggles at the windows. This was too important. The image of Peggy in a bathing suit (please, God, a two-piece) was a fantasy playing out all too often in my dreams. Now the time had come to give my dream the chance of reality.

The parlance of the time regarding sexual advances was coded in baseball terminology. It was called "rounding the bases." I knew that I had reached first base on the grassy hillside, and I knew from teenage banter that sexual intercourse was home plate. It was Bobby Richardson's and Clete Boyer's positions (for New York Yankee fans) that baffled me. Yogi Berra's position was not even up for consideration. Hearing the term *petting* produced only confusion. No matter what I tried, the image of a slobbering Taurus was creeping into the picture. I knew it had another meaning, but reference works on the proper base-running techniques were hard to find. After lengthy deliberation, I was resigned. What the hell, I was a bumbling novice anyway. I decided I would just admit my ignorance and ask for her assistance. It was successful in the past, so why change now.

My parents' flight left Thursday afternoon. I made a date with Peggy for Friday. There was no need to waste time. The plan was simple in order to avoid any complications or difficulties. We would close Baskin Robbins, drive to my house, put bathing suits on, and dive into the pool. The rest of the plan would evolve spontaneously. At least from a comfortable distance, it looked like the perfect plan.

CHAPTER 3

Peggy's parents knew all about us. George and Martha had a special affinity for their only child. You could observe it when they visited the store ostensibly for an evening treat. They always ordered ice cream, but mostly they came to bask in the brilliance of their only child. Parents apparently get satisfaction watching their children work at any job outside the home. Just the fact someone has hired their offspring confirms a history of proper parenting.

George was a fireman, in fact, a captain. He'd been with the department for twenty-five years. At 6'3" and 250 pounds, he cast an imposing shadow of intimidation. His gruff persona heightened the blustery appearance he emitted and his language was usually terse and caustic. The statements he delivered were meant to catch his prey off guard, and his appraisal of people centered on how they responded with their defenses thus anesthetized. Peggy warned me about this aspect of her father and told me to pretend I was not intimidated. Interaction with George was always a contest, though. Recognizing I was outmatched from the outset, I simply played along. One critical practice was avoiding the temptation to venture into smart-ass retorts. He detested that attitude in spite of the fact he frequently lapsed into the role himself.

"Tom, I hear you've been spending time on the football field with my daughter. You better be careful about any contact scrimmages taking place."

"If any scrimmages are called for, they'll be in full uniform."

"With uniforms tucked in, you mean."

"Yes sir, Coach."

Peggy would always chime in, "Dad, that's enough." She would shoot him a cowering yet respectful stare then turn to me and wink. Her wink was masterful and incredibly sexy. A girl can wink at a boy and absolutely melt him. From a girl, it's a signal of a shared secret or connection that is exclusive, intimate and arousing.

George liked to dwell on the subject of "Catholic boys from Prep." It was a subject he thought open to tons of humorous material.

"So who's Prep recruiting this year? I hear there's been a Jesuit sighting in North Omaha. Anybody in particular they going after, Tom?"

"I don't know. I believe they're just trying to show that we're not a segregated school."

"Yeah right, 980 white kids from West Omaha and twenty black kids from the north side. Isn't it amazing these twenty black kids happen to include the starting backfield on the football team and three of the five starters in basketball?"

"Just a coincidence, sir. Simply a coincidence."

The Catholic church has a plethora of material for anyone with comedic aspirations. George and Martha, on the other hand, were Missouri Synod Lutherans. (Why their religion required the label of a specific state was a mystery to me. Peggy guessed some friction years ago prompted a break from another group. Neither of us were interested enough to find out more.) Lutherans, I presumed, were like Catholics, who viewed religion as an adjunct to normal life. Attending weekly and following the guidelines fulfilled the duties of membership. Showing up seemed to be the crucial component. Comfort was the hallmark to showing up. Timothy Leary's mantra of "Drop out, turn on, and tune in" was anathema to people like George and Martha. They interpreted this exclamation as a battle cry for chaos, and such disorder rightfully scared the shit out of people who were both comfortable and content.

Martha was not especially quiet by nature. In George's presence, however, she deferred by staying in the background. Away from him, she manifested both a vibrant personality and sparkling sense of humor. Peggy's engaging style and wit were definitely inherited from Martha. Why her mother dissolved into the woodwork when George was present remained a mystery. Most likely, she had decided it was her concession to marital unity. The fall from grace introduced all of us to the world of compromise. Making choices gets complicated within the daily grind of living together under one roof. Self-killing submission or enduring utter hell are the extremes of the marriage pendulum. Finding the middle ground, while taking care of yourself, while being selfless, is nothing short of miraculous. Most couples only see the middle ground while passing through it for short periods of time.

Martha watched me like a hawk. She looked intently for any sign of danger or alarm. Peggy was the family jewel, and Martha protected her precious gem. Her constant refrain was not about "Catholic boys from Prep." It was about Catholic women having so many children. To her, birthing twelve children was like thirty-one flavors of ice cream. It was just plain excessive. The thought of twelve pregnancies immobilized her. She believed that sanity seldom survived three or four. Going above four certainly exhausted anyone's ability to parent. Without any explicit proclamation, she judged my mother certifiably insane. As for me, her verdict was still pending.

Peggy had implicit permission to communicate openly and often with her parents. I envied her that freedom. It allowed her to discuss any issue or situation openly and without disruptions. To George and Martha's credit, they practiced the art of patient listening and Peggy benefited from their choice.

In a household dominated by twelve children, the art of active listening required impossible concentration, much like selecting the sound of one violin in a symphony. My mother did her best, but there was no one-on-one time. My brothers and sisters and I competed for airtime. The experience either made you proficient at asking for help or becoming solitary. At fifteen, I was too young for classification.

CHAPTER 4

Friday night was drawing near. I mentally orchestrated my plan, and the only loose end was getting permission from the young married couple. Until my parents left, I couldn't check that item off my list. The young married couple arrived with suitcases in hand. Obviously, they needed cash. No other motive could explain their decision. A new team signed on each time my parents went on a trip. One experience lasted a lifetime, so young married couples never made a return visit. After a week with us, they discovered poverty has merits too, that cash wasn't as important as they once thought. Food preparation, dishes, laundry, diapers, and the decibel level of a house filled with twelve children all amalgamated into potential insanity. Not many people were capable of undertaking this task once, none twice. As different young married couples came and went, the experience with our family influenced their decisions regarding the number of children they would bring into the world. We served as early proponents of world population control.

This young married couple, Susan and Jim, listened intently to my mother as she gave them the list of instructions. Her litany was documented in a ten-page booklet called the *Manual for Self-Preservation*. Some of the pages were stuck together with gum and ancient food. Upon closer examination, there were also smatterings of dried blood. In a household with this many bodies, medical emergencies occurred on a regular basis. The manual contained all the phone numbers Susan would need. The only number not listed was for a good clinical psychologist. After a week with us, most young married couples went directly to the yellow pages for that information.

When I got home from work on Thursday night, Jim and Susan were slouched on the couch watching television. Johnny Carson was their choice for evening entertainment. They had finished retiring the brood to their respective beds, and Taurus was fed and lounging peacefully by the pool. With their mission seemingly accomplished, they both look *relieved*.

Their relief would be short-lived because eventually the laundry room would be discovered. Twelve kids times four articles of clothing equaled forty-eight items per day deposited on the laundry-room floor. Our washer and dryer were commercial models normally sold to entrepreneurs opening Laundromats. The constant low-pitched sound reverberating through the house at all hours was the whirling and spinning of these mammoth machines at work. The terror of laundry haunts many young married couples for months after they left us.

I seized the moment, briefly describing my working relationship with Peggy. I explained that I just wanted to have her over after work so we could use the pool. When I finished my innocent discourse, they peered at one another in silence. Neither one seemed able to make the call. Finally, after a long silence, Jim said, "Okay."

Susan wouldn't allow such a simple response. Her femaleness demanded more intensive inquiry. "You're sure she's old enough to drive?"

"Yes, she has her license."

"Will her parents know she's here?"

"I'll be sure to remind Peggy to tell them."

"What time is her curfew?"

"It's twelve thirty."

"You're not planning to leave the property, are you?"

"No, we are just going for a swim and want a little privacy."

Jim had heard enough. His wife of a few years was moving dangerously close to territory formerly inhabited by his mother. This was frightening to him. "That's enough, dear. I'm sure Tom will take care of everything. It'll be fine," he said.

They were nine years older than me at the time and probably into that territory where the years began to slide by. Apparently, though, Jim could still remember his first romantic encounter. With a somewhat sly grin, he looked at me and nodded his head ever so slightly. No other grown man had given me this gesture before. Immediately, I knew what it meant. He was saying, *You got permission. Good luck! Now get out of here before you say something stupid and blow the whole thing.* I promptly got out of my chair, walked to the kitchen, and dialed Peggy's number.

As I lay in my bed, I was ecstatic. The last item on my list was now in place. I had their permission, and my dream had a pulse, a chance of becoming a reality. Peggy sounded excited when I called to invite her. I'm not sure what her intentions might have been, but I was reasonably confident we were at least on the same page.

Excitement and anticipation were impediments to sleep. I tossed and turned for hours with images of Peggy in a swimsuit. Her skin was slightly darkened by the summer tan and was both radiant to the eye and luxurious to the touch. Standing in the shallow end of the pool, our legs would make contact under the water. My hands explored regions never visited before. Her lips, moistened by pool water, welcomed mine. As her breasts rubbed against my chest, I softly slid my hands down to cup them for the first time. My palms massaged the fabric of her suit. Carefully, I slipped my fingers under her suit and gently touched her nipples.

With a sheepish grin on my face and a delicious twinge of Catholic guilt in my subconscious, I looked forward to my grand adventure. The love of my life was coming tomorrow. We would share each other's company, and in the waters of our pool, I will be baptized in the sacrament of sexuality. I finally fell into a deep and intermittently pulsating sleep.

The only glitch in all my plans was a seemingly minor one. Peggy was given a early release from work because the business traffic was slow for Friday night, and it ended her workday at 6:30 p.m. Instead of viewing this sudden reversal as an omen, I suggested that she simply meet me at my house. I would get a ride home from another coworker and get everything set up around the pool. I told her we had a bathroom right off the laundry room where she could change. I told her I would be home by 10:45 p.m. and would wait in the pool. I told her all my siblings would be in bed fast asleep. I told her the pool was heated so the water would be perfect. I told her so many things she finally extended her hand and placed her finger on my lips. My silence gave her the opportunity to assure me she would be there and everything would be all right. She was off to meet some friends at Memorial Park. The kiss she gently administered to my cheek was her signal that she was leaving. She sauntered out of Baskin Robbins and drove away in her car.

Her smile and subtle hip movement reinforced my belief that her anticipation for the evening matched mine. She just chose to remain less vocal about it. How could she remain so calm? I was a bundle of frenetic energy barely able to manipulate ice cream and she appeared completely composed. Why do guys anticipate encounters with the opposite sex with such tension and fervor while girls have this languid air about the whole thing? Perhaps it has to do with the fact that we are apt to erupt uncontrollably at any time and they know it, while they can choose any level of activity or passivity they find comfortable and they know it. Girls, I think, are quite able to match our desire, but they have none of the anticipatory anxiety that overwhelms us guys.

What is it with time? Why does it crawl so slowly when you're anxious? I finally get the last customer out of the store, clean the place up, and say good night to the owners. At least the ride home is quick, and now I'm floating in the pool on a raft awaiting her arrival. There are no clocks to check so occasionally I swim to the side of the pool where my towel and watch are resting. It was four minutes to eleven the last time I checked. Any minute now, I'll hear the completely unique sound of a VW engine as she turns into the driveway. Then I'll see the headlights as they reflect off the retaining wall that borders the house. Finally, I'll hear her cut the engine and slowly exit the car.

I swam to the side of the pool and looked at my watch. It was 11:03 p.m. I jumped out of the pool, dried myself off, and entered the house through the sliding glass door into the kitchen. Picking up the phone, I dialed her number and listened as it intoned the familiar ring. After numerous unanswered rings, I set the phone back on its cradle. Nobody at her home and no VW in sight.

Taurus was awakened by my activity, and he plodded beside me. Maybe his instincts were telling him to check if I needed his assistance. I wanted to tie a message around his neck and send him out in search of Peggy. St. Bernard's have a long history of retrieving lost sojourners in the Alps maybe he would be capable of checking out Memorial Park for sights of Peggy. But unlike his distant predecessors in the monasteries, Taurus's retrieval techniques were dulled by living a tranquil suburban life. I petted him on the head and told him he wouldn't be much help tonight.

If something came up requiring a change of plans, she would have called. It was her modus operandi. Something had happened, and she was unable to get to a phone. A car malfunction or an emotional crises with a friend, maybe even an emergency medical problem, had to explain her absence. Sooner or later, a call would come, and a simple explanation would clear up the entire episode. Instead of going back into the pool, I spread the towel on a lounge chair and reclined facing the driveway.

Around eleven thirty, I called again. No answer. At midnight, I called again and received no response. At a quarter to one, I walked to the shed and turned off the lights in the pool. I adjusted the water temperature and began to lock up. The thought of sneaking the station wagon out and attempting to find her briefly crossed my mind. This thought ended quickly as I heard the sliding glass door open. Susan emerged from the doorway.

"Has she left already?" she asked.

"No, she never came. Something must have come up."

"Did you call her house?"

"Yeah, three times. There's no answer."

"Well, I'm sure there's a good reason for this, and you'll find out tomorrow."

"I hope it isn't anything too bad."

"Me too. Listen, Tom, you finish out there and go to bed. If there's a call later, I'll come and wake you."

"Thanks."

By two o'clock, no call had been received, and I retired to my bed. I was bewildered and upset because this was so unlike her. The high promise of the evening had drained away. All the adrenal glands ceased their function hours ago. Any sexual thoughts had evaporated into the damp night air. Puritanical Catholicism tried to raise its ugly head in the form of thoughts that I might have caused some tragedy to happen to Peggy through my lustful intentions. God, I wish I could exorcise these nonsensical beliefs. Taught to me as a child, they appeared to have a long radioactive shelf life. Even though my image of God was not patterned on a judgmental and vindictive judge, these crazy thoughts continued to periodically resurface despite my best efforts. With a heavy heart and a troubled soul, I fell asleep issuing a prayer to God. My prayer was contrite and authentic, wholly unpolluted by sexual intentions. I asked God to send an angel to watch over Peggy and bring her home safely. Fr. Sherman had told us in religion class that praying for others was a higher form of prayer.

CHAPTER 5

Humans sleep as angels keep watch over the night. Nighttime is always ripe for angelic patrols. Evil doesn't necessarily disdain the daylight but seems to abound when the sun surrenders. Crime happens all the time, but truly hideous crime seems always associated with the night. Nightfall provides cover for evil's soft whispers and blatant invitations. The darkness is receptive to terrifying noises that echo unfathomable fright. Like a snake that startles its prey, evil survives best when it sneaks up from the cover of night. Adam and Eve most likely succumbed after dark.

Angelic patrols have their work cut out for them. There is only so much they can do to protect and serve. God's primal command to the offspring that share his image is free will. Humans are not robots who mechanically follow orders. Their greatest and most dangerous of God's gifts is the right to choose. Therefore, angels are restricted anytime they venture into the human arena. They are ministers of observation and spiritual guides who can only attempt to impart the sacrament of hope. They witness evil from close range and intercede only to the degree where free will is not violated nor negated. In the litany of horrendous acts that have plagued human civilization from its inception, this night was just another entry. The angels had gathered in West Omaha.

James Hill was an uninstructed soul burdened by voices of terror. These voices led him astray. He feasted to an uncommon degree on the mental delusion that power was achieved by dominance over other humans. In real life, he was devoid of power. In his delusional life, he gained power violating the sanctity of other lives.

He was a cunning observer of movement in his own private world. His eyes adjusted best to darkness, so the cover of night became his domain. James's talent as an observer was severely negated, however, by his psychotic interpretation. His observations passed through a prism that defined human nature as not whole, not a part of, and insignificant. This was his core belief. All his mental activity orbited this conclusion, and so his whole world was abnormal. For James, life was meaningless and inconsequential. In other words, he was a predator.

From the time he came into this world, the only consistent messages he received were proclamations that he didn't belong and wasn't wanted. He had endured twenty-three years of physical and verbal abuse from the hands and lips of his parents. They systematically created a private hell where James resided, and they made certain he was unable to escape. Shut off and deprived of any healthy nurturing, his psyche became a haven that attracted a hoard of venomous snakes. The snakes constantly whispered mischievous invitations, half-truths, and promises. If the invitations were only accepted, then the promise was made that someday he would be the master of his world.

*****

Peggy left Memorial Park and drove home. It was a humid evening, so the thought of diving into cool blue water sounded refreshing. As the radio blasted out music, she steered her VW into the driveway of her home. She just couldn't bring herself to strip naked in unfamiliar surroundings of our bathroom so she had come home to change into her bathing suit and then head for the pool. It was 10:30 p.m., and she was right on schedule.

James had been scoping out the darkened house minutes before she arrived. He was in the neighborhood casing potential homes to burglarize. Breaking and entering was his specialty, and he took pride in his craft. It was incredibly erotic entering strangers' houses and checking out their stuff. The danger and excitement always gave him a hard-on. He would look for significant valuables that he could stuff in his pockets. He never indulged in large items because his method of transport was by foot, and he always wanted to make a quick getaway. He prided himself on the skill he thought he had honed over the years of never attracting attention to himself. In truth, James was a natural at not being noticed.

Normally, the fruits of his labors were currency, coins, jewelry, and female lingerie. The booty he pillaged was transported to the home he shared with his repulsive mother. There, within the cinder-block walls of his domicile, he enshrined the jewelry and lingerie. Any money he was able to steal kept him in cigarettes and pornography. Between the naked photos and the stolen bras and panties, James had all the props he needed to masturbate frequently. The voices in his head encouraged him to adopt and then repeat this lifestyle endlessly. They claimed repetition would eventually make him a powerful sexual master.

When the headlights came down the street, James had just finished casing the house and was walking to the backyard where he could break a window and gain entry. When the headlights suddenly turned into the driveway, he threw his body up against the exterior siding of the house and remained motionless. A shrub in front of him served as camouflage, and he remained immobilized as he inspected the occupant of the car. His heart was pounding inside his chest, and his thoughts centered on a plan of escape. There was nowhere to exit at the moment, so he concentrated on blending to the house. The initial terror of the headlights began to lessen as he recalled his skill at playing the game of being invisible. What the hell, he was in no hurry, and it was a relief this person arrived before he broke the window in back.

Peggy turned off the headlights, opened the car door, and fumbled with the key ring. Her thoughts were on the bathing suit she had come back to get. It would only take five or ten minutes to put on the two-piece bathing suit, along with pants and a shirt. Tom's house was only a few minutes away, so there was no need to rush. She walked to the front door with her house key in hand.

James peered around the side of the house, and his eyes followed the girl making her way to the front door. She was beautiful even from a considerable distance. He glanced around the neighborhood and detected no sign of movement from any of the houses. It was a quiet summer evening. Because of the heat and humidity, the homes were locked tight while air conditioners strained. Hot summer nights provided the cover he needed.

The house appeared empty. The girl was alone. The snakes whispered. Lives are changed in seconds. James began to move silently toward the front door. As he closed the distance between himself and the girl, his heart began to thump loudly and his muscles flexed. Just as she unlocked the door and removed her keys, James made his critical move. He hurled himself with reckless abandon the few remaining feet that separated him from the girl. She heard a rustling noise coming from the hedges, but the noise coincided with someone slamming into her back and propelling her into the house.

Reaching with one hand for the edge of the door, James slammed it shut. With closed fist, he let fly a right hand shot to the head. It caught her flush on the chin, and the beginning sounds of her potential scream were dulled and muted by her broken jaw. The only other sound she emitted was a gasp for air as her legs buckled and her body crumbled to the floor. James quickly pounced on top of her and hit her again. The blow was solid and caught her just below the left eye. All she could see was a vast blackness with tracers of light shooting from all directions. It seemed like the onset of sleep until suddenly horrific stabs of pain shot from her face and rendered her completely powerless to think or function.

He tore open her shirt, and the buttons ricocheted off the wall. Turning her on her side, he pulled the shirt from her jeans and navigated the sleeves from her arms. As he steadily worked on her, he remembered himself as a small child being pummeled by his father. Moans and groans emitted from her mouth, but the decibel level was minimal. James observed her swollen and bloody face but felt no remorse for the damage he had inflicted. He had already decided that brute force was mandatory for complete domination. Besides, he needed to be sure she was incapable of retaliation or escape.

James held her white cotton shirt out by the cuffs and twirled it. As he stuffed the body of the shirt in her mouth and tied the sleeves into knots behind her head, her entire body was writhing and her features were becoming distorted. He looked around the living room for something to tie her hands and feet and spotted a ball of yarn with two plastic sticks only six feet away. He got up, grabbed the yarn, and returned to coil it time and time again around her wrists.

She tried to move, but it was useless. The intense facial pain immobilized all commands shouted from her brain to the rest of her body. As the pain oscillated in her head, all she could do was watch this thing tie her hands with the very yarn her mother used to crochet. His facial features were a blur as the sight from her left eye diminished and the swelling of her cheek increased. Everything appeared to be moving in slow motion, yet she was incapable of any physical response. A sense of dread began to seep into her thoughts, and the pain that enveloped her quickly mutated into utter panic.

James secured her hands to the post that anchored the entryway lattice work. Any movement she made to free her wrists would now only tighten the yarn. Her legs were next. James grabbed her ankles and pulled them toward the sofa. The change in position extended her arms farther above her head. As he began coiling the yarn around her right ankle, her left leg bolted from the carpet and slammed into his thigh.

The blow struck muscle, and the force of the kick jolted him off balance. James grimaced for only a second then quickly recovered his balance. He reciprocated with a kick of his own. His leg drew back and arched with speed and force toward her left side just below her kidney. The thud of his boot on her body was absorbed into the upholstered furniture of the living room. The air in her lungs was expelled in one mighty gasp. Her only open eye bulged like a balloon as her pupil rolled to the back of her eyelid. Slowly, her head moved steadily to the right until it came to rest on the living room carpet.

Peggy lost consciousness as a pitch-black darkness wrapped around her senses.

James finished securing her ankle to one of the legs of a cocktail table. Quickly, he immobilized her other leg by kneeling on her thigh. As he peered down to look at her it was obvious she was unconscious. As he viewed her inert body lying on the living room carpet the sense of power, control, and domination began to swell within him. The fantasy played out for years had finally come to fruition. The voices in his head had promised this day would come. All he had to do was follow their orders and be patient. This moment validated the authenticity of all their promises.

James unbuttoned her blue jeans, unzipped them, and pulled them down her legs. He removed the pant leg over the one ankle and bundled the jeans around the ankle secured to the cocktail table. As he spread her legs apart, his eyes feasted on her body clad only in a bra and panties. Yarn was stretched from wrists to ankles, and the scene became James's work of art. He stood up to view his new creation.

Peggy was frozen. As she slowly regained consciousness, her eye locked on the man standing over her. He was hideous. Oily, scraggly hair framed a pockmarked face that leered down at her nude body. He was scrawny and disheveled. How absurd was the realization that this pathetic person suddenly had complete control over her life. If she had encountered this man in public, he would have warranted no interest. Yet here he stood over her with absolute power to rape and possibly kill her. She tried to muster hatred, but the pain once again overwhelmed her. She formed a prayer to God, "Please God, make him stop. Make him go away."

Unbelievably, it appeared her prayer was answered immediately. The man walked out of her line of sight. Peggy couldn't see where he went. Her view of the living room focused on furniture and pictures. This was the room she had known all her life. Until tonight, it was always a sanctuary where she was comfortable and safe. Her mother and father sat in their respective chairs and conducted nightly rituals throughout the years of her childhood. So many ordinary, mundane evenings were spent in this room, and she couldn't fathom how the present horror could be real.

James had quickly scanned the living room for scissors. He wanted to cut off her bra and panties. They would become his new trophies, and he would use them to commemorate this night. The snakes always implored him to steal underwear and enshrine them in the secret chamber in the basement. Late at night, when his mother was asleep, he would bring out a few of them as he masturbated in his bed. Until tonight, he always had to select a naked photograph from one of his magazines to provide the visual element. Now he had a real woman, and her nakedness would become indelibly etched in his memory. Just the sight of her underwear would arouse him as he recalled this incredible evening. Finally, he was becoming someone significant.

He walked into the kitchen to find a pair of scissors. After checking four drawers in a cabinet near the refrigerator, his impatience grew and he looked for another cutting tool. Next to the stove a large knife was stuck in a block of wood. He picked up the knife and marched back to the living room. As he viewed the girl with her legs spread on the carpet, his penis began to swell in anticipation. The voices promised he would fuck a woman someday, but they hadn't told him it would be one so pretty as this.

CHAPTER 6

Athanasia is a seraphim angel. Her charisma is the comforter of women who are in the throes of sexual violence. She has worked countless miracles shepherding souls of women out of a violent inferno into a dimension she called the "beatific vision." Being assaulted, raped, or murdered attacks the soul with a diabolical force that threatens to corrupt even the victim. Athanasia's ministry is the establishment of a sacred bond with the victim so that defilement and desecration only violate the body. She cannot prevent an act of sodomy from being committed, but she can use her power to protect a soul from being consumed. Her invitation to the victim is a glimpse of resurrection and the assurance that the pain will eventually end. If a victim accepts Athanasia's offer, then the torture of the assailant erodes into a despicable act that does not harm or extinguish the most integral component of life. Athanasia is a protector of souls.

Cleverly, she first appears to her women bearing facial features that resemble a loved one who has died. The sight of someone known and loved during life diminishes the sight of an apparition. By negating fear, Athanasia is able to communicate directly to a person the reassurance that life is not ending, it is simply changing. There is little time for introduction, and trust needs to form immediately.

Athanasia is the angelic answer to the holocaust some women suffer at the hands of men.

The numerous angels hovering above Peggy parted as Athanasia entered their midst. She began by calling Peggy's name. Softly and with deep affection, she was signaling for her attention. Then with supreme tenderness, she stroked Peggy's battered face. The sheer warmth of her presence mysteriously dimmed the excruciating pain. When she had Peggy's gaze, she situated her spirit directly in front of her. This blocked out the sight of the assailant as he conducted his deviant crime.

After establishing contact visually, Athanasia began her dialogue.

"Peggy, my name is Athanasia. I'm here to help you. Don't be alarmed. The pain you are experiencing is great, but if you follow me, I'll take you to a place where he can no longer hurt you. All you have to do is focus totally on me. Your eyes can never leave me."

"Oh god, I will. Please make him stop. Don't let him rape me."

"Peggy, shortly you will feel pain and spasms between your legs. There will be a heavy weight on your body. Don't be alarmed. It will not last long, I guarantee this. Simply lock your eyes on me, and I will take you on a journey. We're going to another dimension. I promise you will experience healing. Follow me Peggy, we're leaving shortly."

"Please take me...don't leave me here."

"I will never leave you, Peggy. We are together now forever."

The keys to Athanasia's spiritual power were her words and invitation. She always led entrusted souls with both her voice and message. Drawing off their own recollections, she guided them to a place that was familiar, a place where they sensed safety. The battered and brutalized had always been her ministry, and she knew her role well.

CHAPTER 7

James set the knife under the strap of Peggy's bra. With a thrust of the blade, the strap was severed. He could feel his penis swell incredibly as he roughly grabbed her tits and pinched her nipples. He had seen many pictures of tits. Magazines that featured them were the main inventory of his basement library. James never bothered to read what was written in the magazines; he only dwelled on the naked women and the allure they emitted by their pose. His reading comprehension level barely allowed him to navigate the comics in the newspaper, and so his main sources of education were visual.

He had no clue how to touch, hold, or sexually relate to a woman because he viewed women as things whose sole purposes in life were to satisfy his sexual desires or to abuse him with verbal taunts. His mother fulfilled the one role and his pornography the other. Women were objects to be collected monthly by going to the store and purchasing a new issue. They were things he used to stimulate an erection anytime he felt like it. James could only fuck things. His touch was harsh, aggressive, and warlike because he had never, in his entire life, experienced a caress.

After only a minute with her tits, he lost interest and looked at her panties. Taking the knife, he cut through the fabric on the left side of her hip. It exposed the perfect triangle of curly hair that

James had only seen in the pornographic magazines that were available from behind the counter at a store he liked to frequent. He searched through the pubic hair to find the opening he knew was there to welcome his penis. The mere thought of sticking his penis inside her produced a small splatter of semen in his pants. Upset that he was so close to ejaculation, he stood up and removed his clothes. As he descended on her body, his hand clawed clumsily at her crotch. Just as his filthy finger found the way, he happened to glance at her face. Startled at her visual deportment, he temporarily halted his molestation. Her face no longer registered terror. The eye that wasn't swollen shut was glazed and focused, but it wasn't looking at him. She appeared to be in a trance and was oblivious to his presence. James was pissed. How dare this woman disregard the fucking he was about to give her. She damn well better pay attention to him. At that moment, he violently thrust into her.

*****

What James did not know or comprehend was that Peggy had detached from him minutes before. She was departing on a journey with Athanasia to a dimension where neither he nor his violence could follow. She was protected by an enveloping force, and for her, there was only a tranquil serenity permeating the moment. The image was of a garden in a dimension Peggy could dimly recall. Her recollections were filled with mystery, but the mystery did not alarm her. The garden was simply calling her to a memory deep in the recesses of her being. Somewhere in her subconscious, she knew she had been there once before, but she was unable to remember when. The how, why, and when remained questions without an answer. Suddenly, there was a sharp and stabbing pain between her legs. It threatened to destroy the spiritual connection, so Athanasia drew very close and whispered, "Shhhh, in a few seconds, it will end."

*****

With little fanfare and none of the expected sense of accomplishment, James ejaculated his genetically pathetic semen into Peggy. He had fucked women many times in fantasies, but now he had experienced the real thing. It was unfortunate the moment passed so quickly. In his dreams, it seemed to last a lot longer. Instead of spilling onto his hands and sheets in his basement dungeon, he had finally deposited himself inside a woman. This would truly make him complete. The explosiveness of the act would vault him into a position of power and mastery. This is what he wanted and tried to believe as he panted foul breath on Peggy's face. Unfortunately, James was beginning to sense deceit. The whole event began to seem like being alone in his basement. An inert body was lying beneath him, and he felt no connection, no significance, and, worst of all, no power.

James became suddenly enraged. All his waiting and effort and still nothing was felt. He pulled himself out of her and stood up. Goddamn it. This had to be her fucking fault. She had fucked him over like every other woman he had ever known and in the same way as most. She was detached and distant from him. What he had just done mattered nothing to her. In rage, he screamed, "How dare you act like you didn't like that. Goddamn it, talk to me, scream, do something!"

He might as well been yelling at his basement walls. The only response to his tirade was the reverberation of his voice as it traveled through the empty house. He picked up the knife and stuck it into her.

CHAPTER 8

Athanasia told Peggy there would be sharp pains as her soul struggled to release. Somehow, trusting those words shaped Peggy's response to the knife penetrating her stomach. Even though her body withered, her soul remained in Athanasia's embrace. Peggy yearned to fully reside in the presence of this loving spirit who had initially resembled her grandmother who had died years ago. She felt herself moving up toward the ceiling.

She viewed the pathetic features of her assailant as she looked down into her living room. Masked in the shadows, she could only distinguish a colorless outline of someone repeatedly plunging a knife into a corpse. The sight was gruesome, and the assailant was both loathsome and pathetic. Slowly, she came to the realization the corpse was hers. Athanasia patiently and silently watched as Peggy's spirit wrestled with hate and wrath. Athanasia knew that Peggy had to make a free will decision regarding the scene below.

The iridescent light Peggy basked in was strangely absent from both the assailant and the corpse. As the pitiful creature continued to lash the lifeless corpse with the knife, Peggy decided to slowly let go of her initial hatred because the figure wielding the knife exhibited none of the light she was now basking in. Pardoning the killer was not possible yet, but she started on the journey to forgiveness. It was a free will decision she made without knowing that it would determine all that followed. It was her last and greatest epiphany as a live human being.

*****

James was alone once again. His shriveling penis receded like a frightened snake. Having sex with this woman provided no order, connection, or significance in his life. The snakes were screaming for revenge. They told him, "She tricked you. Women do that, you see. They lure you, then leave you, and provide no satisfaction."

James decided to deal with this woman the same way he dealt with centerfolds that lost their luster. He cut them up and threw them away. When the voices in his head finally subsided, he had plunged the knife into the girl precisely thirty-one times. Blood had spouted in torrents on her body and on his. The beige carpet, Martha's pride, had absorbed most of it and became the color of port wine. Tied up, raped, and cut to pieces, Peggy's remains laid in a pool of blood, on the floor, in the living room of a middle-class home in the city of Omaha.

James went to the kitchen to clean up. As he was washing his hands in the sink, the telephone startled him by its sudden clamor. It was 11:05 p.m. The sharp sound shocked and frightened him. Paranoia attacked him, and he began his flight from the scene. As the phone rang incessantly, James grabbed the bra and panties from the floor and slipped out the door. Remaining in the shadows, he worked his way through the neighborhood, careful not to disturb. He was heading for the safety of his basement where he could lie down and sleep. Into his musty bed, he would slide and close his eyes to the events that had just transpired.

As James crept from the house, the ringing echoed off the walls of the kitchen and whistled through the living room where death resided. It floated within the context of time and was greeted only by the spiritual guides who had stayed behind. The call was a summons from a fifteen-year-old boy. The love of his life was missing, and he thought he actually wanted to know why.

CHAPTER 9

Athanasia's and Peggy's spirits commingled. As they entered the new dimension, Peggy looked back on the earthly landscape. George and Martha were on the dance floor in tight embrace. To the sounds of country music, they swayed across the floor. Without a care or concern to trouble their thoughts, they glided like a couple enthralled to be with each other. It was a night to express love, and imbibing alcoholic spirits only deepened their affection. Any interruption of this shared intimate moment would not be tolerated. Life appeared to be very good.

Sadness began to permeate Peggy's spirit. She realized what they would discover when they returned home. She made an attempt to dislodge from Athanasia and cried out, "I need to go warn them, comfort them, tell them how much I love them."

"Peggy, you cannot return now. The faith which brought you here is the faith they taught you. Trust that they will be provided guardians. Angels will watch over them."

"Athanasia, I don't believe they can handle what they are going to see. It will kill them. I'm all they have in their lives."

"They have each other, Peggy. I agree it will be difficult for them. There is nothing you and I can do. Trust, Peggy, it's all in the hands of faith."

Peggy viewed Tom as he lay on the lounge chair next to the swimming pool. He looked anxious and worried as he waited for her arrival. "Let me reassure him that I'm all right."

"You can't, Peggy. This tragedy will take its toll on so many people who were connected with your life. All of them will deal with it in their own way and at their own pace. You will need to accept and trust this fact. More importantly, you will come to know why."

"Athanasia, how could I ever know why? I don't even understand who I've become or where I am."

"Let me reassure you eventually you will understand."

"What am I, a speck of light?"

"Oh, Peggy, you are so much more than that. We have an existence which resembles illumination because we are reflecting the light of creation. You have returned to your place of birth."

"So the reason I glimpsed being here before is due to some faint recollection of my past?"

"Exactly. You've returned home."

"Athanasia, all of this is overwhelming."

"I know. Resolution requires wisdom and patience."

"But what about those I left behind? My parents, is there any way we could tell them?"

"Those left behind have a difficult task to face. It may appear to them you are gone forever. Out of physical sight sometimes translates into lost forever. If your parents adhere to this point of view, then your death will be very traumatic, and they may not recover spiritually."

"Athanasia, my parents are good people. I don't want my death to harm them. They believe in God. We went to church and attempted to pray. They believe in heaven, at least I suspect they do. Will their belief be strong enough?"

"I don't know."

"You don't know? You're an angel, you're supposed to know. If you don't know, who does?"

"The faith of your parents will be the key."

"Athanasia, you didn't answer my question. Will my parents be able to handle this?"

"All we can do is observe."

"Athanasia, you're being evasive."

"I know. Peggy, your question will be answered. My ministry is to help you accept it."

"Will Tom recover too?"

"It will be up to him, Peggy. The difficulty he may face is that he might think he caused this to happen."

"Athanasia, he had nothing to do with this. I was heading over to see him."

"I know, Peggy. But tragic death can cause numerous negative responses from people. Evil thrives on those responses because they can diminish the Creator's light from their souls. Without the light we are both immersed in now, evil seeps into the vacuum."

"Athanasia, can you make sure it does not touch my parents or Tom?"

"Peggy, I cannot."

CHAPTER 10

George and Martha noticed Peggy's VW in the driveway as they approached the house. With senses dulled by alcohol and bodies craving sleep, the oddity of her car parked in the driveway was more of an annoyance than a cause for alarm. Peggy always parked her car on the street, but she was also a teenager, and so small lapses never surprised them.

As George guided his car to a stop, he asked Martha to get Peggy's keys. His tone of voice reflected the irritation he felt. The alcohol consumed earlier only heightened his aggravation. This was just one more episode involving a teenage daughter with a license to drive. One more parental encumbrance he would have to endure.

As Martha opened the front door, she felt a chill deep in her body. This was not a chill based on temperature but one that seemed to be in her muscles and bones. She saw the kitchen light on, and although unusual, her mind had no time to register the thought. In a millisecond, her eyes saw an image on the floor to her left. Her hand reached involuntarily for the living room light switch.

A primordial scream emanated from her diminutive frame and reverberated throughout the house. It pierced the night and sent shock waves through the neighborhood. Accompanying her scream was the chill as it seeped from the recesses of the house. Both the scream and the chill entered other houses, and bedroom lights flickered on next door. The aftermath of evil sometimes has an odor. It can even have a color or a taste. But there's always a chill. It's evil's calling card, the signal there's been a visit.

George was standing by the door to Peggy's VW waiting for the keys. When he heard Martha, scream, he froze for an instant, then leaped forward. His run to the door, the movement of his wife's body to the side, and the clear view of his daughter's naked and bloody body blended into a single instant in time.

As a fireman trained in rescue, he knew and understood danger. He had sensed it, felt it, and responded to it many times as a professional. The learned skills he had acquired told him to kneel down in her blood and gently reach out his hand to check her neck for a pulse. The instant his fingers touched her skin, he knew she was dead. In his many years of responding to danger and death, one factor remained unchanged—the cold touch never lied.

When it's someone else, someone you never knew or saw before, it's customary to follow all the procedures. Your mind simply responds to the training received over the years. You secure the crime scene and alert the proper authorities. When it's your daughter lying dead beneath you, everything becomes confused and disjointed. You instinctively want to clean her up, remove the shirt from her mouth, cut the yarn binding her wrists and ankles, wash the dried blood caked to her body, close her legs, and cover her with a blanket. These steps seemed like the obvious things to do. Any father would do them no matter how difficult they appeared.

George was about to respond as a father until recognition filtered into his conscious thought. This was a crime scene. He stood up and turned to his wife. Martha's pose was a transfixed vignette. Frozen in shock, her hands were clutched in her teeth. Except for an occasional tremor, she remained absolutely stationary. Her eyes were riveted to her daughter's body, and the bulging of her pupils reflected the horror she was seeing. George grasped Martha's shoulders, bent down, and collapsed her knees with his forearm. With one swift surge, he lifted her off the ground, then carried her out the door. Setting her on the front steps, he turned back and gently closed the front door. When a neighbor from across the street inquired about assistance, George simply responded, "Ed, call 911. Peggy's been murdered."

What more could he say? How many words were necessary to convey what they just saw? Words were so useless anyway. Silence seemed a natural response to the numbness he felt. He knew shock had a certain duration period whether you talked or remained silent. He sat down next to Martha and tightly held her in his arms. Martha responded by gasping for air as tears cascaded down her cheeks.

CHAPTER 11

Within minutes, squad cars screeched to a halt and flashing red lights blanketed the neighborhood. Lights bounded off the vinyl siding and rooftops of homes now illuminated by the eerie flashing signal of alarm. Neighbors awakened from their sleep and were hypnotically drawn to the scene. Police officers, detectives, and a coroner assembled to dissect every inch of the crime scene. Horrendous murders were uncommon in Omaha, and George's association with the fire department sparked additional attention. The common theme resonating in all those present was a fervent desire to apprehend the son of a bitch who was responsible for this massacre.

Peggy's remains were photographed from every angle. Her shirt, jeans, the yarn, and the murder weapon were bagged and tagged. There was a recognition by the detective that her bra and panties were not present at the scene. He marked that on his report. Carefully, her body was lifted and slipped into a black travel bag. When the zipper was closed, the final vestiges of Peggy's earthly life disappeared. After the coroner transported her body from the scene, all that remained was a VW in the driveway, photographs on the walls, clothing in her bedroom, and a white chalk outline drawn on the bloodied living room carpet.

The detective looked around the neighborhood and observed houses sealed shut as air-conditioners waged a war against the summer humidity. Every home probably had one. He made a comment to an officer that each advance in technology carries a price that is not always apparent. In the case of air-conditioners, homes are closed off and neighbors isolated from one another. No one heard or saw anything unusual that night. Peggy's murder went unnoticed by an entire neighborhood. His only response was to shake his head in dismay.

*****

James tossed and turned in his bed as he struggled to fall asleep. What made slumber so difficult was the hissing sounds emanating from all the snakes that shared his bed. They were gleeful and festive as they congratulated James on his masterful accomplishment. Tonight was a crowning achievement because it plunged him into a deeper level of dependence on them. The snakes' mission was to obliterate the light from his soul. Since the light was so powerful, it was always a monumental endeavor to extinguish it completely. Consuming an entire soul required patience and the subtle art of deception. Rarely did they ever achieve total mastery, but tonight was a major victory. If they could just take him a little further, then he would be theirs; with some more coaxing, they could take him beyond redemption.

CHAPTER 12

The phone call came at 6:04 a.m. The ring startled the young married couple as they slept on my parents' bed. The wife answered.

"Hello."

"I apologize for disturbing you at this hour, this is Detective Jack Warner from the Omaha Police Department. Is this the woman of the house?"

"No, ah, I'm Susan. The parents are out of town. My husband and I are house-sitting for the children."

"Susan, is there a son named Tom?"

"Yeah, sure. He's asleep. Do you want me to wake him."

"Thank you, I would appreciate it."

As she placed the phone on the night stand, her husband asked, "Susan, who is that?"

"A police officer. He wants to speak to Tom."

"What about?"

"I don't know. I'm going down to wake him."

She descended to the lower level of the house and knocked on my door. "Tom, Tom, wake up. There's a police officer on the phone, and he wants to talk to you."

"What about?"

"I don't know, he didn't say."

"Okay, I'll be right up."

Deep in the mind of every teenage boy is a silent alarm system. It activates whenever he is summoned by a teacher, a coach, a boss, a priest or pastor, and most especially, by a policeman. This unspoken mental alarm is universal. *What'd I do?* This is a genuine question because usually we truly don't know what or—more accurately—which. Between bed and phone, my mental alarm had finished the question, failed to find an answer, and began searching other data banks. The word *Peggy* was just forming in my brain as I put the receiver to my ear.

"Tom, this is Detective Warner from the Omaha Police Department. I'm sorry to wake you, but I need to ask you some very important questions. It's about your friend Peggy."

The sensation was exactly that of being awakened from a short nap taken at an unusual time. I couldn't get myself oriented.

"Peggy…she's…okay?"

"No, Tom, she isn't. I'm sorry, son, there's just no other way to say this. She's dead."

This news was received just like any male received the proverbial low blow. Time, and everything in it, ceased to exist. No voluntary action, including breathing, was possible. There was no pain, just the sure knowledge of pain to come.

"What…happened?"

"She was murdered in her house."

A second low blow before the effect of the first had even begun to morph—the purest form of numbness, like having molecules of Novocain attach to every living cell of your body in the same instant. There was some precise period of silence. I had no idea of its duration.

"Tom, her father told me she was coming to your house last night. Did she come over?"

"No…but she was supposed to."

"What time were you expecting her?"

"Around eleven."

"Where was she going before that?"

"Memorial Park, I think."

"Do you know the names of the friends she was with?"

"Cindy...Patty...I can't think."

"It's okay Tom. Would you happen to know where they live or their last names?"

"They...ah...go to Burke."

"It's ok, son. Did you talk to Peggy yesterday?"

"Yeah...about 6:30...at the store."

"That's the last time you saw her?"

"Yes."

"How late did you work?"

"Ten thirty."

"Did you go straight home?"

"Yes."

"The babysitter, ah, Susan, she heard you come in?"

"Yes."

"So she saw you the whole evening after you got home?"

"No...I went out to the pool to wait for Peggy."

"You didn't get into your car and drive somewhere?"

Something that had been growing inside me for weeks burst open at that instant like a malignant, overinflated aneurysm. I knew what he was asking and why. It was my first lucid thought since picking up the phone. I also knew that I didn't kill Peggy, and I didn't really care that this man actually thought I might have. What was flooding through me was the soul-staining certainty that I had caused it. The date at the pool was just Satan's tool. His fuel had been my filthy, lustful thoughts. Fr. Sherman and all those before him knew. God himself knew.

"I'm only fifteen."

The rest of our conversation was strangely mechanical and automatic.

"How did you get home from work?"

"Ted. He works at the store."

"What's Ted's last name?"

"Robinson."

"And where is the Baskin Robbins you work at?"

"Seventy-Eight and Pacific."

"In the last few days or weeks, did Peggy notice anyone frequenting the store who bothered her or simply stared at her?"

"I don't remember anyone."

"Listen, Tom, you've been a great help, and I am terribly sorry about your loss. It's tragic and—"

"How did she die?"

"She was stabbed to death with a knife."

"Should I call her parents?"

"I don't know, son. They're devastated, and what they really need right now, probably no one can provide. I don't know how well you know them, so I really can't give you any guidance there. Take care of yourself. You need to talk to someone. You'll need help dealing with this. Good-bye."

"Good-bye."

I hung up the phone and saw Susan standing in the kitchen. The look on her face confirmed that she knew the essentials of what I had been told.

"She's dead?"

"Yes."

"Was it a car accident?"

"No, she was murdered in her home."

"Dear God. Where were her parents?

"They were out."

"Jesus. They came home and found her?"

"I think that's what happened."

"Are you going to call them?"

"Do you think I can, I mean…should I?"

"I think you should. At least you'll find out what happened."

"Yeah…I guess I should."

I don't know why the thought of taking a shower came to me at that moment. It just seemed to be something I wanted and needed to do. I needed to clean up and wanted to wake up from some horrible dream, I guess. Walking like a zombie, I entered the bathroom, locked the door, and turned on the shower. As was my habit during the hot summer months, I adjusted the water temperature a bit to the cool side. As soon as I stepped in, I realized that I didn't feel hot.

In fact, I felt cold. I raised the temperature. I raised it again. Again. The entire bathroom was enveloped in steam. I actually burned my skin without feeling warmth. It was eerie and strange, and I had never experienced any sensation like it before. Evil had entered my life for the first time, and at some level, I recognized it. I was learning that evil does not wash, scrub or melt and it has the sensation of being cold. I gave up and got dressed.

A phone call to Peggy's house yielded only a busy signal. So did the next three times. Frustrated, I finally asked Susan to drive me to Peggy's. As the car turned onto the street where Peggy lived, I felt cold again. This time I made no futile effort to warm myself. I absolutely didn't want to be here, but I had no choice. I had to be involved, and there was no other way. After reminding Susan that there were eleven other children back at the house and reassuring her a couple times that I would be all right, I watched her drive off. As soon as she was out of view, I regretted asking her to leave. I felt an incredible need to be older and an equally strong desire to be younger. Any slim possibility of being comfortably fifteen vanished.

CHAPTER 13

The VW was in the driveway, and George's car was on the street. The house appeared empty and the neighborhood eerily quiet. I was completely out of my element. I was plunging into something that was way over my head. Coming to her house was a simple reaction, the only option I could think of. Besides, I needed to see George and Martha. Maybe I thought they would tell me it was all an incredibly cruel hoax.

The front door to Peggy's house was crossed with yellow tape, just like in the movies. This *was* a crime scene. As I turned and looked helplessly around the neighborhood, a man across the street signaled me to his front porch. He told me George and Martha were inside. I walked to the house and felt even more out of place.

The man who had called me introduced himself, "I'm Ed. You know George and Martha?"

"Yes, I do…I'm Tom. Peggy and I work together at Baskin Robbins."

"George and Martha are in the kitchen. Please follow me."

As I entered the kitchen, George's presence filled the room. He was talking on the telephone. Martha sat on a chair in the far corner of the room with her hands covering her face. As George talked on the phone, Martha cried.

Leaving Ed, I walked up to Martha and, not knowing what else to do, awkwardly placed my left hand on her shoulder. Somewhat startled, she glanced up to my face. Slowly, she rose from the chair and wrapped her arms around me. Her embrace was amazingly forceful. She seemed to be holding on to me for dear life, and it somehow made me feel better. As her tears soaked my shoulder, she spoke, "Tom, oh Tom, someone's killed my baby."

George hung up the phone. He stepped over and placed his hand on my neck. He squeezed firmly just to let me know he was there. It was a unification of our sorrow, and the three of us were thus joined in some communal embrace. No words were necessary, and I was truly grateful for that.

Eventually, Martha released her embrace and lumped back in the chair. She was past exhaustion and beyond consolation. I knew it wouldn't be long before her body would just collapse under the strain. She needed a deep and restful sleep, but she wanted, I thought, to do something for her daughter. Being conscious was all she could do so her vigil continued.

I was introduced to all the people in the room. When they finished, I couldn't match even one name with a face. Shared shock mercifully reduced verbal exchanges to an absolute minimum, and we all stood around wondering what came next.

George gave me a nod and beckoned me to follow him. The kitchen was the land of women mourning the dead, and George obviously didn't want to be there. I was thankful he invited me to go along. We walked through the living room past the maze of people gathered in conversation. Somehow, word had passed from the kitchen that I was the "boyfriend." The unknown kid Ed had ushered into the house was now adequately identified. The conversation had returned to the world going to hell and how Omaha was now an active member. Horror had invaded their very neighborhood.

George led me out the door, down the porch, and across the street to his house. Like a private following an officer, I marched behind him. When we reached Peggy's VW, he stopped abruptly.

"Did Detective Warner call you?"

"Yeah."

"I'm sorry, Tom, I should have called."

"It's okay. I can barely believe any of this, so it didn't make any difference who told me."

"God, that's the truth. I'm praying sweet Jesus will wake me and all of this will be nothing more than a horrible nightmare. Unfortunately, I've been up all night and it's real. Goddamn it, it's real."

"What happened? The detective asked me some questions, but he didn't say exactly what happened."

"Tom, I don't know if I should do this, but I know how much my daughter thinks…ah…thought of you. And I suspect I know how smitten you were with her. You at least deserve to know how she died before you read it in the newspapers. Come on, we'll go through the back door, and I'll tell you what I think happened."

The instant we entered the back door, I knew the origin of the chill that had earlier assaulted me. It was more than something *in* the house—it was *of* the house. The air was rank in some direction-less way like a home long inhabited and never cleaned, yet two days earlier, it had smelled of nothing more than Martha's baking and the faint remains of Peggy's perfume.

Like a homicide detective, George outlined his theory of the crime. Step by step, he delivered a dissertation that was logical, complete, and precise. Midway through, George told me Peggy had been raped. It was the only time his voice cracked, "Tom, the fucker raped my little girl."

I had somehow known it all along, but now I had to face it. I knew my anger and hate could never match. He was a huge bear of a man who could and would snap a pervert's neck in one motion. I was a puny fifteen-year-old. More importantly, his rage was pure and unencumbered and just. Mine was burdened by the knowledge that I had dreamed endlessly of having sex with Peggy. I was too young to understand the difference between fucking and making love much less the nature of rape. I felt emasculated.

George was obviously coping with his daughter's death through his continuing rational analysis of the crime scene. He seemed terri-fied of turning on the emotional faucet. His paralysis, I guess, gave him some detachment from the horror. It allowed him to function. At this point, it was all he could do for his daughter.

The chalk line traced Peggy's final position in this world. The image spoke volumes about what had transpired in this room. Suddenly, my hatred for whoever had done this, whoever had violated and slashed my Peggy, rose several notches. As I stood staring down at a roomful of beige carpet, my gaze slowly fixated on the twelve good wide bloodstain and, finally, on the small chalk outline. The hatred continued to swell inside my stomach until my face was red with rage. I made a solemn vow. After George's fire had faded, maybe after he was dead, I was going to find the son of a bitch who did this. He would pay. God would he pay. I remembered Fr. Sherman's stupid warning to us in religion class: "Be careful what you pray for because it might be given to you." In this case, I hoped with all my heart it would.

George's voice intruded on my thoughts, "Tom, can you remember anyone coming to Baskin Robbins who seemed weird or unusual? You know, someone who came in and stared at Peggy or hung around the store?"

"I don't know. I really can't recall anyone. The detective asked me the same question."

"It's just a thought. My mind is racing for some explanation, and I thought maybe it was someone who was stalking her. Did she ever say anything to you about someone following her?"

"No, George. Peggy…well…she never mentioned anything like that. I'm sure if there was, she would have said something."

"You're right. Peggy never had a problem expressing herself. Did you call when Peggy didn't show up at your house?"

"Yeah…a couple times. But nobody answered. I'm not sure why I even called here. Peggy was going to Memorial Park, and I thought she would come from there."

"Maybe that's it. Some psycho followed her from the park. God, all I want is two minutes with the bastard."

With that, George seemed to be spent. We left the house in silence and walked back across the street.

*****

I left George, Martha, Ed, and all the neighbors gathered in mourning. Even though I was three or four miles from home, I declined George's offer to drive me. I wanted some time, and it had to be away from George. It was time I was going to use imagining *my* revenge. I had already decided that it would involve a sharp knife and the killer's genitals, but I had many details to think over.

People always say that the young have rich imaginations, and I certainly had one twenty-four hours earlier. Somehow, though, when I tried to stoke my fantasies with hatred, I couldn't keep the fire going. What was wrong with me?

I finally sat down on a curb and began to cry—for Peggy and for me. A woman backed down her driveway and made the reverse turn in the street right in front of me. We made eye contact. Something in her face told me she was going to roll down her window or even come out of her car. She had a sweet, kindly face that made me feel pitiful. I bolted. I ran to the east as fast as my legs would carry me. I ran until I was home. The tears were gone. I felt nothing.

CHAPTER 14

James awoke Sunday morning eager to see the newspaper. This surprised him because reading was a real chore. In Omaha, there was only a morning edition of the Saturday paper. Since the timing of his crime didn't allow enough time for Saturday coverage, it had to wait for Sunday. Television and radio, though, had covered every aspect of the murder, and James had listened with fascination. He wondered whether he might be on the front page.

As he climbed the stairs, he knew he had some explaining to do. Normally, he slept until noon and he *never* gave a shit about what was in the newspaper. He had to be careful not to arouse his mother's suspicions. The fat old bitch was always looking for something.

"Jimmy, what the hell are you doing up? Goin' to church? Hah, hah, hah."

Whenever she laughed, she sounded like a man—a dirty, leering old man. Her laugh always ended with a thick-mucous-plugged cough. He hated being called Jimmy. He associated the name with beatings administered by his father the drunk. His mother attempted to continue the tradition of physical abuse until he threw a fist in her direction. When the drunk died, so did her protection, so she sat on her fat ass with her legs on a footstool hurling verbal abuse. Her life consisted of the paper, coffee, cigarettes, television, and doughnuts.

As her size increased, the only article of clothing she could put on was a tattered housecoat. When she died, James planned to burn it. The worst part about her was the odor she spread through the house. The smell made him continuously nauseous.

"I couldn't sleep. Why the fuck do you always yell at me when I first get up? How about 'Good morning, James'? By the way, for the last time, my fucking name is James. Get it right for Christ's sake."

"You son of a bitch! You're just like your father, that worthless piece of shit. Apples from the same tree you are, rotten apples at that."

"Ah, shut up, you bitch. He couldn't stand your fat ass, an' neither can I. Give me the fucking front page so I can go get some peace. Taking a shit is the only thing I can do without you being around."

"Oh, big shot. The front page. Don't you think the comics would be more your speed?"

"Fuck off."

James grabbed the front section of the paper and went to the bathroom. Locking the door gave him some measure of privacy. There it was, bold as hell, right on the front page: GIRL BRUTALLY MURDERED IN BEL-AIRE HOME.

James began to plod through the story. He read out loud while sitting on the toilet. He truly comprehended maybe a third of the words but enough to realize the cops didn't know shit about who did it. James knew that should be good, yet he felt vaguely the same way he had felt after screwing the girl. Goddamn it. The article should be about him.

He learned her name was Peggy. He liked it. In future fantasies, with her bra and panties, he would use her name. James sat on the toilet peering at the newspaper he had dropped to the floor in front of him. At least the story talked about something he did, something significant. By god, he *was* important, even if he could never tell anyone. The snakes began whispering right there in the tiny bathroom. They told him the more times he did it, the more important he would be. James had the thought that if he just raped the next one but didn't kill her, then there would be someone left to know his role in the significant event. He congratulated himself for having such a "good" thought, then flushed his shit down the toilet and left the room.

CHAPTER 15

I read the articles on Sunday morning. I found myself searching for the part that said Peggy had been killed because she left her friends to be with me or the part that said the police even thought I might have done it. I even had the irrational thought that the police might have divined my own sexual thoughts about Peggy. I was relieved to find my anonymity intact. But I did have the sense my soul was burdened.

Later in the day, Susan asked me when the funeral would be. I didn't know. Susan said the information would likely be in the obituary section. I hadn't a clue where that was, but I finally found it. There in black and white was the tiny box and small lettering announcing Peggy's funeral arrangements. Visitation was Monday evening at 7:00 p.m. at the John A. Gentleman Mortuary. Services was on Tuesday at 10:00 a.m. at Calvary Lutheran Church. Interment to follow at Evergreen Memorial Cemetery.

One way or another, all of us get our name in the local newspaper. Peggy's time had arrived.

*****

"Athanasia, how do we know about faith?"

"What were you taught?"

"I was taught about heaven and hell. I don't know, it wasn't very important to me at the time."

"You were told about eternity."

"Yes, but who can understand eternity?"

"You've been a part of it forever."

"How?"

"Your soul is eternal. The journey of the soul is not to a place. It simply returns to its dimension of origin."

"So we came from here, and we all go back. Where's the here?"

"Peggy, this dimension is impossibly away and also right before our eyes. It's a mystery that we call the 'beatific vision.'"

"I haven't a clue what that means."

"Peggy, you are now part of the beatific vision."

"I'm sorry, Athanasia. I just don't get it."

"You see me don't you?"

"Of course."

"I'm the first stage of the mystery. Other stages will follow."

"So...you are an angel who leads me to this vision?"

"Yes, I'm part of the vision. And my ministry is to guide souls. But there is so much more."

"So...I'm still me yet I am absorbed in you. Is that right?"

"For now, it will do. We are in communion. Your light commingles with mine."

"Will I remain in communion with you Athanasia for eternity?"

"Only to a degree, Peggy. Souls which achieve their destiny reside in communion with all creation. Each soul has a ministry which defines them."

"What's your ministry?"

"What I'm doing now."

"Did you guide me while I was living?"

"No. Another angel did that."

"How come I didn't notice?"

"You noticed, Peggy. Tutorial angels guide through invitations communicated by whispers. Often, the clamor of one's life makes the whisper barely audible."

"Why don't angels speak louder so we can hear?"

"We don't interfere. The whispers can be heard clearly if the person prays and meditates. They're a gift, and it's up to each soul to either accept them or ignore them."

"So this tutorial angel was whispering to me all my life?"

"Yes."

"Athanasia, I didn't pray much, and I don't know anything about meditation. Is that why I didn't hear the whispers?"

"Oh, Peggy, you prayed unceasingly, and you responded to the whispers frequently. The free will decisions you made in your life were prayers, and many of them reflected the light of the Creator quite brilliantly."

"Athanasia, could you get a tutorial angel to whisper to my folks?"

"Peggy, it's up to your parents to listen. We are not allowed to infringe on their free will."

"Could I be a tutorial angel for them?"

"Your ministry, Peggy, is not mine to determine."

"Will God determine it for me?"

"The Creator will reveal it to you."

"When?"

"Patience, Peggy."

"Every soul then…goes through this experience when they die?"

"Every soul encounters corporal death. What happens after death is determined by the condition of one's soul."

"Athanasia, I don't understand. Was I supposed to learn all this in church?"

"Religions can be instructive. They have ample revelation available. Unfortunately, all of them flounder to varying degrees in confusion."

"What confusion?"

"Let me give you just one example. Sometimes religions play a part in people's obsession with the corporal body. The body simply dies and decays. Yet observe all the rituals taking place for you. Notice how much importance is placed on your earthly remains. Services for the dead should always focus on the soul and its journey. Sadly, most of the emphasis seems to be placed on the cadaver."

"Athanasia, my parents don't know what to do. They're in shock and just going through the motions."

"Peggy, so many families who lost a loved one experience the pain of letting go. Ministers assist them, and their intentions may be noble. But they often get trapped treating the corpse."

"I see what you're saying. Makeup to cover my wounds, clothing and body posture that makes me look like I'm sleeping. It's a bit much."

"There's even more, Peggy. Your parents have to make decisions about your service, casket, grave site, and headstone. The obsession is on your body, while your soul is receiving meager attention."

"Why don't religions correct this?"

"To some degree, they try. Many emphasize resurrection and eternal life. But their teaching expands into so many areas that people become overwhelmed with the enormity. What's vitally important gets lost."

"It sounds so simple. Why don't they get it?"

"Stages of the mystery are simple. Religions can help people navigate through the stages. And some religions do it well. One problem they all encounter lies in the central concept of attaining one's destiny. Attainment of destiny demands moving toward self-actualization. Some religions focus more on how to control people instead of empowering them."

"You're losing me again, Athanasia. This isn't as simple as I thought."

"That's why it's done in stages, Peggy."

CHAPTER 16

My first experience with a mortuary was the death of my grandfather Hugh. I was nine years old. He was laid out in the casket in his favorite suit, and I could have sworn he had just decided to take a nap with his suit coat on. That's what it looked like until I touched his face. My grandfather was ice cold and hard as a rock. This was no longer the man who impressed me as a child, who gathered me in bear hugs and conducted talk sessions around the kitchen table. There was something missing. A piece of him had disappeared. It wasn't in the casket, and it wouldn't be buried in the ground. The body in the casket may have resembled my grandfather, but it wasn't him. I wondered why we were all pretending it was.

On Monday evening, I put on my most formal attire—a navy blazer, tie and gray pants. These were the uniforms of the Jesuit school I attended. As I stood before the mirror finishing the knot in my tie, it suddenly dawned on me that for the first time ever, the two ends of the tie had come out even and the knot was straight. I believed it had to be significant. The thought came to me that I was going on a formal date with Peggy. Suddenly, it was all clear. This would be all our homecomings, all our winter formals, all our proms rolled into one evening.

Susan had volunteered to drive me, but there was no way I was going to have a chaperon on my only real date with the love of my life. And so there I was, dressed in my finest, pedaling my bicycle down the streets of Omaha. Tie, coattails, and small tears flying in my wake.

As I entered the parking lot of the mortuary, it became crystal clear my bicycle had been a completely unique and childish choice of transportation. I suddenly didn't feel like I was on a date at all. I felt like a little boy who, while trying on his dad's coat and shoes, is spied by an adult who remarks how "cute" it is. I tried to melt into the crowd.

The entry way was filled with people. A notorious death or an especially young victim of a horrendous crime always draws a large crowd. The combination had produced a mass of people, probably ten times the number at my grandfather's wake. As I walked down the aisle to the room where Peggy's body was placed, I dodged groups of couples engaged in conversations. From tidbits I extracted, it appeared most of the people were connected with the fire and police departments. They came in force to offer condolences to George and Martha. His twenty-five years of faithful service to the community was paying its dividends tonight.

As I neared the room, a line was forming. People were signing a book placed on a podium by the door. When my turn came, I picked up the pen and printed my name. I wanted to write something else. A heartfelt message, some expression of how much I already missed her, or may be a little poem. I was full of feelings and empty of words and spent too much time at the podium holding the pen. The woman behind me gave me a gentle nudge. It was a polite way of saying, "Move along, young man. Others are waiting."

Flowers covered the front of the room, bouquets and wreaths of varying sizes and colors. The two dominant colors were white and red. Instead of providing serenity to the setting, they instilled in me a sense of dread and sorrow. My mind returned involuntarily to the image of a chalk line and blood on the living room carpet.

The arrangement of the flowers were peculiar, I thought. They flanked the casket on both sides and gave the impression that Peggy's body had fallen asleep in a botanical garden. As I slowly followed the procession to the casket, I observed her folded hands, closed eyes, and heavy makeup covering facial wounds. The mortician had obviously attempted to make her appear angelic. All it did for me was confirm she was truly dead. I didn't view her body very long. Any fascination with cadavers had ended when I had touched my grandfather's cheek. Like George, I received my lesson years ago. The cold touch never lies.

I embraced Martha and gave her what I thought to be my best look of condolence. There was nothing I could think of saying to this poor woman, so I moved onto George. He hugged me and murmured words to the effect that he was grateful that I came. God only knows how many times he had said those words. He looked like a beaten prizefighter, one who stayed in the ring way past the point of no return. The ordeal was slowly sucking the life out of him, and it would take more than just a crowd of people to replenish his spirit. I left him and took a seat in the last row of the chapel.

When 7:00 p.m. arrived, the minister walked in and stood by the podium. He was getting his thoughts in order, and his presence silenced the murmurs of the crowd. I couldn't imagine what he would say.

"Dearly beloved, we gather tonight in sadness and sorrow to mourn the loss of a young girl taken from us tragically and painfully in the prime of her life. We turn to scripture in times like these to hear the consoling message that God provides. Blah, blah, blah............"

The minister droned on in a sound reminiscent of Peggy's VW engine. I grew tired, restless, and discontent. He had obviously delivered this talk many times. It was a speech he had repeated for many people in many funeral homes throughout the city. The only preparation required was having the correct name on the deceased. It sounded rehearsed, and I thought Peggy deserved something better. A little Old Testament violence, I thought, would have been much more in order. Quickly I returned to Fr. Sherman's class on Genesis.

*****

Now Abel became a shepherd and kept flocks,
while Cain tilled the soil. Time passed and Cain
brought some of the produce of the soil as an
offering for Yahweh, while Abel for his part
brought the firstborn of his flock and some of
their fat as well. Yahweh looked with favor on
Abel and his offering. But he did not look with
favor on Cain and his offering, and Cain was very
angry and downcast. Yahweh asked Cain, "Why
are you angry and downcast? If you are doing
right, surely you ought to hold your head high!
But if you are not doing right, Sin is crouching at
the door hungry to get you. You can still master
him." Cain said to his brother Abel, "Let us go
out"; and while they were in the open country,
Cain set on his brother Abel and killed him."
(Gen. 4:3–8)

Thus, Cain became the first soul who went astray. What was
it that made Cain feel less than, not whole, and insignificant in the
presence of God and his brother? Was Cain evil from birth or did he
become that way? What the hell would someone do to become like
Cain? But, most of all, why didn't God stop him?

Yahweh asked Cain, "Where is your brother
Abel?" "I do not know," he replied. "Am I my
brother's guardian?" "What have you done?"
Yahweh asked. "Listen! Your brother's blood
is crying out to me from the ground. Now be
cursed and banned from the ground that has
opened its mouth to receive your brother's blood
at your hands. When you till the ground it will
no longer yield up its strength to you. A restless
wanderer you will be on the earth." Cain then
said to Yahweh, "My punishment is greater than
I can bear. Look, today you drive me from the

surface of the earth. I must hide from you, and be a restless wanderer on earth. Why, whoever comes across me will kill me!" "Very well, then," Yahweh replied, "whoever kills Cain will suffer a sevenfold vengeance." So Yahweh put a mark on Cain, so that no one coming across him would kill him. Cain left Yahweh's presence and settled in the land of Nod, east of Eden." (Gen. 4:9–16)

Maybe Peggy's murderer was a descendant of Cain. I only wish I knew where Nod was because I would go there and hunt the son of a bitch down.

*****

The Lutheran minister droned on. What could he say to a crowd of mourners reeling from a tragedy too awful to comprehend? I certainly didn't have any wisdom to share with George and Martha because we were all swimming in the same cesspool of anger and hatred. The minister was harping on grief, forgiveness, and resurrection. Granted, these concepts are the central core of Christian belief, but those who needed healing the most were too caught up in something else. I was wishing he had just walked into the room and screamed, "The son of a bitch who did this to Peggy will pay in eternal hell!" Then after describing hell in gory and specific detail, he could have talked a little about Christian concepts of emotional recovery. Absent any acknowledgment of our shared hatred, the rest got tuned out. Tuned out by me. Tuned out by George. Tuned out by Martha.

The service ended, and I slipped out the door, got on my bike, and rode home. My final date with Peggy had been a total bust. I vowed to do better with the funeral, but my vow felt weak because I was lost, and I knew it.

CHAPTER 17

Susan drove me to the Missouri Synod Lutheran Church the next morning. I told her I would find a way home. The funeral was like a Catholic service in many ways. The major difference centered on the hymns. Lutherans sing a lot, and they sing every verse. As a Catholic, I was accustomed to closing the hymnal after the second verse. Rarely did we venture to verses three, four, or five. Those verses are window-dressings for Catholics, seen on the page but never sung. The liturgy had Germanic overtones of stoicism and piety. There weren't many personal touches nor even glimpses of emotion.

Ed offered me a ride to the cemetery. I had no plan on how to get there so I gratefully accepted. Conversation with Ed and his wife was limited, self-conscious and superficial, like a long elevator ride with workplace acquaintances.

Funeral processions seem to be rooted in military traditions. They are orderly, precise, and preempt civil traffic laws. For the vast majority of human beings, their final ride is the last time they receive a moment of total respect and deference from family, friends, and strangers in the community. Also, you get to go through all the red stoplights without any recourse.

After another service conducted in front of the grave, not one word of which was truly memorable, everyone slowly dispersed. I told Ed I could walk home, we were only a few blocks from the Baskin Robbins, and I knew the route very well. He seemed relieved.

As I exited the ground littered with graves, it was eerie and way too quiet. The only other people in sight were the men who were waiting to cover the grave and remove the green tent and folding chairs. They kept their distance from me, but I was sure they were thinking when was this punk kid going to leave so we can do our job. As I tried to get all those thoughts out of my mind, I made a conscious effort to clear all the clatter in my brain and tell Peggy I loved her and I was sorry that I may have played a part in what happened to her. Faintly, I thought, I heard a whisper. Maybe my lack of sleep over the last few days was playing a trick on me. Even so, I decided to stop for a moment and listen.

*****

Peggy and Athanasia had viewed the entire proceedings of the last few days. Their spirits were present at the services, and their warmth was available to all in attendance. Peggy saw Tom lingering near her grave, and she began to verbally echo words of assurance.

"Tom, I'm at peace. Please don't worry. My soul is with an angel. Go on with your life. But be careful. Sin and darkness are always at the door."

*****

The faint echo in my mind sounded like Peggy's voice. It was frightening and reassuring at the same time. The voice was not coming from the grave or any other specific point. It just existed apart from space or time. For the first time in my life, I felt completely and totally alone. For the first time in my life, I uttered a genuine prayer without any confidence that it would be heard, "God, please help me. I don't know what I'm doing."

Peggy would be a fractured memory for me. There was the soft, sweet, exhilarating and perfect Peggy from the grassy hill beside the football field echoing her familiar line, "Silly not to."

75

That Peggy would be softly and lovingly cradled in my soul for the rest of my life. There was also the butchered and violated Peggy, the small white chalk outline in the huge circle of blood. I had no idea where to put that Peggy, but I knew she wasn't going away any-time soon.

PART II

1977

CHAPTER 1

"Tom, when are you leaving for the cemetery?"

"It's not cemetery, Mark. It's seminary."

"Ohhh."

Mark was in first grade, but my other brothers knew immediately what seminary meant. They came over to me and said, "Thanks for taking one for the team."

Celibacy was now out of their lexicon. I would be the priest for the family.

I was twenty-five years old and partially removed from the throes of innocence, contemplating a profession as a Catholic priest. That was a long ways from scooping ice cream at Baskin Robbins. I had attended the University of St. Thomas (no relation or connection of any kind) in St. Paul, Minnesota, and had achieved a degree in philosophy. I was truly a schizophrenic philosopher because I marveled at the brilliance of Aristotle, Thomas Aquinas, Immanuel Kant, and Rene Descartes, but I also was intrigued with writings by Friedrich Nietzsche.

Mark's question was more appropriate than it may seem. Death and abandonment were intriguing factors in my life for the last ten years. Mark was not the youngest anymore. He was succeeded by two girls, the thirteenth and fourteenth children in our family. My mother's reproductive plumbing was retired, but she's a first-ballot cinch to receive induction into the Maternity Hall of Fame.

The family lost one member. Taurus, the St. Bernard, was placed on waivers and picked up by a rancher in Western Nebraska. The gigantic slobbering behemoth, who received a diploma from Dog Obedience School, dove through the neighbor's plate glass window. He wreaked havoc on their living room decor and traumatized their spaniel, Skippy. Skippy was a bantamweight who constantly messed with the heavyweight champion of the neighborhood. Bantamweights are small, but they're also coy. Skippy understood the metric system. Taurus was kept on a fifty-meter chain, and Skippy would stand fifty-one meters away. He tormented the living hell out of Taurus until one fateful day.

My brother Pete was making the transfer from the backyard chain to the walking chain. In the mere seconds it took to unhook one chain and leash another, Taurus sensed a window of opportunity. Needless to say, he took advantage. Skippy's one option for survival was a doggie door in the garage, which led into the house. Skippy made it safely through the door just as Taurus plowed head first into the entrance.

Skippy blew a sigh of relief, and the smart move would have been to call it a day. For some inexplicable reason, Skippy assumed a position on top of the sofa in the living room and taunted Taurus with indignant yelps. He had the metric system down, but he was ignorant about calling it quits when cajoling heavyweights. Taurus backed up and used their front lawn as a runway. In the spirit of Evil Knievel jumping the Snake River, he crashed head first through the picture window.

My father refurbished the living room and acquiesced to their demand that Taurus must go. All of us cried like babies as the rancher drove away with our dog. Skippy lived through the ordeal, but he was altered both physically and psychologically. Nightmares of flying glass haunted him the rest of his days.

Taurus left for greener pastures, and I was about to do the same. In the ten years since Peggy's murder, educational attenuation occupied my life. Armed with a BA degree in philosophy, I was beginning a four-year sojourn in a place called the seminary. I would be pursuing the theological inquiry of Holy Mother Church. Ordination to the priesthood was the goal of my enterprise, and achievement depended on my ability to analyze, collate, and synthesize the dogmas, doctrines, and opinions of the church. It was time to see whether I was wheat or merely chaff.

Leaving Omaha had its merits. As Simon & Garfunkel sang in a song titled "Old Friends," "Preserve your memories, they're all that's left you."

CHAPTER 2

In 1974, James Hill was nabbed while attempting to rape a coed from the University of Nebraska in Omaha. The crime took place in Elmwood Park, which bordered the campus. He needed more than yarn to dominate this woman because she struggled free, called the police, and James was picked up lurking behind a row of bushes. Peggy's kick to his left thigh was the right idea but the wrong target. This coed had both areas covered. She planted her size-7 foot directly in James's scrotum. Any violence he intended to inflect was immediately negated when her foot hit the target. Her one masterful kick probably saved her life, and it brought James into a cubicle with Detective Jack Warner.

Detective Warner became involved with the case because there was a suspicion James would attempt this crime again. All rape cases passed through Warner's desk. When a murder of a police officer or fireman occurs, it usually receives critical attention. For Detective Warner, the murder of any family member of these professions received the same scrutiny. Unsolved murder cases can sometimes go into the classification of a cold case. Peggy's murder haunted him, and he was willing to look anywhere for a break to solve this case. Perpetrators who had a penchant for rape were his best bets.

When he initially viewed James, he saw a shriveling, pathetic man whose personal terror seeped out of his pores like sweat. Studying him from behind the two-way glass yielded a decision to befriend this poor creature instead of tormenting him. An intuitive hunch said James had lived with torment all his life. After so many years, anyone could develop defenses that would be hard to penetrate. He looked like a loner who might bite if offered a sympathetic ear instead of a tongue-lashing. What the hell, Warner figured it was worth a try. Besides, the poor bastard declined legal representation, so he would have free reign to probe. All Warner wanted was a few minutes to determine whether this guy had a murder lurking in his resume. There had been so many dead ends encountered with Peggy's case. Years had slipped away without rendering a shred of new evidence or any plausible leads. The case was cold, and he was not willing to allow it to become frigid.

I needed to commend Detective Warner for periodically keeping me informed about the case, and I was especially thankful that he, years later, gave me a transcript of his taped interrogation. It certainly filled in many blanks about the man who killed Peggy.

"James Hill, I'm Detective Warner. We need to talk."

Warner carefully withdrew the chair situated on James's left side. James kept his eyes lowered to the ground and made no response.

"Last night, you were apprehended on Fifty-Seventh and Happy Hollow Boulevard, hiding in the backyard of a private residence. James, what were you doing?"

"None of your fucking business."

"James, we're going to find out eventually. The girl in Elmwood Park gave the police a description, and it matches you to a tee. Sometime this morning, she will pick you out of a lineup, and you'll be charged with attempted rape. It doesn't matter what you do or what you think—all of this is going to happen. It's out of your control now."

"So why ya hasslin' me? Just shut the fuck up and leave me in peace. I'm not talkin'."

"James, I'm here for one reason, just one. If you talk to me man to man, your cooperation will be noted. Judges always look at my

83

notes. They want my opinion on the people I talk to, and believe me, my opinion carries weight."

"Man to man, huh? Yeah right. I tell you I did it to the girl, you lock me up, and case closed. Fuck you."

"James, the case is closed already. I'm just trying to find out if this girl lured you. Did she come on to you in the past? You know, tease or flirt with you. We both know women do it sometimes, even young ones."

"She might have? What's the difference?"

"Well, there's a huge difference. Let's say she wanted it. Girls can't openly ask for it. That damages their reputation. But we both know they flirt, don't we?"

"Damn straight."

"So did she do that to you—flirt or tease you?"

"She might have. I was being careful so I may have missed it. Yeah…I guess there's a chance."

"See, James, already we made progress."

"What you writing?"

"I'm simply stating there's a possibility she teased you. I'm putting possibility because you told me you weren't sure yourself. Maybe you were encouraged by the girl."

"The judge will read that?"

"Without a doubt. Judges always want to know as much as they can about someone before they come into their courtroom. The judge doesn't know you, James. He's never seen you or heard of you."

"Then write down the fucking cunt flashed me a beaver."

"This is your life, James. This is no fucking game we're playing. This pen in my hand is more powerful right now than a knife or a gun. This pen decides how long you will be locked up. Do you understand that?"

"Yeah right, if I had a knife last night, you and me wouldn't be here."

"A knife's pretty powerful, isn't it?"

"Fuckin' A it is! It shuts up witnesses, don't it?"

"Yes, James, I guess it does. So last night, had you ever seen this girl before?"

"Nah, I was jus' walkin', mindin' my own business."

"Did she say anything to you? Like call you a name or something?"

"Nope. She jus' walked by me."

"Did she smile at you or wave?"

"No, she never looked when she went by."

"Ohh, so she saw you and pretended you weren't there, kind of like you didn't exist."

"More or less, I guess. Rich college girls do that all the time. All impressed with themselves. Think their cool bitches or something, better 'n everybody else."

"What did you do next?"

"I dunno, it was stupid really. I jus' turned around and followed her."

"Did she hear you?"

"After 'while she did."

"What, did she look back?"

"Nah, she walked faster. You know, picked up the pace."

"Okay, what happened next?"

"Well, it was dark, nobody around. I decided to chase her. You know, give her a little thrill. Somethin' she could tell her bitch friends about."

"So you ran after her?"

"Yeah, it was easy. Girls run like wounded dogs."

"When you caught up with her, what happened?"

"I grabbed her."

"Where did you grab her?"

"I grabbed her arm and turned her around. All I was going to do was tell the fucking bitch she wasn't so cool. You know—"

"What happened next, James?"

"She yelled at me and started waving her arms like a mad woman. She began hitting me. I got pissed. The bitch was slugging me."

"Okay. What did you do next?"

"I slapped her, grabbed her mouth, and we wrestled a bit."

"Is that when you ripped her shirt?"

"Yeah…I guess."

"If you just wanted to tell her something, why rip her shirt open?"

"I dunno, I guess I wanted her quiet."

"Oh, so the shirt was going to be used to gag her? What, put it in her mouth?"

"No, I'd tie it around her mouth. Like this."

"That's a good idea, James. Then you keep both your hands free."

"Yeah…"

"Man James, why outside, though? People could come from anywhere. You had to know that."

"Stupid. I knew it was fuckin' stupid."

"Now indoors, James, in a house, you control it. You're in charge, and you don't have to worry about anybody else. Right?"

"Yeah…sort of…'cept the fucking voices are always there."

"Voices. Whose voices?"

James drew back physically as his eyes drooped to the tile floor. He never talked to anyone about the voices. He was frightened of their capability to retaliate against him. At one time, they were his companions, but now they were wearing him down with the weight of their demands. After the murder, they implored James to repeat the violence. Their incessant babble became a constant nagging scream in his head. It was endless and deprived him of any peace.

The detective appeared to be interested in hearing more about these voices, so maybe he would just tell him. Sharing it with him might reduce the volume level and frequency of their tirade. They were becoming too burdensome for him to handle, and maybe this detective knew something he could do to make them go away. Besides, the detective had treated him with decency. Not once had he called him Jimmy like his fucking father or mother did.

"Oh, it's those damn voices, the ones that don't stop. You know, the ones that jus' keep talkin' and talkin' and talkin'. Can't turn 'im off or turn 'im down to sleep."

"How long have you been hearing them?"

"Since I was a kid."

"What did they say to you then?"

"They told me they'd help me get back at my father for hitting me."

"He beat you up a lot, didn't he?"

"Every time he was drunk, he'd pound me. I'd hide, but he always found me."

"What about your mother? Didn't she ever stop him?"

"That worthless bitch loved to watch. Sometimes she joined 'em."

"Is he still abusing you?"

"Nope. The voices told me they'd get 'em and he died. After he bit the dust, I trusted 'em."

"What about your mother?"

"She can't move her fat ass quick enough. Besides, she's scared of me since the old man died. The fat ass lost her protection."

"Does she know about the voices?"

"Nah, but she damn well knows I'm powerful."

"James, do the voices have names?"

"Nope."

"Have you ever seen them?"

"Not really, but at night, I think they look like snakes."

"Snakes. Doesn't that scare you?"

"You get use to 'em after a while."

"When your dad died, did you help the snakes do something to him?"

"I wanted to, but he jus' keeled over with a heart attack."

"What makes you so sure the snakes caused it?"

"They promised me he would die."

"So they caused the heart attack?"

"That's what they said."

"Have the snakes told you to hurt anyone else?"

"Sometimes."

"Who?"

"Girls."

"Which girls?"

"Ahhhh, jus' any…young ones."

"James, you're drifting away from me. I need you to be clear about his. I'll write all this down and give it to the judge. If you're honest with me, it will help. Judges appreciate cooperation, and when someone comes clean about what they did then, it will go better for them in court. This could make or break your case."

"So…you think the judge wants to know about the voices?"

"James, they make all the difference in the world. These voices are the most important things in your life right now. You better tell me now because later it won't make any difference. If it's not in my report today, the judge is going to think you just made them up. You know, scared of going to jail, so you made up some story about hearing voices. If he thinks this is a con, be prepared for the worse."

"For sure the judge will read what you write?"

"Guaranteed."

"And…you think it's important?"

"Most important thing you have in your life right now, James."

"Okay. But the fucking judge better read this, or I'll jus' deny it."

"He'll read it, James. Believe me he'll read it."

James had found someone who listened to him, someone who took the time to show the slightest amount of interest in the events of his dismal life. He had lived for years without anyone being remotely interested. Accepting the invitation offered by the detective seemed like the right thing to do.

"If I tell ya stuff…stuff about the voices and all. Will you help me get rid of 'em?"

"The voices?"

"Yeah."

"I can't help you there, James, but the judge can get you the treatment you need."

"A mental hospital?"

"I don't know for sure, James. But we'll do our best to help you if you tell me everything. And, James, I mean everything."

"Some of this stuff…I didn't want to do. You know…some was bad."

"That's what I need to know. The really bad stuff."

James spilled his guts about every aspect of Peggy's murder, including certain facts of the case that were never released to the press. Later on, the police searched his bedroom in the basement and found the lingerie James accumulated from his burglaries. Peggy's bra and panties were part of the collection. As Warner sat that day and heard the gruesome details, his only consolation was closing Peggy's murder case. The details James spewed out made him nauseous. The victory of closing the case was tempered by the horrible way Peggy died. He always hoped she went quickly. Now he knew she suffered a lot. Later, he would claim it was all pure luck to stumble into this pathetic killer. Intuition told him to befriend the guy, and every once in a while the advice from one's gut proved best. Who knew where intuition came from, he was just thankful he had it.

James was charged with two counts of assault and battery, two counts of attempted rape, and one count of murder in the second degree. He could have been charged with the Nazi Holocaust, the assassination of King Ferdinand, and the destruction of the temple in Jerusalem, it made little difference to James. He got a court-appointed attorney who viewed the case as an interesting attempt to plea insanity.

The attorney's advice to James was simple. "Don't say one word to anyone until you clear it through me first. Your legal defense will be a plea of not guilty by reason of insanity. With voices and some drug use thrown in for good measure, you've got a chance at a hospital instead of the pen."

In the late 1960s and early 1970s, people who heard voices presented the criminal court system with a mounting dilemma. The voices of society seemed fractured by the Vietnam War and escalated drug use. If someone heard voices, then the illegal drugs pervading the youth culture definitely played a part. Besides, it went a long way to explain how such a senseless act of violence could be perpetrated on an innocent girl. There were a lot of people who wanted to put the unsolved murder to rest. If this son of a bitch was loony, then it helped explain how something so horrible could occur in Omaha.

Over the past three years, George and Martha's fervent intensity for revenge had drained. The emotional trauma dissipated with time. After all, it requires loads of energy to sustain hate. Psychologically, the continuous bombardment hatred dispenses wreaks havoc with every neural fiber of one's body. More importantly, your extended family and friends will eventually implore you to move on with your life. If you don't, they will gradually distance themselves from your company. You can't constantly rehash a tragic episode for years without social side effects. After a while, many people run for cover. I stuck around for as long as I could.

George and Martha's tragic error was remaining at the scene of the crime. Replacing the carpet in the living room was mandatory, but they needed to do more. It really didn't matter that the carpet was green now instead of beige—both of them could still see the blood and the chalk line on the floor. This memory required more professional skill than a carpet installer could provide. They needed to move.

The house became a shrine to Peggy. Her room remained perfectly intact. The time Martha spent in Peggy's room slowly debilitated her reservoir of spirit. Pictures of Peggy and personal memorabilia adorned every nook and cranny of the house. Candles became Martha's devotional repository, and they burned incessantly as a vigil to her daughter. Without knowing it, Martha was becoming more Catholic than she would ever admit.

Whatever drained from George and Martha in the three years since the murder was replenished by the trial. Both the trial and Peggy's parents became burdensome to witness from afar in St. Paul. The plea of not guilty by reason of insanity incensed George and probably raised his blood pressure a hundred points. Hatred began to consume him, and the physical toll it exacted was plainly visible even through a phone.

When the defense attorney introduced expert witnesses who claimed James was suffering from hallucinosis, George went on a rampage. The attorney presented testimony that James suffered from a mental disorder caused by hallucinations. The voices he heard were by-products of his disease. Drugs he ingested, a screwed up mental circuitry, and years of parental abuse combined to render James incapable of discerning what he was doing. His lawyer presented a formidable argument.

I was swayed by his line of defense. The story of James's tormented home life, his decadent sexual fantasies, and the sketchy information about drug use combined to create a pathetic photograph of misery and deprivation. It was hard not to feel pity for the poor son of a bitch. George and Martha didn't buy it for a minute. They didn't give a shit about hallucinosis; they wanted James to fry in the chair.

My trouble with sharing their view was an intuition that you can't stay in the book of Exodus forever. An eye for an eye and a tooth for a tooth is the early biblical view. If you read on, the message changes to something more benevolent. Killing someone through cold-blooded murder or throwing a switch for the electric chair both require death sanctions. Rationalized any way you want, death is the final goal in both pursuits. Whenever death is freely sanctioned there's a risk of being on a shaky moral precipice. What gets accomplished if you become consumed advocating that someone has to die for their sin? Someone gets obliterated, and you run the risk of being devoured by hate. I couldn't see any winning combination in the entire scenario.

James Hill was given a life sentence for his crimes. His new subterranean domicile was the Nebraska Psychiatric Institute for the criminally insane. The voices he claimed to hear intrigued me in a way I could not explain. Who did these mysterious voices belong to, and what did they say? James and his psychological condition remained an enigma. I had no interest in solving the riddle because I wanted to distance myself from him as far as I could. The ass hole was probably insane and I didn't want any further intrusions in my life from James. I welcomed the decision of the court. The Institute could have him.

At the psychiatric hospital, James would be confined under a roof and banished from sight. All his abnormal delusions would be diffused by some form of therapy and massive quantities of drugs. The terrifying noises would still echo within him, but he would not be able to act them out on unsuspecting victims. He had found a temporary confidant in Detective Warner. Now what he needed most was a good confessor.

George retired from the fire department in 1979. Thirty years of work marked the distinction of his commitment to service. In February of 1980, just six months after retirement, he fell like a towering oak tree on the driveway of his house while shoveling snow. Medically speaking, he suffered a major cardiac arrest. It was quite some time before Martha saw him lying facedown in the snow. She ran outside and applied the lesson George had taught her over the years to check his neck for a pulse. Martha's fingers sensed nothing warm. Once again, the cold touch never lied.

*****

"Athanasia, I have so many questions."

"I know you do."

"Why am I with you and my father is not able to join us?"

"When you died, you witnessed the man plunging a knife into your corpse. The sight demanded a response, and you were free to choose any reaction you wished. Hatred was present, yet you chose pity. Do you know why?"

"The man was dark. He didn't have any light within him. I was saddened by the sight."

"Your choice was indoctrinated by a lifetime of judicious responses. You chose to live in accordance with the will of the Creator by sharing your gifts and avoiding the temptation to hoard. Seeing another soul deprived of light induced sympathy rather than hate."

"But I only lived for a short time."

"In that short time, you modeled creation. It's never been about quantity of years—it's the quality attained. When your father died, what did you observe?"

"That's difficult because I love him dearly."

"Now you're being evasive. What did you observe?"

"His soul was marred and tattered."

"Was it painful to see?"

"Yes."

"Hatred deteriorates souls because it inverts light. Instead of refracting the gift for all creation to bask in brilliance, it redirects the gift inward. When someone attempts to contain, manipulate, or control the Creator's gift, it tears the fabric of a soul. Your father's soul was impaired."

"Is that why he's not sharing in our communion?"

"Yes."

"Will his soul recover?"

"It's possible."

"When?"

"Recovery has stages also. Movement is predicated by the damage sustained and the reservoir of grace accumulated during one's life."

"My father had grace, didn't he?"

"Yes. Light was visible."

"What happens to souls which have no light?"

"That's revealed in another stage. Patience, Peggy."

"So, Athanasia, we accumulate grace by sharing the Creators' gift with others?"

"Exactly. Peggy, you're making progress."

"We say 'Creator' but I was raised with the name *God.* Is there a difference?"

"There have been many names given to signify the Creator. All souls have a symbiotic connection to creation but only a partial comprehension. Free will demands the autonomy for self-discovery."

"We haven't discovered the same name yet?"

"Discovery is a process, and the Creator has been called many names throughout the history of human learning. You mentioned God, there has been YHVH, Elohim, Shahadah, Allah, Jehovah, Buddha, Shiva, Oodin, Varuna, Izanagi, Isis, Inana, Ishtar, Astarte, Anat, Persephone, Izanami, Tara, Kuan-yin, Totantsi, Freyja. This list goes on and on. The struggle to understand completely is arduous."

"So the different names are guesses we make?"

"They're pieces of the puzzle."

"Why is it so hard if we've been here before?"

"Because partial comprehension agonizingly labors for identity and soul's struggle to rediscover the communion they once shared. The search for identity yields so many interpretations and the names denote varying levels of comprehension."

"Athanasia, all the different names come from many religions. Why don't they all agree?"

"Comprehension has obstacles, and people have struggled to overcome them. All religions embody revelation from the Creator, but they differ in their degree of assimilation."

"I don't understand. Why do they struggle so hard with something so simple?"

"Peggy, you've only experienced one stage. From your vantage point, it appears simple, but there is so much more to learn."

CHAPTER 3

Entering the seminary begs one giant question. Why the hell would anyone in their right mind desire to become a priest in the Catholic Church? The profession is somewhat defined by the boundaries of celibacy, poverty, and unwavering obedience. All of these are in direct opposition to the current maxims of our culture. Freedom of sexual expression, the opportunity to financially succeed, and personal autonomy are the slogans of the day. The Church demands that priests live in opposition to these maxims. As I said, who in their right mind would choose to live this way.

I entered the St. Paul Seminary in the fall of 1975. Situated on the banks of the mighty Mississippi, its breathtaking view provided a divine panorama. What a glorious setting to invoke on a journey into the world of a transcendent God and a mysterious Roman Catholic Church. Eagerly, I read about the history of the seminary grounds. Built in the late 1800s, the brick and mortar used to construct the buildings gave the campus an austere ambiance of antiquity and order. It looked old, and it felt Catholic. The three main dormitories were five stories high and shaped like brick boxcars. The administration building was architecturally designed to resemble a train station. I found out they were gifts of a St. Paul railroad tycoon who was a philanthropist at the turn of the century. His name was James Hill. God, I'm haunted by that name.

To presume I was in my right mind would have been an error. Peggy's murder, the arrest of James, and George and Martha's hatred produced confusion. Out of my bewildered state, I fashioned a BA degree in philosophy from St. Thomas University. It's not that I was unable to function, rather I appeared to be functioning normally. As we all know, appearances are sometimes deceiving.

My standard comic reply to anyone who asked why I wanted to be a priest was the fact I grew up in a household with five brothers and eight sisters. When the church offered me my own bedroom with a private bathroom, I immediately accepted. The real reason was much more mystical.

The study of philosophy from Socrates, Plato, Aristotle, Augustine, Aquinas, Spinoza, Kant, to Nietzsche was a progression from logical, rational thought into areas of muddled quandary. Even though my mental faculties yearned for a stable hierarchical view of life, my experience and intuition screamed there was chaos and confusion out there. I thought the key for resolution of this dilemma had to be contained in mysticism. Since the Catholic church was a mystical encyclopedia ranging from Arianism to Zealotry, it seemed natural to delve in head first. It's highly advised to plunge into mysticism with professional assistance. Anyone who tries to go it alone might find insanity lurking in the shadows.

The courses for study in the academic environment called major seminary were as follows:

- Liturgical rites, rituals, and rubrics
- Church history: patristic period, Middle Ages, Reformation, Modern, and Postmodern
- Ecclesiology, Christology, Trinitarian theology, Sacramentality, theodicy, and eschatology
- Moral virtues, moral dilemmas, and canon law
- Clinical pastoral counseling

- Sacred scripture: Pentateuch, Prophets, Judges, Kings, Wisdom literature, Gospels, Epistles, Acts, and Apocryphal writings
- Homiletics

If the original Apostles were given this curriculum, they would have stayed in their boats. Fishing would sound a lot less burdensome even on days when you don't even get a bite. Tending nets they knew, this stuff would be completely foreign material.

Scripture was my favorite, and the book of Genesis provided consolation in times of tumult. It never provided concrete answers to the dilemmas I faced, but the stories detailed incidents that sometimes coincided with my own experience. If I just kept searching, maybe the answers would appear.

> Throughout the earth, people spoke the same language, with the same vocabulary. Now as they moved eastwards they found a plain the land of Shinar. They said to one another, "Come, let us make bricks and bake them in the fire. Let us build ourselves a town and a tower with its top reaching heaven. Let us make a name for ourselves, so that we may not be scattered about the whole earth." Now Yahweh came down to see the town and the tower that the sons of man had built. "So they are all a single people with a single language! This is but the start of their undertakings. There will be nothing too hard for them to do. Come, let us go down and confuse their language on the spot so that they can no longer understand one another." (Gen. 11:1–8)

If jargon is looking for its moment of conception, then the tower of Babel may be the point of consummation. The language of the Catholic church has its roots in Hebrew, Aramaic, and Greek. But when viewed in terms of longevity, Latin reigns. Even though the church changed in the 1960s to adopt the practice of allowing each country to speak in their mother tongue, they still retained a distinct theological language. Theology, like many other disciplines, entered into a covenant with jargon centuries ago. The tower of Babel may have only been a ziggurat in terms of size, but it's impact in the world of language elevated it to celestial proportions.

I began my studies in a major seminary with an open mind and a willing heart. Coming to St. Paul was a watershed moment in my life. I was determined to discern whether or not I had been called to the priesthood. Even though the bulk of my energy would be focused on academics, there was a lingering hope my heart and soul would be healed from the mental image of the blood and chalk line on the carpet. The image festered in a subterranean cavity, and it vacillated between an active and dormant state. Either way, it was always there. Unfortunately, I knew I was powerless over it, and I was becoming alarmed by certain behaviors I had chosen as a way to cope.

Psychologically, a case could be made that seminary was my refuge and safe haven. I was running away instead of seeking something new. What the hell, is there a better place one could choose to seek sanctuary? From the standpoint of being remote and outside the confines of the real world, the seminary was only a few degrees removed from a cloistered monastery. The reason a monastery never sounded appealing was the fear of having to spend an inordinate amount of time alone. We may all be solitary to a degree, but just the term *monastery* sounded too foreboding. I opted to simply trust my intuition and pray a spiritual power guided me here.

The first professor to have a major impact on me was a Jewish rabbi. The seminary invited Rabbi Aserial to introduce first year clerics to the study of the Torah. We quickly discovered we were in the hands of a professional.

Standing a mere five and a half feet, his height did not negate his stunning presence. A little bulky in the midsection and a face camouflaged by a thick black beard minimized any physical fear, but his gait and stern stare magnified the appearance of intellectual prowess. Some people simply look intelligent. The rabbi had the look.

Walking into class the first day, he carried a bundle of newspapers. Passing one to each student, he told us to examine the front-page headline: FEDERAL RESERVE RAISES INTEREST RATES.

Peering at the huddled mass of priestly candidates, he asked us if this headline was true. Befuddled by the simplicity of the question and intimated by his presence, no one answered. He calmly walked to the first row of students and reassured us this was not a trick question. After we all nodded our heads yes to his question, he directed us to the editorial page. He told us to read the column by Art Buchwald. Once again, he asked us if this was true. A faint glimmer crept into the room as we began to see where the rabbi was leading us.

The rabbi defined a newspaper as a collection of written articles and illustrations that vary in style, context, and purpose. Each section contains articles chosen to form a cohesive whole that attempts to describe the events of yesterday. Readers select articles that sate the multitude of appetites they wish to satisfy. When scanning the sections, it's imperative the reader is able to differentiate between fact, fiction, advertisement, entertainment and opinion. Truth has different levels, degrees, and manifestations. It's up to the reader to discriminate.

Someone taught us how to read a newspaper or at least guided us in the right direction. The instruction required was minimal. Over time and with experience, we acquired the skill. When dealing with scripture, the task is much more demanding. Scripture is seriously studied from numerous criticisms. The criticisms are schools of inquiry that examine scripture on different levels. The major criticisms are as follows: textual, historical source, form, redaction, canonical, structuralism, narrative, rhetorical, social, and advocacy. This is one hell of a lot of criticism. I'm not sure whether God looks down with pride on his lowly subjects for the complex scrutiny they put the Bible through *or* if He simply shakes his head in dismay. Either way, scripture scholars do not adhere to the keep it simple stupid approach regarding biblical study.

Rabbi Aserial's expertise was source criticism. His penchant in the field was identifying writing styles and categorizing their frequency of appearance in the text. Biblical scholarship identified four separate sources or traditions of authorship in the first five books of the Old Testament. They were labeled J, E, D, and P. These initials do not signify four individual authors; they reflect four separate schools of thought. Because the Hebrew people were divided through conquests and exiles, their experiences varied. Recording their history and interpreting moral lessons fell on generations of eyewitnesses. Four separate accounts survived, and they shared similarities along with numerous discrepancies. A redactor needed to collate the accounts into a readable manuscript.

The rabbi told us a redactor functioned like an editor. Newspapers are products of journalists who write articles requiring editorial approval. Journalists sometimes work for editors who think they are god, but the redactor who blended J, E, D, and P had the monumental task of speaking for God. Rabbi Aserial claimed current research presented by a team of scripture scholars pointed to the court of Solomon as the time frame and locale for a redactor. Investigation was leading to a woman in Solomon's court who edited and revised the four accounts. Only a theory at this stage, it still possessed enough credibility for serious consideration. Since Wisdom literature uses the female pronoun to designate the virtue of wisdom, how ironic is it that the redactor might have been a woman? From one angle, it makes sense. What man in history would have been capable of demonstrating the parochialism required to render such a glorious account?

Divine revelation plunges the Bible into territory occupied by very few works of literature. The rabbi bluntly stated we were entering the world of mystery and faith. Scripture would become a companion, a tutor, and sometimes a nemesis for the rest of our lives. He said, "Scripture has the unique power to transform and transfigure. Be careful though, like any great power it can be twisted, turned, and demonically abused."

Lecturing for two hours a day, three days a week, he never consulted a note or required the use of memory aids. He held me in rapture with his brilliance. We walked through scripture guided by a pro and assimilated knowledge in prodigious quantities. The Old Testament came alive and vibrated its message with distinction. What a journey for a schmuck like myself! Everyone should be so fortunate, especially Catholics who often display biblical illiteracy.

Besides being the best professor I ever had in my academic life, there was one facet of the man that none of our class knew about until the end of the year dinner in the seminary refectory. By I am sure an accident, one of my classmates noticed at the dinner the black numbers blazed on his wrist. He always wore a long-sleeve white shirt with cuff links and a black suit coat in class. On this night, maybe due to the fact it was a hot summer day, he had a short-sleeve shirt on under the suit coat. The sign these numbers conveyed were the self-expression that Rabbi Azerial endured the concentration camps. As word passed among my classmates, all of us were in both shock and astonishment. His credibility and character were already at the highest level attainable, but now they reached the zenith level.

Catholics have a schizophrenic history with scripture. For centuries, most of the population was truly illiterate so the Bible was communicated through sermons and stained glass windows in church. The windows illustrated various biblical stories. As the priest read or lectured, the people could look up and see the story depicted. When more people learned to read and Bibles were readily available, the book adorned most Catholic households. Not as a book to be read, but as a place to document family history. All the important events of family life were recorded on the front pages of the Bible. It was passed down to future generations as an heirloom. Unfortunately, the only worn and tattered pages were the ones before the book of Genesis. Catholics rarely ventured into the printed text. It remained sacrosanct territory open only to those who received some mysterious invitation. Most people were relieved they never received the invite.

Scripture begins with a resounding, breathtaking, and intoxicating story of creation. The stories of Genesis are mythological masterpieces laden with wisdom, insight, and numerous levels of interpretation. Launching into the book is a festive love song. The characters are so inventive and the lessons played out are multileveled dramas. But like all love stories, the honeymoon quickly ends. The books that follow Genesis descend into areas of myopic legalism, names that are impossible to pronounce, and battles or exiles that

invoke endless lamentation. If this isn't bad enough, the authors torture us further by writing lengthy genealogies of ancient family trees.
Many readers lose their focus and put the book down. Divine revelation or not, the material is difficult to trudge through. Eventually,
the Bible is placed in a bookcase where it's conspicuously seen but
rarely handled. Scripture accumulates dust as it atrophies on a shelf.

The long history of biblical neglect presents Catholics with a
religious dilemma. They are easy fodder in an argument for anyone
with just a meager level of biblical proficiency. Quoting a biblical
book, chapter, and verse to bolster one's case completely immobilizes
most Catholics. It doesn't matter if the verse is taken out of context
or incorrectly quoted because simply the mention of scripture freezes
most Catholics. Citing anything from the Old Testament produces
complete paralysis.

Rabbi Aserial was poignantly clear when it came to citing scriptural verses to bolster an argument. He said, "The scriptures contain both descriptive and prescriptive ethics. Obviously, they differ
in degree and intent. Be extremely careful when enlisting scripture
as *the* source for a position on a particular issue. Like a two-edged
sword, it can be quoted to defend or disclaim almost any position.

"Descriptive ethics is 80 percent and prescriptive ethics accounts
for the final 20 percent. The difficulty is knowing which is what.
Descriptive ethics is a teaching style that uses the life experiences of
people throughout history, demonstrating what they decided to do
with their lives and what consequences followed from their choices.
Morality is derived from their experience. Prescriptive ethics is a more
direct approach stating distinctly how everyone should live and what
decisions they ought to make. Recognizing the difference between
these two teaching disciplines is key to understanding scripture."

CHAPTER 4

It didn't take long before I surmised the magical word underpinning all theological inquiry is *mystery*. The Trinity is a mystery. Transubstantiation is a mystery. The Immaculate Conception is a mystery. The Incarnation is a mystery. Even God remains a mystery. Theology can cloak itself in superlative dialogue and discussion, but the reality remains that it ultimately invokes a giant leap of faith from each and every believer. Just because it can't be empirically proven is not grounds for complete dismissal but it does necessitate a spiritual awakening. Without a leap of faith, agnosticism would prevail as the only logical option.

Two areas of theology in Holy Mother Church that do not make it into the realm of mystery are infallibility and celibacy. Both of them exhibit deep strains of befuddlement. Why in the world the church wants or needs to proclaim certain pronouncements above the capacity to be in error is beyond me. Almost two thousand years of communal existence with periodic revelation from the Holy Spirit should be ample grounds to rest your case on. Why the church, in the late nineteenth century, felt compelled to issue this dogma is a *mystery*. Better yet, why would they even want to?

This stance begs the question of how can fallible human beings who are obviously flawed in so many ways and on so many levels proclaim that they are totally incapable of error? I recognize that infallibility only occurs on matters of faith and morals and it is only proclaimed from the chair of Peter but was it truly necessary that Holy Mother Church broadcast this to the entire world? It does infer that in some area we have a monopoly on truth that no other religion can possibly obtain because God is talking directly to us. Even if God is talking directly to us, why not just state the case without saying it's infallible. All matters of faith and morals are leaps of faith anyway. Thank God, the church rarely proclaims infallibility. There are enough issues that provoke exclusivity from other religions and this particular mystery seems to say we are totally closed to any rational debate. Why?

Celibacy is an entirely other matter. The church of the twentieth century invokes the decision by Jesus not to marry as the prime reason for celibacy. It also contends the apostles left their wives when Jesus called them to follow him. Depending on whom these guys were married to, this could have been justifiable abandonment.

Historical research paints a gradual progression toward the implementation of celibacy as a discipline in the church. It began as a restriction against a second marriage. For whatever reasons, once someone lost their wife, they were implored to remain single for the remainder of their days. Within a couple hundred years after Jesus, it was recommended that the episcopate (bishops) refrain from marriage altogether.

Whether you appeal to Justinian in AD 529, the Gallican Councils, Toledo in 653, Chrodegang of Metz in 755, Pavia in 1022, or Gratian's Decretum in 1142, it wasn't until Pope Innocent III, in 1207, when legislation regarding celibacy for all clerics was universally enforced. Prior to 1207, some priests, some bishops, some cardinals, and even some popes were married and having children. How many clerics were married throughout the period of history would be difficult to determine. Their reasons for resisting the prior statements regarding the goal of a celibate priesthood were not published as far as I know. It just doesn't take a rocket scientist to figure out a couple of their reasons.

Holy Mother Church provides volumes of fairly sound scriptural and theological grounds for its position on the matter of celibacy. One area that received minimal coverage is the business of finances. When the monastic influence in the church increased to levels unparalleled in history, the church witnessed large communities of men living together in poverty and growing in holiness. St. Augustine, St. Benedict, and St. Boniface were only a few examples of spiritual brilliance directly attributed to monastic life. The church began to see how inexpensive monastic life was because it didn't have to house and feed wives, children, and in-laws. This had to be seen as a glorious financial windfall. In today's terms, the idea would probably get someone installed as a cardinal and nominated for the Nobel Prize in economics. Defined, rationalized, or justified in any language available, the discipline of celibacy had monetary roots.

From Innocent III to John Paul II of today, the best an aspiring cleric could do is debate the issue with select classmates and spiritual directors under the cloak of confidentiality. Making any public noise about the negative features of celibacy usually renders stern consternation from the seminary staff. It's best to keep your mouth shut and take lots of cold showers. I did both as I began searching for classmates whom I could trust and confide in.

With partnership in mind, I scanned my fellow sojourners looking for likely candidates. Even though we came from different locales, ranged in age from twenty-one to fifty-two, obtained undergraduate degrees from various universities, and had diverse employment experience, groups formed within the class. It didn't take long to find out who fit where. Mark from Iowa intrigued me the moment I met him.

Mark is an instructed soul. His soul is shrouded in an elegant tapestry that confirms he has benefited from excellent instruction. Sound architectural guidance nourished him for years, and arriving at seminary was a natural response to a spiritual invitation. All the men arriving at seminary were responding to a call, but Mark appeared to have been formally invited. After a short period of time, it was easy to distinguish which seminarians received an invite like

Mark's. His invitation brought me once again to the book of Genesis, courtesy of Fr. Sherman.

> Yahweh said to Abram, "Leave your country, your family and your father's house, for the land I will show you. I will make you a great nation; I will bless you and make your name so famous that it will be used as a blessing. I will bless those who bless you; I will curse those who slight you. All the tribes of the earth shall bless themselves by you." (Gen. 12. 1–3)

God authored both calls, and Mark possessed incredible gifts to offer the church. He would never rival Abram in worldwide impact, but his presence guaranteed an impression. His footprints would be visible in every parish he served. Since my call appeared to be more informal, I knew I'd benefit from Mark's wisdom. Hopefully, I had something to give in return.

Mark was tall, lean, athletic, and approachable. With his curly brown hair, handsome facial features, and an abundant intellect, he appeared to be the kind of person I would want to talk to if I ever needed to see a priest. Compassion for others and a natural propensity to be empathetic ruled Mark's life. I fell in love with his sense of humor and marveled at his musical and artistic talent. He painted and sketched while listening to music, which ranged from Mozart to Tom Waites. Even with the music off, he could belt out lyrics from memory. His retention astounded me.

Mark and I were both devout heterosexuals. Whether or not sexual preferences are guided by genetic wiring or predisposition's, all our circuitry veered in the direction of good-looking women. Mark's handsome qualities put him a notch or two above me in the arena of deflecting advances from the opposite sex. He had the features that would ultimately tag him as "Father What-a-Waste" by women following his ordination to the priesthood. Regardless of this distinction between us, celibacy would definitely be an arduous struggle for both of us.

There were men in the seminary who probably would not have to fight so hard when it came to sexual advances made by women. Some of them were literally "baby priests." They discovered at a very early age in life that priesthood was their call and vocation. Because of this early knowledge, they never bothered to mess around with the details of dating girls, exchanging kisses, and fighting horrendous nightly battles focused on areas of the female anatomy. Even if a girl innocently wandered across their path, they had a defense against the girl wandering too close. The defense was normally their mother.

When some Catholic mothers get wind that their son is entertaining thoughts of a vocation to the priesthood, they become barracudas. Any girl who messes with one of these mothers will have scars to prove it. Their baby priest will not be tampered with by anyone wearing a plaid skirt. The only women who are even allowed to get near their son are nuns in full habit. These mothers have a specific role to play in their sons' vocation. They have to ward off all female intruders until the day he walks down the aisle of the cathedral to receive ordination.

> When Abram came back after the defeat of Chedor-laomer and the kings who had been on his side, the king of Sodom came to meet him the Valley of Shaveh. Melchizedek, king of Salem brought bread and wine; he was a priest of God Most High. He pronounced this blessing; "Blessed be Abram by God Most High, creator of heaven and earth, and blessed be God Most High for handing over your enemies to you." And Abram gave him a tithe of everything. (Gen. 14: 17–20)

Abram is our model of faith but Melchizedek epitomizes our destination. The goal centers on hearing a particular proclamation issued by Holy Mother Church, "You are a priest forever, in the line of Melchizedek."

This line declared we made it, and believe me, many mothers of baby priests weep like infants when they hear it proclaimed. Mostly, they are happy for their sons. But they are also relieved that they're laborious work is finally completed. From here on out, their son is now in God's hands, and He better damn well watch over him.

CHAPTER 5

Part of seminary training was weekend work in one of the local parishes. Mark and I were assigned to St. Matthew's Church in Minneapolis. We were sent out like early disciples to experience the world we would eventually inherit. It was the seminary's way of asking the question, do you really want to do this for the rest of your life?

Sent in pairs because alone might be dangerous, our mission was to observe typical parish life. Dressed in white shirts and ties, we resembled Jehovah Witnesses evangelizing to a given neighborhood. Thank God, Mark and I weren't required to go door to door. Our mission centered mainly on staying out of the way while closely observing the actions and words of others. The pastor of the parish served as our instructor and guide. Our responsibilities were to do whatever he told us.

Fr. Christopher appeared to be an instructed soul, but there were moments when he gave signs of going astray. He had been ordained for twelve years and was made pastor of St. Matthew's two years before we arrived. It was his first assignment as pastor. In our first meeting, he welcomed us and outlined the role we would play in parish life. Since we were neophytes in the eyes of the church, our tasks for the first year were simple. In terms of power or responsibility, we were one rung under the maintenance supervisor (aka the janitor).

Fr. Chris was immensely proud of the new architectural feature recently completed in the church. A brand-new, state-of-the-art baptismal font was constructed. The *anowien* would descend into a pool of flowing water for full immersion. The sacrament of baptism would now resemble its biblical origin on the shores of the Jordan River. Mark and I participated in the initial ribbon-cutting ceremony.

The newborn baby's name was Alexander, the first prodigy of Steve and Regina. Their parental pride beamed as their son was presented for immersion in the waters of baptism. As Fr. Chris stood in the water cradling the infant, his prayers for the child rose like incense to the heavens.

"This is our faith. This is the faith of the church. We are proud to profess it, in Christ Jesus our Lord."

"Amen."

"Steve and Regina, is it your will that Alexander should be baptized in the faith of the Church, which we have all professed with you?"

"It is."

"Alexander, I baptize you in the name of the Father, and of the Son, and of the Holy Spirit."

The water was warm and refreshing to Alexander, much like the previous nine months in the womb of his mother. Alexander responded to the warm water by discharging urine in a steady stream into the waters of the baptismal font and on the vestment of Fr. Chris.

Mark and I spent the remainder of our Sunday draining the pool and cleansing the font with an assortment of chemicals. The sacrament removed original sin from Alexander; it was our job to remove the urine from the pool. Sacramental rituals attempt to address the theological dimensions that link us to a transcendent God. Once in a while, we forget to consider impediments that afflict newborn babies. Full immersion is an excellent baptismal entrance into the life of the church; it's just better practiced with individuals whose sphincter muscles are more fully developed.

CHAPTER 6

Both Mark and I were products of the mass of the Roman Rite. We grew up in a church that celebrated the *missa cantata* in Latin.

"In nomine Patris et Filii et Spiritus Sancti. Amen. Dominus vobiscum."

"Et cum spiritu tuo."

Mass anywhere in the world followed a preordained formula. Walk into a Catholic church in any foreign country, and the celebration would be identical to what you experienced at home. Mark and I began our journey at the baptismal fonts in the churches where we were born. Every Catholic has a sacramental history, and it is meticulously recorded in registries at the church of their baptism. No matter where you receive first communion, confirmation, the sacrament of marriage, and, ultimately, death, a notation is sent to your home parish. From womb to tomb, your sacramental life is entered and recorded by the church of your birth. Holy Mother Church keeps track of her children.

The highlight of our Catholic youth was the elevation to altar boy. It usually occurred in the fourth grade at the tender age of nine. Now along with the *Baltimore Catechism*, we had to memorize and regurgitate certain prayers of the Latin Mass. The Confiteor was my personal favorite.

Confiteor Deo omnipotenti, beatae Mariae semper virgini, beato Michaeli Archangelo, beato
Joanni Baptistae, sanctis Apostolis Petro et Paulo,
omnibus sanctis, et tibi pater, quia peccavi nimis
cogitatione, verbo et opere: MEA CULPA, MEA
CULPA, MEA MAXIMA CULPA. Ideo pre-
cor bea tam Mariam semper Virginem, beatum
Michaelem Archangelum, beatum Joannem
Baptistam, sanctos Apostolos Petrum et Paulum,
omnes sanctos, et te pater, orare pro me ad
Dominum Deum nostrum.

Once you've done the mea culpas, there's no turning back.
You're a Catholic for life. Whether you practice the faith or choose to
abstain, it remains the Latin dance of your soul.

My most poignant experience as an altar boy occurred when
my great-uncle came to visit our hometown. He was an ex-marine
chaplain during World War II. The war had been over for years, yet
Fr. George still looked like a marine. He was gruff, rough, and ready
to rumble. His stark stare conveyed to me that he was a no-nonsense
priest who didn't take shit from anybody. When he was present in a
room or church, he commanded attention. I was told to be at Mass
the following morning at 6:00 a.m. I would be his altar boy.

I went home and practiced my Latin. Even though I knew my
responses, I wanted to make sure. The bulk of my serving experience
had been at the 6:00 a.m. daily mass where I practiced the ritual
in front of small congregations. Mistakes tend to be overlooked at
six in the morning. Serving for my great-uncle would be my first
assignment under a spotlight. The priest I normally served for was
old, retired, and hard of hearing. Altar boys could recite any gibber-
ish they wanted, and he would never know the difference. Once in
a while, he would fall asleep in the chair during post-communion
meditation. It was the altar boy's responsibility to gently wake him
up for the final prayer and dismissal. Serving for Fr. George would
not be like that at all. His marine corps background prompted my

imagination to run wild with visions of monstrous penalties for mis-pronunciations or ritual errors. He scared the hell out of me.

I was doing a perfect job all the way up to the offertory. For some unknown reason, I became immobilized as I stood in front of him with the cruets of wine and water. He held out the chalice to receive what was to become the blood of Christ, and I went to pour the wine in. Then I froze and thought maybe it's the water first—no, it's the wine—wait. After an agonizing moment of indecision where I feigned the wine cruet, then the water cruet, then the wine cruet again, Fr. George leaned over and whispered, "Thomas, are you with me or against me? Pour the wine."

In a millisecond it was clear how the hell could I have stumbled. I knew it was the wine first—it was so simple. I immediately wanted to recite chapter and verse of the altar-boy lesson Sr. Alfredine made us memorize, "When someone offers only wine, then the blood of Christ begins to exist without us; but when it is only water, then the people begin to exist without Christ. Wine comes first, water then follows, just as Christ comes first and we follow."

I wanted to tell Fr. George I knew all along. My stumble was not based on ignorance or a lack of study. I had the ritual down pat. I even remembered Sr. Alfredine claimed the lesson was taken from some saint named Cyprian who lived a long time ago. Unfortunately, I couldn't communicate anything to him because I needed to move on to the washing of hands. The moment was over, the ritual contin-ued, and my blunder would live on in infamy.

As I look back, I'm sure Fr. George forgot the incident by the time he reached the Cannon Actionis. It was just a minor trans-gression by an altar boy whose hands trembled in fear. Fr. George undoubtedly witnessed miscues by servers on a regular basis. Why the hell I still recall it and can see it so vividly is one of the mysteries of memory. Why certain events stick with us for so many years is a quirk of human nature. Like the indelible mark made on our souls when we receive the sacraments, some memories don't wash away with time.

When my family moved to Omaha, I just finished the eighth grade. St. Lawrence Church was beginning its adaptation to Vatican

II, and Latin was replaced by English. The mass was now called a "liturgy," and a new altar facing the people had been erected in the church. The leisurely stroll along the altar rail holding the paten while the priest distributed communion on the tongues of the faithful was changed. People came standing instead of kneeling and had the option to receive on the tongue or in their hand. The role of altar boy diminished to a minor level that seemed inconsequential. All the glory, majesty, and mystery had been expunged from the ministry. It was a perfect time to retire.

The changes from Vatican II came suddenly and, for most Catholics, without warning. They were welcomed by some and disdained by others. With the blink of an eye, Holy Mother Church became a new woman. Private adoration, the mystery of ritual, and the priest as the sole spiritual and temporal rulers of a parish were transformed into communal worship, audience participation, and numerous lay ministries. The transcendent God of my youth was now visible to see, hear, and touch. As a teenager, change was exciting. For older Catholics, it must have been difficult. I overheard many murmurs of protest from people who felt betrayed.

Since I had moved to a new city, a new school, and was surrounded by new faces everywhere, participation in a new Catholic church simply blended into the overall confusion. Like everything else, I simply tried to make the best of it. At least that's what I intended until I came down from the bleachers in the gymnasium to receive communion at the opening liturgy of my freshman year. I was in an all-boys Jesuit prep school. Packed in the bleachers and surrounded by 999 fellow classmates, I watched in amazement as guitars were strummed and voices sang the lyrics to hymns I never heard before. It was upbeat and celebratory, a lot like the football pep rally we had the week before.

Our focus was supposed to be on God, but now we were talking to Him in an entirely new way. It sounded like He had become one of our buddies. Someone we knew well and conversed with many times before. I had no idea what my classmates thought because they were still strangers. So I decided to play along and pretend this was nothing new. Coming down the bleachers I placed my hands, left over right, to receive holy communion. The Jesuit scholastic intoned the words, "The body of the dude."

I'm not sure if I ever recovered enough to respond "Amen."

*****

"Athanasia, I never spent much time with the Bible. Does it give all the answers?"

"No one or no book is capable of having all the all the answers Peggy."

"Well...does it give the ones we need?"

"It does."

"Where was I supposed to look? There's lots of stuff in the Bible."

"There certainly is. The simple answer is found in the beatitudes. All you do is pay attention to the description of those receiving the blessing. Notice what's not mentioned. Being wealthy, powerful, or famous, along with other temporal efforts are not listed. In spite of their absence, people tend to invest an inordinate amount of time and energy pursuing them."

"Does this mean the wealthy, powerful, and famous are doomed?"

"No, not at all. Material resources provide both opportunities and responsibilities. When someone attains wealth, power, or fame, certain privileges become available. These privileges afford certain freedoms, but they also demand reciprocity."

"What do you mean?"

"People with material surplus have an obligation to share. Just as the light from the Creator disdains being hoarded, material goods share this same response. Whenever a person accumulates entities of creation for the sole purpose of attainment, the gift becomes refractive instead of reflective."

"Athanasia, you're losing me again."

"Okay, I'll simplify it. All souls have the gift of light. When light is freely shared with others, souls become luminous. We are modeling the Creator, who gave us the gift. Hoarding is contrary to the nature of creation because it presumes ownership and control."

"So being selfish is sinful, right?"

"Yes, but there's more to it. Selfishness with any element of creation has the power to destruct. Refraction obscures because it points inward instead of outward. Whenever the power of light is misdirected, it can burn and destroy."

"But people accumulate things because they fear not having enough when they really need them. Why is that wrong?"

"Peggy, it's not wrong to prepare, plan, or save. What sometimes happens, though, the effort expended excludes recognition that everything is essentially a gift. Ownership declares this is mine. Control contends I'll do whatever I please. Both attitudes are refractive because the emphasis is directed inward. Whenever someone attempts to hide light, even for safekeeping, the power is distorted."

"Back to the beatitudes. Those are people who have little or nothing. Correct?"

"They are attitudes, Peggy. Attitudes transcend material goods. Souls who realize they own or control nothing in the eyes of the Creator and offer everything back to the source are blessed. Anyone is able to become part of the beatitudes."

"All they need to do is share what they have?"

"Exactly. Those who have an abundance are offered an opportunity to become magnanimous beacons of light. Brighter than the stars in the sky."

"Too bad so many don't realize it."

"It is sad, Peggy. It's very sad."

"Don't tutorial angels whisper to them?"

"Constantly."

"So what's the problem?"

"Often, wealth, power, prestige, fame, and all the rest takes hostages. Souls enamor to pleasure and become addicted to the sensation."

"Athanasia, pleasure is not all bad, is it?"

"Not in proper portions, it's not, but pleasure is insatiable."

"What does that mean?"

"It's limitless. There's no boundary a soul can reach where ultimate fulfillment is attained."

"You always want more?"

"Exactly."

"Why do we chase after it so hard then?"

"Because the allure and enticement promises a final destination."

"Which is what?"

"We'll become like God. Sound familiar?"

"The snake in the garden of Eden."

"Correct. The lie told centuries ago continues to deceive today. Sadly, the lessons available to everyone go unnoticed by many."

"What happens to their souls?"

"Souls like your father, Peggy?"

"Yes…I really want to know, Athanasia."

"You will, Peggy. Indeed, you will."

CHAPTER 7

A priest has daily responsibilities in a parish, but his main contact with the community is reserved to two days. The flock gathers on weekends to be fed. The litmus test of priestly ministry is defined by the spiritual nourishment offered during this short time span. If your call is to sate the spiritual thirst of the faithful, then you better be well prepared on Saturday night and Sunday morning.

We heard Fr. Chris preach many times, along with other priests at the seminary and those in our parishes as we grew up in the faith. The term *homily* replaced what used to be called a sermon. Sermons had taken on a negative connotation associated with fire and brimstone or lectures on personal sinfulness. Homilies were going to be the crowning spiritual jewel of the revised liturgy following Vatican II. The priest would make the scripture readings come alive and relate them to the communities' spiritual thirst. They would do more than hold our attention. The priest would be an architect of our souls as the homily served as his blueprint.

Homiletic preparation in the seminary contained one tragic flaw. The time allotted for this exercise was minimal at best, so it could be presumed they were satisfied with the levels of our public-speaking ability. It is the one area where all of us needed a ton of work. The greatest gift any seminary could give to the Catholic faithful in the pews would be to train seminarians more exhaustively in both public-speaking technique and homily content. Talk about sheep being sent to the wolves—we were all sent out with varying levels of training and confidence.

The church had prescribed to the notion that a priest will learn best how to deliver a homily by on-the-job training. Simple repetition over the years will hone both his delivery and message. In this area, the church is about as far removed from infallible as it can get. The dribble that spews out of some priests on a weekly basis is enough to establish valid grounds for the canonization as saints of every parishioner who has to listen to it week after bloody week. Some priests are so bad that martyrdom begins to look promising for the faithful because it will end one's obligation for weekly attendance.

Our homiletics professor never advocated preparing a homily while you are putting on your vestments in the sacristy, but Mark and I heard a few that sounded like this method was employed. The worst instances were usually when the priest finished the gospel and then preceded to tell the congregation what he just finished reading. "Retelling the story" is what we nicknamed this homiletic practice. It sure doesn't give much credit to the faithful in the pews. Do we really think they are that stupid? Surely, they've heard these readings read before because we repeat the entire cycle every three years. Most of the time, it appears to be a quick and easy way to notch one more homily on your belt and simply get it over with. Unfortunately, it also appears that there is a direct proportion between the time spent on homily preparation and the actual length of the talk given. As preparation time dwindles, the length of the talk increases.

Without a doubt, there are excellent homilists in the Catholic church—priests who sincerely regard the time spent with their parishioners as valuable real estate. They educate, elucidate, and present their material in a straightforward fashion to the audience that is present at each individual liturgy. Their talks have a beginning, a middle, and an end. There is a central theme running through those separate parts, and it's bolstered by personal examples of how they themselves confront or overcome the burdens of life which sometimes run counter to the gospel message. When a priest proclaims a homily such as this, the faithful are truly uplifted and the liturgy is celebratory. They serve as witnesses to the crowning jewel of liturgical nourishment for thirsty souls. Mark and I began to venture out in search of this jewel.

Once in a while, when our duties allowed it, we attended another parish a few miles away. Joan of Arc Church was labeled progressive. Catholicism has a history of divergent expressions of faith, but Joan of Arc Parish tended to push the doctrinal envelope to the edge. My grandmother would be in full, major cardiac arrest before the offertory. As an avant-garde liturgical celebration, only certain Catholics were encouraged to attend. With rhythmic gyrations and vocal exclamations of praise, the community lifted their prayers to heaven. Their main prayer should have been giving thanks to the archbishop, who tolerated this unique religious expression. His tolerance level had to be huge.

The congregation was an eclectic mix of souls who traveled miles to attend. Many Catholic parishes were passed on their journey to the celebration, so dedication was never a matter to question. The celebration on Sunday morning began at ten thirty, and the size of the throng necessitated using the gymnasium in place of the actual church. Everyone was warmly greeted regardless of your status as a regular or a first-time observer. A festive environment permeated the worship space as people milled around and musicians rehearsed. A baby grand piano, violins, oboes, drums, guitars, flutes, and a saxophone provided accompaniment to a congregation committed to participate this community-defined liturgy as a celebration and tirelessly prepared for the event. Each week provided an opportunity for a new adventure.

Besides an excellent ministry of welcoming and a talented group of musicians, Joan of Arc also brought in outside speakers to deliver homilies. It was here where the envelope went past the point of progressive. One Sunday, Mark and I witnessed the most peculiar homily ever heard in a Catholic liturgy. The guest homeliest was Gloria Steinem. Following her spiritual message based on readings specifically chosen for the occasion, she invited questions from the people. One woman stood up and asked, "Ms. Steinem, you constantly talk about women becoming liberated, is there a simple maxim you advocate on how we can accomplish this?"

"Yes, a liberated woman is one who has sex before marriage and a career after."

Next, a man posed this question, "Ms. Steinem, may I be so bold to ask why you never married and had a family?"

"Because I don't endorse breeding in captivity."

What we heard wasn't the normal fare for Joan of Arc, and it wasn't one of the liturgical jewels we were searching for. This episode went way beyond the boundaries of their unique expression. Ms. Steinem joined the ranks of Walter Mondale, Jesse Jackson, and Hubert Humphrey as nationally known guest speakers at this parish. Periodically, the pastor scheduled speakers to enlighten the faithful and provide notoriety for the parish. Mark and I just happened to stumble in at one of those periods. It was a lesson to both of us that sometimes the practice of relevant messages that are shared with the faithful can swing to the other side of the pendulum and be totally counterproductive. Her message that day had a beginning, a middle, an end, and a central theme. It just wasn't Catholic by any stretch of the imagination.

We decided not to mention this experience in our weekly notes since we really weren't supposed to be there, anyway. What purpose would it serve, the archdiocese was fully aware of Joan of Arc's propensity to dwell on the edge. This particular Sunday, they simply chose a loftier precipice.

CHAPTER 8

There was something strange about Fr. Chris. Mark and I could never identify exactly what it was, but we knew some odd behavioral quirk existed. We began to hypothesize that all priests were strange to some degree. The nature of the profession demanded a slightly different mental circuitry and a somewhat radical otherworldly view of life. We called our hypothesis the "weirdidity factor." The scale ran from 1 to 10, with 10 representing strangeness beyond belief. Mark hovered around 1 or 2, while I was probably a strong 6 or 7. Fr. Chris tended to vacillate too often, so it was difficult to pin him down on any given number. In fact, it was hard to pin him down on anything. Some intangible component was lurking in Chris's repertoire, and shortly after concluding our assignment at St. Matthew's in May of 1980, the St. Paul Pioneer Press ran a front-page headline: PRIEST INDICTED FOR CHILD MOLESTATION.

Prior to his arrest, I never heard of pedophilia. If you asked me what it meant before the indictment, my guess would be some foot disorder because the Latin word for foot is *ped*. It was not a term or topic of conversation in the seminary. Little did I know it would become a melanoma tumor in the soul of the Catholic church. Physically, psychologically, spiritually, and financially, the disease penetrated Holy Mother Church and inflicted devastation like a plague contaminating everything it touched. Fr. Chris was not the first case in the church, nor would he be the last. Pedophilia invaded like a tempest totally intent to rape and pillage. Hostages were rendered psychologically impaired, and the church ended up paying billions of dollars in medical assistance and legal settlements in the United States alone. For most institutions, multiple cases of pedophilia would inflict a terminal blow. The church reeled in the wake of this malaise, but it lived to see another day. Hopefully, it learned a lesson. I looked to Genesis once again.

> When the two angels reached Sodom in the evening, Lot was sitting at the gate. Lot saw them he rose to meet them and bowed to the ground. "I beg you, my lords," he said "please come down to your servant's house to stay the night and wash your feet. Then in the morning you can continue your journey." "No," they replied "we can spend the night in the open street." But he pressed them so much that they went home with him and entered his house. He prepared a meal for them, baking unleavened bread, and they ate.
>
> They had not gone to bed when the house was surrounded by the men of the town, the men of Sodom both young and old, all the people without exception. Calling to Lot they said, "Where are the men who came to you tonight? Send them out to us so that we may abuse them." (Gen. 19:1–5)

Fr. Chris entered Sodom years ago. He became immersed in an area of sexuality that triggered alarms in his conscience. As the alarms blared, his response was a slow and steady effort to turn down the volume. Gradually, the decibel level decreased to a point where his conscience ceased to function as a barometer of sexual behavior. Without any investigation or research on the issue, I privately wondered if priests who had this disorder had been sexually molested when they were young. Because this abuse was possibly never dealt with, maybe they chose priesthood because it just might be a viable block to them never acting out on their own sexual dysfunction. The decision to become a priest was a safeguard, not an abomination. Unfortunately, the dysfunction became more powerful than their ministerial profession. As I said, I had no idea at the time if this was even remotely close to a proper diagnosis. Even if there is credibility to this thought, it in no way serves as a justification for the enormity of this horrendous behavior and, more importantly for Holy Mother Church, to handle this epidemic with secrecy and a substantial checkbook. Once again, a decision based more on finances rather than morality.

When Chris turned nine years old, he got a job cleaning an outdoor drive-in theater during the summer. For twenty-five cents an hour, he removed the remnants of trash deposited by the patrons the night before. It was a solitary job, walking the rows of speakers picking up the garbage. He was making pocket change, getting some exercise, and discovering the world of sexuality. The first condom he found lying on the ground was a complete mystery. Filled with fluid of some kind, he had no clue of its purpose or function. Using a hot-dog wrapper, he deposited it in his sack. He would ask Peter for an explanation later.

Peter was an uninstructed soul who rapidly went astray. Chris got the theater job through his friendship with Peter. Despite their eight-year age difference, Chris enjoyed spending time with his neighbor. Peter was a seventeen-year-old hellion who looked after Chris like an older brother. Chris had an older sister, but she showed little interest in him. The most he could expect was an occasional cursory greeting. Since he found it difficult to talk with kids his own age, Peter became his only friend. Peter was a purveyor of excitement and electricity. His behavior pushed the boundaries of social acceptability, and he was branded a juvenile delinquent by many neighbors. Chris's parents viewed the pairing as harmless. Curiosity enticed Chris into Peter's world. He had no idea the world included a den of snakes.

Each morning, Chris walked next door to Peter's house and entered through the garage. Peter's late night frolics rendered him unable to wake up in the morning. It was Chris's responsibility to rouse Peter from sleep so he could drive him to the theater. The owners of the drive-in were paying Peter seventy-five cents an hour for trash removal. The cunning move to hire Chris for a quarter was another creative scam he engineered. Academic disciplines were abandoned years ago because he failed to see a measurable reward. Scams were easier, quicker, and more lucrative. With a little deception and a healthy dose of manipulation, Peter was becoming good at these ventures. The snakes promised him rewards. Repetition would eventually deliver what he fervently desired. Peter wanted to fit in, feel a part of, and become significant.

While Chris worked, Peter occupied himself with the latest pornographic magazines. He sat in the refreshment stand engrossed in the latest monthly offering. The pictures didn't excite him anymore. Frontal nudity lost its luster after years of observation. Letters to the editor depicting sexual escapades fueled his interest. He fantasized scenarios where he participated in these wild adventures. Peter didn't care whether the letters were real or fictitious; he just wanted a taste of the action. Since women found him crude, rude, and repulsive, Peter could only engage his imagination as he frequently masturbated. Once again, the snakes promised him it was only a matter of time.

One morning, Chris came to rouse Peter, and the snakes hissed a delicious invitation. The time had come for Chris's introduction to new allurements and enticements. When Chris began as Peter's alarm clock, he simply knocked on the door and waited downstairs. Over time, Peter coaxed Chris to come in his room and wait for him to get dressed. Today, Peter was going to invite him into one of his lurid sexual fantasies. The twerp would be putty in his hands.

"Peter, it's time to get up."

"Hey, runt, what time is it?"

"It's nine."

"Is everybody gone downstairs?"

"Yeah, why?"

"Come over here, I want to show you something."

"What?"

"Goddamn it, just come here."

"What's the matter? I didn't do anything wrong."

"Who said you did? Chris, put your hand under the sheet. You're not going to believe what I got."

"No way, Peter."

"Shut up, and give me your hand."

"Why are you doing this?"

"Relax, Chris, all I'm doing is teaching you something every kid needs to learn sometime. Hey, have I ever hurt you?

"No…but I don't like this."

"I didn't either when I was taught. I was just as scared as you are now."

"Why do I have to do it?"

"Just let me teach you. Believe me, you got to learn this someday. And you're better off letting me teach you instead of somebody who might hurt you."

"Peter, I want to go home."

"Come on, Chris, just relax. Give me your hand, and I'll show you what to do. Remember that plastic thing you found at the drive-in? I told you I'd explain it later. That's what I'm doing now. I'll show you what it's used for and why all guys do it. Come on, Chris."

"You promise this isn't bad?"

"When did I ever do something bad to you?"

"I…guess never."

"Give me your hand, squirt. I'm teaching you something your classmates won't learn for a couple more years. What the hell, you're better than any of those bozos anyway."

"You promise?"

"On the Bible, squirt."

"Well…okay."

Alarms, whistles, and sirens screamed for attention as they implored Chris to leave the house. *Get out! Run as fast as you can!* Why he chose to ignore his conscience would remain a mystery. Maybe it was his age and inexperience. Maybe he feared reprisals from Peter.

Maybe only God knows why he stayed. Whatever it was, his decision that day haunted him for the rest of his life.

Chris hated what he felt in his hand. It was disgusting to touch Peter down there. What became immediately apparent was the pleasure Peter took from his touch. He seemed to love it as he barked instructions for Chris to follow. Morning wake-up calls to Peter now included masturbation courtesy of Chris's hand. As the sessions grew in number, Chris grew accustomed to the ritual. Peter started buying him gifts, and the bribes were working. Their friendship changed as Peter began to treat Chris with more affection. One thing did not change. Chris disdained the milky substance ejected from Peter's penis. He despised the shit.

If Chris thought masturbation was the only lesson, he was sadly mistaken. Peter had much more in store for him in the coming months. Chris simply complied with Peter's demands. Your imagination can fill in the rest.

Chris struggled with his sexual identity. He never heard the terms *heterosexual, homosexual,* or *bisexual,* but he felt sure sin penetrated his life. Guilt, remorse, and shame over the actions with Peter dominated his once tranquil existence. He wanted to stop, but he also began to take pleasure from his actions. Peter guided him to sexual arousal and orgasm. Even though participating with another male haunted Chris, Peter reassured him it was normal. He told him this was a male secret and society simply chose not to talk about it. With no one else to guide him, the episode buried itself in a subterranean cavity of his soul. The image he didn't fit, wasn't whole, and insignificant dwelt in his soul like a cancerous tumor. Peter introduced evils calling card into Chris's life, and the snakes were right around the corner.

Chris used academic studies as his coping mechanism. With rigor and commitment, he achieved honor roll status among his peers. Dating girls required social skills he lacked, so he didn't venture there. Books and the knowledge offered through voracious reading became his dominant activity. Relationships appeared burdensome, so he applied minimal effort in the social arena. People remained distant from his world. Even Peter faded away as Chris grew older. Distance from everyone was the preferential choice Chris desired.

Sexually, Chris fantasized about younger boys. Fear impeded acting out the fantasies, but they surfaced in his dreams and were the images he would dwell on while masturbating. Vivid sexual dreams with young kids frequently haunted him. Despite every intention never to follow through, he agonized over the power of his sexual drive. The intensity was real and couldn't be ignored. Chris searched for a profession where these cravings could be held in check.

One Sunday, a visiting priest came to his church and spoke about vocations to the priesthood. Despite never considering it in the past, certain statements aroused his curiosity. The major impediment echoed often by others was celibacy. For Chris, it sounded perfect. Celibacy provided protection from his evil inklings. Viewing the chance encounter as a divine revelation, he entered college seminary and, eight years later, received ordination to the priesthood.

His proclivity toward pedophilia was camouflaged and difficult to detect. Without an actual episode involving a young boy, Chris kept the issue buried. For all intent and purposes, it didn't exist. Back in the 1960s, recognizing the malaise exceeded the scope of any tests available. Psychological testing measured intelligence, work ethic, social skills, and stability. Even though he showed deficiencies in two areas, his superior intelligence pulled him through. Evil's calling card slithered out of view. Unfortunately, this card proved to be his demise and ended up costing the church a bundle.

CHAPTER 9

The trial was a spectacle. The media smelled blood and a feeding frenzy dominated the airwaves and news printed a sad commentary on the pluralism of both the crime and the journalists who reported it. The facts of the case were clear from the onset. A Catholic priest sexually molested six boys.

Fr. Chris received a three-year prison sentence for his crimes. Some people in the courtroom thought it was too severe, while another group believed the judge was too lenient. A father of one victim screamed for the death penalty. As the judge pounded his gavel, the voices were silenced and everyone exited with the sound of murmurs clouding the air. Fr. Chris remained stoic and expressionless during the sentencing. Despite his obvious humiliation, the facial features he presented were detachment and aloofness. God only knew what life he would encounter following his prison term.

Along with three years of incarceration, the judge placed severe restrictions on any future contact with children. Similar to the mark placed on Cain, Fr. Chris was tattooed for life. In the eyes of the court, he would forever be a child molester. In the eyes of the church, it appeared the jury was still out. The archbishop suspended his priestly faculties but remained silent about his long-term future in the church. The archdiocese withheld their verdict till another day.

Mark and I prayed for Chris. It was the only support we could offer. We learned from others in the seminary about a treatment program that could offer a sliver of hope. Apparently, Chris was not alone in this malaise. The penalty concerning association with children would not be an insurmountable impediment. The church offered many ministries. A desk job in some agency could satisfy the court and allow him to return. We wished him the best, but we also realized his actions inflicted incredible damage on everyone involved. Sometimes the magnitude of damage is only comprehended after future consequences surface.

Benjamin was one of the six molested boys. His father shouted for the death penalty at the sentencing. He brought back memories for me of George wanting James to fry in the electric chair. Following the court case, Benjamin continued treatments for clinical depression. The church provided all the affected parties with excellent care. Highly trained and experienced professionals were instructed to provide carte blanche assistance. Recovery required time and resources. The church could only provide the resources.

On a cold January eve six months after sentencing, Benjamin descended to the basement of his family's home. Huddled on the concrete floor by the furnace, he decided to adopt a treatment method guaranteed to silence the tumult and pain of his life. He propped his back against the concrete blocks and positioned his father's shotgun, barrel first, into the cavity of his mouth. With a prayer asking forgiveness, he gently squeezed the trigger. Instantaneously, his head was splattered on the wall and the floor. His father heard the blast and found his son in a pool of blood and brain matter on the concrete floor. The force of the blast negated any attempt to check his neck for a pulse. His father yelled, "Goddamn you God! Why?"

*****

"Athanasia, why were we drawn to Benjamin?"
"Because of the violent nature of his death."
"You mean his death resembled mine?"

"To a degree. A shotgun blast to the head removes the word *attempt* from the action performed. Resolution is attained immediately. In your case, someone else made a decision and acted. Yet both your souls arrived because of a violent death at a young age. Your kindred association with Benjamin shared this similarity."

"I thought some religions believed suicide sent a soul to hell?"

"Some teach that."

"Well…Benjamin is here."

"Peggy, when you saw his soul, what did you observe?"

"A bright radiant light shrouded in pain."

"Exactly. Benjamin's struggle was not about hoarding the Creator's gift. He modeled a beatitude. Blessed are the poor in spirit, for theirs is the kingdom of heaven."

"What about his suicide? Isn't taking one's life against the Creator's wishes?"

"It is, Peggy."

"What makes Benjamin different?"

"He was preyed upon by a person who inflicted tremendous damage."

"The priest?"

"Yes."

"How could a priest do such an awful thing to a child?"

"Peggy, how could anyone do it?"

"Benjamin trusted him, didn't he?"

"There was no reason not to."

"What will happen to the priest?"

"He was preyed upon too. It will require work for him to expel the demons in his soul."

"What about Benjamin's parents?"

"Peggy, once again, we can only observe."

"But a priest did this. Who do they turn to now?"

"Granted, when a religious figure inflicts damage of this magnitude, those affected feel betrayed. After all, the perpetrator represented God by their profession. Hatred is directed at the person and the religion."

"So…where do they turn?"

"Their religion betrayed them, and it appears God allowed this to happen. Neither is true, but it's all they see. Hatred will consume them if they refuse to consider forgiveness. The difficulty is, who do they listen to?"

"Athanasia, why doesn't the Creator simply wipe out the demons? You know, just command them to be gone. What they do is monstrous."

"Demons require an invitation."

"Okay, I understand that, but once they get invited, the evil becomes horrendous."

"It does."

"So why can't angels throw them out?"

"We intercede constantly. When someone listens to the voices of evil, they have a choice to turn away."

"Who's more powerful, angels or demons?"

"Peggy, power comes down to the one you feed?"

"Angels. So why can't you get rid of demons?"

"Without evil, a soul can't exercise free will. There has to be a choice, and the options have to be innately different."

"Athanasia, the world would be glorious without evil. It would be heaven."

"It will be, Peggy. The journey to beatific vision has resplendent moments. You've already witnessed some of them."

"But the horror also continues, and it appears to never end."

"You're getting ahead of yourself, Peggy. Patience. The stages will reveal everything. Patience."

CHAPTER 10

It had been years since Peggy but I was falling in love once again. It wasn't a she, and it definitely wasn't a he. My love affair was with alcohol, specifically scotch. When I first ingested the liquid, it was putrid. I gagged. The strange thing about my reaction is that I repeated the procedure. Why I wanted to drink more of something I initially found disgusting was beyond me. I simply drank until the stuff started to taste good. I forced myself to acquire a taste for scotch. This wasn't new behavior for me because it's the exact same approach I used regarding cigarettes.

Following Peggy's death, I experimented with beer, wine, and marijuana. I had brief interludes with each of them, but they didn't grab a hold of me like scotch. They were like affairs, while scotch became my mistress. It was readily available, it didn't take up too much space in my room, and it was moderately inexpensive. Scotch made few demands on me, and it always delivered short-term relief from emotional stress. From the standpoint of a love affair in seminary, it satisfied all the criteria. Scotch wasn't a high-maintenance lover. Besides, we were good for each other.

Other seminarians drank, so I wasn't unique in that respect. They simply didn't drink as much as Mark and I did. Since we both had high tolerance levels for alcohol, our consumption didn't receive any particular notice for the first three years of study. It wasn't until our final year that the seminary staff began mentioning it in our evaluations. When it surfaced, Mark addressed the issue immediately. He talked to a priest who belonged to something called the Calix Society, and he quit drinking. I talked to the same priest and continued to drink. The only change I made was to conceal the bottle from others and begin lying about my consumption. At the time, it seemed to be my only option because people just didn't understand the love affair I had nurtured with scotch. Most rationalizations displayed a definite weakness of logical analysis. In fact, if I had tried to present a syllogism based on my rationalization, it would be justifiably *invalid*. I simply chose to ignore it.

Most people would have let the issue die right there. I only had to conceal my drinking for another year, and then I would be ordained and in the clear at a parish somewhere. This would have been the logical move to make, but my rationalization network didn't always operate in the realm of logic. I went to the priest from the Calix Society and hatched a plan to put on a two-day seminar on alcohol abuse for the seminary staff and students. I took the idea to the rector and was given his approval. Inviting speakers from all over the Twin Cities who were experts in the field, I put on a hell of a show.

As the rector thanked me for my work at the conclusion of the seminar, the applause I received vindicated my love affair with scotch. It was my first major experience of putting out a fire in my personal life, and I received the message that I was one damn good fireman. It's sad I never went directly to a mirror and peered at my reflection. If I had then maybe I would have seen the slight trace of Cain's mark on my forehead. My life was changing, and unfortunately, I never saw evil lurking at the door. Instead of looking in the mirror, I ran as fast as I could to the chapel.

CHAPTER 11

The chapel on the grounds of the St. Paul Seminary was called St. Mary's. In all seasons of the year, it served as our haven for prayer. It led us like a beacon of light offering nourishment and shelter for our spiritual journey. Sunday evening prayer was my personal favorite.

Diligently trekking the sidewalk path from our dorm rooms, we proceeded to the chapel for prayer. Darkness ruled the campus, but St. Mary's glowed in the distance. Only candlelight was allowed for this service, and the flicker of the wicks illumined the stained glass windows. The silence of the night was only briefly disturbed by our footsteps on the marble floor of the chapel. We took our seats and opened our books in preparation for the days concluding service.

A piano softly intoned a key, and 122 male voices reverently chanted the lyrics of the Psalter. Words lifted from the page and rose like incense to the heavens. Individually, there wasn't the capability to imitate sounds of heaven, but collectively, we sounded like a celestial choir. You could feel the presence of spirits revolving around you. Our voices invited them, and they freely roamed throughout the chapel. Like a gift from God, it provided harmony to our song and serenity to our souls.

The prayer became more poignant as the seminary years came to a close. I was getting ready to say good-bye. Farewell to a city that provided a geographic address, and farewell to a campus that housed, fed, and educated me. Saddest of all, I was preparing to say good-bye to a friend and confidant. Mark was heading back to Iowa, and I was returning to Nebraska.

One evening, Mark quoted Winston Churchill. He stated in simple terms our hope for the future, "This is not the beginning of the end, it's simply the end of the beginning."

"What a journey, Mark. Can you believe it's almost over?"

"Amazing, isn't it? Four years sounded like an eternity when I arrived. Now, it seems like it disappeared in a flash. Where did all the time go, Tom?"

"Four years of theology. Piles of notebooks filled with copious handwritten material that seems too much to comprehend. How in the world can we integrate all this material?"

"Just remember one word, Tom. *Mystery*. Most of what we think and do is largely a mystery."

"Point taken. I'm glad it's over."

"Tom, so am I. I'll miss some of it. The friendships, late-night discussions, sneaking over to Joan of Arc, some professors, and most of all, communal prayer. We're on our own now. It will be harder."

"Agreed. Prayer concerns me. Left to my own devises, I'll procrastinate on both times and frequency. I know I'm doomed without personal prayer, but I don't trust myself, either. Doing good works for others is powerful, but they've amply warned us that this doesn't take the place of personal prayer and meditation. If I don't develop a strong daily habit, I'll forget why I'm doing good works in the first place. Say a prayer for me once in a while, will you?"

"Tom, once in a while won't be enough. I know you need a daily supply. You'll always be mentioned."

"Thanks...are you scared, Mark?"

"Scared shitless, why?"

"I don't know. I think I'm ready, but there are so many doubts."

"Doubts are normal, Tom, or at least they should be. The important fact to remember is you have the talent and ability to be an excellent architect of souls. Never forget that, no matter how burdensome the doubts become."

"Thanks, Mark. I owe you for most of what I'm bringing to the priesthood. You've been my spiritual guide and companion."

"Don't ever tell your bishop that."

"Why?"

"Tom, there's parts of you I don't want credit for. Your bishop is a man of patience and tolerance. Lord knows he'll need large amounts of both virtues to handle you."

"Spoken like a man who knows me all too well, Mark. May God watch over both of us. "

"It wouldn't hurt to have a few angels also, Tom.

CHAPTER 12

In the Roman Catholic Church, the ordination rite is the sacrament of holy orders. A marriage takes place, but the couple joined together represent the priesthood and Holy Mother Church. The ritual celebrates a unique communion of marriage and celibacy simultaneously and in perpetuity. The call to the fraternal brotherhood of clerics is validated by a pronouncement from the vocation director and a seminary representative.

"Into your hands, Lord, we entrust this candidate for ordination".

Our promise is to remain faithful to the teachings of the church, never assent to marriage, and be obedient to the bishop. In professional baseball, a lifetime batting average of .333 guarantees enshrinement in the hall of fame. With the Vatican, nothing short of perfection is demanded.

As I laid prostrate on the marble floor in St. Cecilia's Cathedral in Omaha, hundreds of voices chanted the Litany of Saints. The melodious rhythm reverberated off the granite walls and the marble floor. The prayer was enchanting as my soul reveled to the cadence.

Holy Mary, pray for us.
All holy angels and archangels, pray for us.
St. John the Baptist, pray for us.

St. Joseph, pray for us.
St. Peter, pray for us
St. Paul, pray for us.
All holy apostles and evangelists, pray for us.
All holy disciples, pray for us.
St. Stephen, pray for us.
St. Lawrence, pray for us.
All holy martyrs, pray for us.
St. Gregory, pray for us.
St. Augustine, pray for us.
St. Mary Magdalen, pray for us.
St. Lucy, pray for us.
St. Elizabeth Ann Seton, pray for us.
St. Theresa, pray for us.
All holy women of God, pray for us.

*****

"Athanasia, sends her prayers."
"Peggy, sends her love and her prayers."

*****

Suddenly, I heard a faint whisper. It sounded like Peggy's voice, but it was years since I heard her. It reminded me of the experience at the cemetery following her funeral. Words were difficult to decipher as they competed with the music. The only intelligible sounds resembled love and prayers. Eagerly, I yearned for more as I strained to block out voices chanting the litany. My ears detected no audible sounds apart from the names of saints. Instead of questioning my sanity or dismissing the episode as a delusion, I gently kissed the marble floor. Some experiences defy explanation. I was beginning to learn precious gifts sometimes last only for a moment, even if the moment was still clouded by a white chalk line and blood on the carpet.

PART III

1987

CHAPTER 1

I was thirty-five years old and I had only a pint of innocence. Twenty years earlier, before I met Peggy, I had a gallon. Human life experience had slowly drained my tank.

It was probably a normal human reaction to lose innocence, but I also knew that some of my loss was definitely self-inflicted. There was an awkward subliminal sense that I was causing my own demise, but I could not put my finger on what to do to stop it.

The phone rang at 2:47 a.m., and I reached to grab the receiver and struggle to sound awake. The Our Lady of Lourdes Hospital had a patient near death, and I was the priest on call. Extracting myself from the sheets and blanket, I groped for clothing that was black in color. We wear black for official functions, and ushering a soul to the hereafter is an official function. Within minutes, I was out the rectory and in my car heading for the hospital.

At a stoplight, I reached over and checked the glove box. Safely secure are my stole, oils, holy water, and the book of prayers. I never removed them from the car, but it was always good to check. Besides, this activity gave me something to do instead of lighting up a cigarette. I was smoking too much as it was there's no need to increase the toxic-fume level this early in the goddamn morning. Impatient with the long traffic light, I looked both ways then ran it. I was safe by all counts because my mission precluded simple red-light observance. Besides, there was no one on the streets at that hour anyway. My mind began to ponder the rationalizations I had been making. It sure seems like I've been using a lot of them lately. Time for a self-examination, it appeared things around me were spinning out of control.

I reached the emergency parking area of the hospital and whipped my car into a stall reserved for clergy. Walking through the doors, I adjusted the stole around my neck. Movement was choreographed with the emphasis on speed, a family gathered in a room around the bed of a loved one. People required special attention at times like these—they're lost, confused, and don't know what to do. All they see is impending death, and it emotionally paralyzes them. That's why they call a priest. They figure, at least he will know what to do and say. It's his job, and he's done it many times before.

The patient's name was Peter. He was eighty-two years old. If my memory serves me correct, his wife's name was Anna. They had been married over sixty years and had six children. Two were in the parish, and the rest lived elsewhere. I visited him a week ago in the nursing home. His condition obviously nose-dived.

I reached the room and entered. Introductions were made, and Anna filled me in on her husband's condition. Simply looking at Peter told me more than I needed. I suggested we begin the sacrament of the sick immediately. Peter's time on earth was rapidly coming to a close.

"In the name of the Father and of the Son and the Holy Spirit."

"Amen."

"Peace to this hospital room."

"And to all who dwell within."

"Sprinkle me, O Lord, with hyssop, and I shall be purified. Wash me, and I shall be whiter than snow."

"Our help is in the name of the Lord."

"Who made heaven and earth."

"Let us pray."

"Hear us, Lord, almighty and eternal God."

The rite continued as I anointed Peter's eyes, nostrils, hands, feet, and finally his forehead. With each anointing, I made the sign of the cross with my thumb. The holy oil is used as a symbol of the church's reverence for the final moments of life. The oil is Peter's last contact with the church. From here on in, he's in God's hands.

"May the Lord forgive you by this holy anointing whatever sins you have committed. Amen."

Before Peter quietly and gracefully died, his face illuminated in radiance for a brief moment. A gargled sound passed through his lips, and I thought he called someone's name. The other people in the room heard it too. "Kathy" was the name he uttered, and I asked the family if that name was familiar to them. They said it was his mother's name, and she was someone he loved dearly and missed so much. She had died decades ago. I had witnessed this strange phenomenon before and told the family God sometimes sends angels to comfort the dying. They resembled someone we knew and loved, so fear of dying is partially mitigated through their presence. I couldn't offer proof for this claim beyond the fact it occurred frequently. Hopefully, Peter ventured to a place where death, decay, pain, illness, or suffering didn't exist. He gladly departed from a body he had lived in long enough.

After sharing condolences with the family, I excused myself. I needed to go home and get some sleep. A full schedule awaited me in the morning. As I left the room and rounded the corner, Sr. Madeline stood in the hallway with her arms crossed.

"Sr. Madeline, what are you doing up at this hour?"

"You know, Fr. Tom, if I had a penis, we would never have to call you. I could do the sacrament myself."

"A penis! Oh my god, Sister, all these years I've been anointing with my thumb. Why didn't you tell me?"

"Very funny! Very funny!"

"Sr. Madeline, it's three in the morning. You sure pick the strangest hours to vent your theological opinions on me. What do you want me to do, call the pope and tell him to ordain women? Better yet, why don't you call him. And while you're at it, tell him Fr. Tom would like a beautiful woman waiting for him when he gets back to the rectory. Good night, Sister."

"You men just don't get it."

"At this hour of the morning, you're right, we don't."

I walked away. Staying with St. Madeline is an exercise in futility. My god, did the woman ever sleep? You couldn't escape her, even at three in the morning.

As I got in my car, I empathized with her dilemma. She wanted to be a priest. Sr. Madeline had become an advocate for the ordination of women. Unlucky for her, it's a damn lonely profession. Advocates in the church fight an incredible battle. They see themselves as protectors of truth. Regardless of the issue, it becomes the totality of their existence. One thing is certain: never attempt to engage an advocate in a serious verbal debate at any hour. They don't adhere to dialogue all verbal jousts erode into emotional monologues. In spite of my empathy for Sr. Madeline, I'm incapable of expressing it. She's already decided my gender excludes me from any opinion on the matter. I'm a priest; therefore, I'm the enemy.

Someday, when she's on her deathbed, I'll pay a visit and tell her I admired the ministry she had chosen. Advocates may be royal pains in the ass, but they also serve as reminders for the rest of us. Periodically, we need advocates to wake us up from apathy and indifference regarding issues that may or not be important.

Church history is littered with advocates, and many were branded heretics. They presented positions that countered normative institutionalized beliefs. The church burned a few, slew others, and excommunicated the rest. With privileges revoked, they were expunged from the community. There have been cases where the church sheepishly made overtones of amends decades later. Their views mysteriously became integrated into the doctrine of the church. As a rationalization, the church contended these men and women were simply ahead of their time. Obviously, it's difficult to see the future, so excommunication was a plausible mistake. When the church atones for mistakes, it recites a few mea culpas and moves on. A mistake that resulted in the penalty of death invokes a maxima mea culpa.

Advocates serve as a reminder that all the answers aren't set in stone. I decided long ago to tolerate their opinions. Even though there's little hope for dialogue, I figure hearing their viewpoint compels me to consider the issue they espouse. Besides, advocates would readily point out that the church embraces monologues also. Sr. Madeline often claims no one listens to her.

I returned to the rectory and went to bed. Assignment to Sacred Heart Parish came six months ago. With 2,400 registered families, an elementary and secondary school, two hospitals, three nursing homes, and a psychiatric facility, the demands of the parish seemed endless. The only saving grace was the country club on the north edge of town. Without an occasional round of golf to replenish sanity, I would be doomed.

This is my second assignment as a priest. My prior stint was at St. Bernard's Parish in Omaha with teaching responsibilities in a Catholic high school. Leaving Omaha for an assignment in the country caused some concern. Norfolk was a two-hour drive from Omaha, and the population hovered around 24,000. Living in a town this size required an adjustment. Growing up in Carroll provided a few clues, but that was twenty one years ago. It didn't take long to fall in love with the town, people, or parish. Hospitality greeted me the moment I arrived.

CHAPTER 2

Holy Mother Church dispenses seven sacraments. Sacraments have colors. Baptism, confirmation, marriage, and holy orders are denoted by the color white. Reconciliation and anointing of the sick are violet. The color for the Eucharist depends on the liturgical season in the church year. My fascination resides with the two violet ones.

The anointing of the sick used to be called extreme unction. As a child, the words sounded ominous. I knew the word *extreme* meant something wasn't quite right, but I had no idea what *unction* meant. When I learned it dealt with people about to die, I decided to leave it alone.

My first experience with extreme unction was in a hospital. Uncle Andy was occupying the bed, and my grandmother was rolling the beads. When my grandmother prayed the rosary in a hospital, within a few days, our family gathered for a funeral. My grandmother's ministry extended primarily to the spiritual needs of any relatives in the throes of death. As our extended family decreased in size, she branched out and adopted people who had no one else to pray for them. If the *Guinness Book* contained a world record for being present when people die, my grandmother would be tough to top. Poor Andy laid in a hospital bed, and I knew immediately he was a goner.

Andy was my godparent. From baptism on, he knew some role had to be played. After all, he witnessed the removal of original sin from my soul. Andy acknowledged his role by sending me a check on my birthday. I just received my tenth check.

My father brought me to the hospital and I knew the proper decorum for kids was to stay out of the way. Hospitals were territory reserved for adults. A doctor and two nurses gathered in the hallway engaged in conversation focused on a steel folder filled with pages. Murmurs were all I could hear, as the doctor did most of the talking and the nurses nodded their heads in agreement. Suddenly, the monsignor from our parish walked down the hallway. He had a small yellow vial in one hand and a leather book in the other. Around his neck, with the ends reaching his waist, was a violet stole.

The combination of my grandmother reciting the sorrowful mysteries, the doctor holding a steel chart, and the monsignor wearing a violet stole signaled to Andy he neared the end. The look on his face was stark, living terror. True to my grandmother's form, his funeral followed our visit four days later.

While in Norfolk, I got a small dose of the medicine Andy received. I needed an operation to repair a ruptured intestinal hernia. The surgery took place at Our Lady of Lourdes Hospital, and I requested no visitors. Sr. Madeline was burdensome when I could walk away; confined to a bed, she could torment me for hours. As I slowly regained consciousness following the surgery, my ears detected Hail Marys. When my eyes opened, an elderly priest with a violet stole stood over me. At the foot of the bed were two elderly women joining in the recitation. My first thought was death. Something got botched in surgery and I was departing. For one short moment, it scared me shitless. After discovering they came to my room offering prayers for recovery, I thanked them and requested they leave. Ever since then, I'm extremely careful when I do hospital ministry. Wearing the violet stole can scare the crap out of anyone.

Reconciliation used to be called confession. In the second grade, we were marched by the nuns from the school to the Church. It was our first taste of the box. The *box* was a term given to the confessional by older kids who survived second grade and lived to tell about it.

Parents and godparents spoke for me at baptism; now I was on my own in a dark closet with a priest next door. All that separated me from the priest was a cloth draped on the window between the rooms. The cloth blurred vision but didn't block it out completely. If the priest stayed alert, he could figure out who knelt next door. Another feature of the box was the kneeler. The second my knees made contact, an outside light above the door went on. The light was red. It served as a warning to those waiting in line that a sinner was in the box doing time.

The dark closet, the red light, and the violet stole all signaled terror. This confession business was serious shit for a kid only seven years old. The nun dropped her voice when she spoke about absolution. It meant the priest cleansed our sins, but none of us were real sure how he did it. The imaginations of a seven-year-old sometimes invokes frightening scenarios.

Because there were sixty-four kids in our class, the nun enlisted some eighth graders to help her keep us in line. As we stood waiting our turn, an eighth grade boy whispered to us, "Make sure you tell Father everything. What you don't know and the nun is forbidden to tell, there's a switch in Father's box that opens the floor. If the priest thinks you're lying, he might throw the switch. You'll fall straight to hell. The priest doesn't do it very often, but two years ago, a kid named Jimmy went into this exact box, and nobody's seen him since. Tell Father everything."

One part of me knew it was a lie. He wanted to scare us. I pretended not to believe a word of it, but I took extra time entering the confessional. Staying a little longer than normal, I told the priest everything, even stuff I never did.

After all these years, I'm still doing time in the box. The major difference is the violet stole is now around my neck. Doing time with this sacrament usually includes writing letters and reading books. Catholics decreased their participation with this sacrament over the years. Some people decided they'd go to God directly, while others believe the church spends too much time and energy on sinfulness. What got lost or misplaced is the awesome power reconciliation delivers. When someone experiences a severed relationship with God or another human being, the sacrament can be miraculous.

CHAPTER 3

On a typical Saturday afternoon, as I read Tom Clancy's novel, *The Hunt for Red October*, penitents for confession were sparse. The last penitent passed through about two hours ago. The church door opened, and footsteps made their way to the confessional. I marked the page number of the novel and set it down on the floor.

The scent of perfume identified gender. The nasal sounds and short gasps for air signaled she was deeply troubled. I focused my attention because these were not features of the standard garden-variety confession. The sin this woman bore sounded more serious. Venial transgressions didn't evoke tears or gasps for air.

"Father, I don't remember…what to say. It's been…a long time."

"Let's begin by making the sign of the cross. Then you simply tell God whatever you feel you need to. Speaking as best you can. Take your time, there's no need to hurry, no one else is here. Okay?"

"Okay."

"In the name of the Father, Son, and Holy Spirit."

"Father, I haven't had a full… night of sleep for weeks. When I go…to bed…the dream comes with me. It…won't go away…it keeps coming back. Over and over and over again. Nothing stops it…total…exhaustion doesn't make it stop. I can't take it any…more. I'm afraid I will do something I might…regret. What can I do?"

"Is the dream always the same?"

"Yes."

"Describe it to me. But please take your time."

"It begins…with clouds, blue sky, beams of sunshine, warmth, then a voice…soft voice …not words, at least not…words I understand…I think it's a baby…the sounds of a baby. The whisper of a baby, a plea…an appeal maybe…something to get my attention. I… always wake up at this point…I'm sweating and scared…the whisper is frightening, it haunts me somehow."

"When did you first have this dream?"

"About seven months ago. It would appear only once in a while. The last two weeks, it happens every night."

"Was there a traumatic episode nine months ago?"

"Nine months ago…I had an abortion."

"Talk about it as much as you can."

"I'm not married. But ahhhh, I lived with a man. We lived together for a year and a half. The relationship was difficult. We constantly fought, even over the minutest details. We both drank, and our arguments grew more vicious as the drinking escalated. As I look back now, alcohol brought us together. We met at a bar. Later, drinking became a weapon. Father, it got really nasty."

"Was there physical violence?"

"No."

"Since he left, are you still drinking?"

"Yes."

"We'll come back to that issue later. When did you find out you were pregnant?"

"Nine months ago. I was on the pill, but I wasn't always careful."

"Did you tell him?"

"No. Father, do you think I should?"

"Are you still together?"

"No, he's been out of my life for months prior to the abortion. Should I contact him?"

"You're absolutely certain the relationship is over?"

"I'm certain, Father."

"At this point, I don't see any benefit in telling him. You might decide to tell him sometime later. Tell me about your decision to have an abortion."

"I don't know. It was difficult. I felt alone, helpless, hopeless— and cut off. I never told anyone. My life seemed so screwed up. I couldn't see bringing a child into all that."

"Did you ever consider placing the child up for adoption?"

"Father, I knew only one thing. I wouldn't make it through the pregnancy. I am really all alone here."

"Your family doesn't live here?"

"No. My parents live in Arizona."

"Did you talk to them about this?"

"No."

"Any brothers or sisters?"

"A brother in Las Vegas and a sister in Phoenix."

"Did you talk to either of them?"

"No. We're not a close family. Everybody kind of does their own thing. We don't even get together on holidays."

"Did you consider going to a counseling service?"

"No."

"You were definitely alone. It must have been hell."

"It was, Father. I'm still not sure how I made it through."

"This dream began a couple months after the abortion. Correct?"

"Yes. It's the baby haunting me, isn't it?"

"Well, you don't know what the baby is whispering, right?"

"I can't make it out."

"Then let's not make a judgment on it."

"Father, if I could go back in time, I would have ended the relationship. It was never my intention to become pregnant. I'm not even sure I wanted to marry him. I don't know why I stayed with him. I felt alone I guess. I hate what I did. God …….. I am sorry for killing my baby."

"Coming here today was an excellent decision. Some of the decisions we make in our lives are disastrous. As we look back, we see how destructive they were, and we'd give anything to be able to change them. We also realize nothing can be done. How you choose to deal with the abortion will determine if you recover from it."

"Will the dreams ever stop?"

"Maybe what's more important is to learn what the dream is conveying."

"What if it is a nightmare haunting me?"

"If it is, we'll at least know it and go from there. It could be something else too."

"Like what?"

"The baby's whisper, you can hear it, but you can't understand it. Right?"

"That's right."

"This is just conjecture on my part, but maybe it's a plea or an invitation."

"An invitation to what?"

"It's imploring you to seek help."

"Counseling?"

"Yes."

"Why do I wake up in fear then?"

"Well....what you'll have to go through will be painful. Prior to the dream, you were trying to ignore the whole matter of the abortion, pretend it didn't happen. The dream wakes you up because pretending isn't working."

"God, it would be so much easier to pretend."

"It would."

"What should I do?"

"Get professional help immediately."

"Okay."

"Do you know someone?"

"Not really."

"If you want, I'll give you a name and a number."

"I'd appreciate it."

"There's one other problem. The drinking. If it continues, then you may not ever recover from this."

"Why do you say that?"

"Please understand I'm telling you something based on what I've seen happen to other people. I'm not an expert in this field, but my profession provides many opportunities to observe. The little bit you have told me about your drinking could indicate a potential problem. If my guess is right, then the drinking problem will ultimately sabotage any attempt to get well. The drinking issue is serious."

"Father, drinking wasn't a problem till I met Jeff."

"Jeff's gone and you're continuing at or near the same level. Is that correct?"

"Well...I guess so, but that's because these dreams are driving me insane. Drinking at least gives me some moments of peace."

"Please don't take this wrong. I'm getting a sense you want to protect your drinking. Kind of like a defense. Am I striking a nerve or, am I completely off target?"

"Father ...I don't know. I'm lost."

"Let me make one suggestion."

"Okay."

"The name and number I'm going to give you is the critical first step in getting help. If you decide to continue drinking, then pay attention to how long it takes you to call this number. When you do call, pay attention to how difficult you find it to talk about your drinking with the counselor. These two keys will say volumes in regard to you having a drinking problem or not. Is this clear?"

"I think so."

"Repeat it back to me in your own words."

As is the case with confessional experiences, I don't know if she called. Once she left the box, communication ended, and I could never talk to her about any of it outside the confessional. She would have to bring it up or make a return visit. The sacrament demands anonymity and commands personal responsibility. The act of contrition and the prayer of absolution acknowledge our private personal relationship with God and our willingness to restore intimacy severed by our actions. It's not a quick-fix sacrament where you tell the priest sins and go your merry way without any intention of changing.

Sacramental power is incumbent on the willingness to seek change. Reconciliation acknowledges there are sins that we can't overcome by ourselves. They'll haunt us for life. Power comes when we verbally admit we've tried everything but nothing works. As someone elegantly said, "If you're having trouble finding God, then become powerless. God chooses to dwell there most often. Confession can be an authentic admission of being powerless."

For someone who understands the sacrament so well, it's unfortunate I receive it so seldom. If my memory was accurate, it's been over a year since I went to confession. In spite of knowing the awesome power of the sacrament, I did not allow myself the opportunity for healing. Knowing an action is insane and responding to it requires wisdom. I wish I had some.

Back to Fr. Sherman and the book of Genesis.

> The sons of Noah went forth from the ark were Shem, Ham, and Japheth. Ham was the father of Canaan. These three were the sons of Noah and from these the whole earth was peopled. Noah was the tiller of the soil. He planted a vineyard; and he drank of the wine, and became drunk, and lay uncovered in his tent. And Ham, the father of Canaan saw the nakedness of his father, and told his two brothers outside. Then Shem and Japheth took a garment laid it upon both their shoulders and walked backwards to cover the nakedness of their father; their faces were turned away and they did not see their father's nakedness. (Gen. 9: 18–23)

Wasn't it interesting that both the story of the creation of Adam and Eve *and* the story of Noah both contain a transgression followed by nakedness. One was eating the forbidden fruit, and the other was imbibing wine to the state of being drunk. The story of the flood was Yahweh invoking a do-over. Creation had run amok so it was time to restart. Both of these stories are great examples of descriptive ethics.

Like Aesop's fables, they are learning tools concerning the plight of the human condition. No matter how many chances Yahweh gives us humans, we tend to screw it up. In creation, we learned it was dangerous to believe we *are* GOD, and with Noah, we learned that overdosing on sensual pleasures has major negative consequences.

There is an expulsion in both stories. Cain was banished for killing his brother Abel, and poor Ham was cursed for seeing Noah naked. One punishment fits the crime and the other remains a mystery to me. My personal dilemma is more akin to Noah.

My alcohol intake has increased to proportions that have become alarming. I am descending faster than I can lower my own expectations. I have tried to control my intake time and time again, but eventually I have always failed. The rationalization I used in the past was alcohol is my mistress. She has protected me and got me through so many difficult situations. Unfortunately, my mistress has begun to rule my life. I should heed the same advice I gave to the woman penitent. I gave great advice to someone else, but I have been unwilling to follow that advice in my own life. Not only was I lacking wisdom, but I certainly needed a healthy dose of courage.

CHAPTER 4

The Norfolk Regional Center was a psychiatric facility in the boundaries of the parish. My assignment included weekly visits to minister with the patients. Presiding in the sacraments of reconciliation and Eucharist on a locked ward opened new ground in my priesthood. But it didn't take long to figure out why the ward remained locked.

I presided in the liturgy of the Eucharist in a room next to the nurses' station. If necessary, I could shout for assistance. Most of the residents attended the services. Near-perfect attendance had nothing to do with me—these people would show up to any function that deviated from their daily routine. They starved for something different. Laboring for hours on a homily became pointless since I competed against numerous channels and voices playing in their heads. Some of the residents received the full cable subscription package and didn't have to pay any monthly dues. All those channels make it impossible to pay attention. Remarkably, I obtained a partial audience by simply reciting the names of Jesus, Mary, or John the Baptist. When these names were spoken, certain residents stood up and approached the altar. Initially, it alarmed me. When they got to the altar and innocently asked what I wanted, my fear turned to pity.

My congregation had two people who thought they were Jesus, one Virgin Mary, and one John the Baptist. Occasionally, one resident claimed he was Judas Iscariot, but he vacillated too often to be taken seriously. The rest of the congregation were content simply being themselves. As one resident remarked, "I have enough insanity to contend with. Why would I want to add another identity into this mess?"

After the first liturgy, I removed the names of Jesus, Mary, and John the Baptist from the prayers and scripture readings. They were replaced by God's Son, His mother, and Elijah the Second. Using these aliases ended future excursions to the altar. Once in a while, I'd slip up and inadvertently say one of the names. Remarkably, they detected my slip and began their journey. It served as a reminder to never underestimate their ability to hear when called by name.

What baffled me was their choice of religious figures. I asked the psychiatrist if this was common or an isolated incident. He told me the preponderance of schizophrenic patients choose religious entities. Rarely does a schizoid venture into delusions of being a famous politician, doctor, lawyer, or entrepreneur. The overwhelming choice by locked ward residents is biblical figures. At least mine went right to the top echelon with their choice.

The woman pretending to be the Virgin Mary presented a tragic case of extreme scriptural orthodoxy. The New Testament became a curse rather than a spiritual blessing. No one on the hospital staff cared to investigate which biblical verse commanded her action. It could have been Matthew 5:29, Matthew 18:9, or Mark 9:42. It made no difference as they documented her injury. "And if your eye should be your downfall, tear it out and throw it away; it is better for you to enter life with one eye, than to have two eyes and be thrown into the fire of hell" (Matt. 18:9).

A Bic pen served as her instrument to heed the call from scripture. Surgery was able to only partially repair the damage to her eye. The Virgin Mary became outfitted with a black eye patch. When I broached the subject of literalism one day, she claimed her orders came from the Gospel of John. She alone should know since Mary issued the verse a long time ago: "Do whatever he tells you" (John 2:5–6).

Interpretation of the Bible was the dominant topic on the ward. Most of the residents read and quoted scripture on a daily basis. It amazed me they were able to memorize and correctly quote countless verses of scripture. Partiality extended primarily to the New Testament, but the prophets surfaced once in a while too. When I read the gospel during the liturgy, it was common practice for several residents to join me. I read from the lectionary while they recited from memory. Word for word they kept up with my pace. Unfortunately, a prodigious memory is not a viable remedy for mental illness.

Not all the residents who came to the religious services shared this devotion to the Bible. Two men who came every week occasionally added a new feature to our celebration. The new feature wasn't Biblically inspired. They masturbated during the Eucharistic prayer. As the bread and wine transubstantiated into the body and blood of Christ, these two went into orgasmic jubilation. They were warned, reprimanded, and threatened repeatedly. Faced with permanent expulsion from the liturgy, they restrained themselves for months at a time. Then out of the blue, some Sunday I would catch them again. Their penchant for doing it during the Eucharistic prayer was chosen solely on the grounds it would be less detectable by me or other residents. The staff informed me that most of the male patients suffered from an inordinate propensity to masturbate. I never condoned it, but when people are locked up for life, some things get overlooked.

Reconciliation was the unanimous choice as the favorite sacrament on the locked ward. They prepared in earnest when their turn came to confess. True to their obsessive compulsive natures, they wanted to receive the sacrament every week. For my own sanity, I only allowed them confessional privileges bimonthly. I played a numbers game. I could only tolerate five penitents a week, so bimonthly was based on ward population. The list of sins they confessed was as tortured as their present mental condition. Assassinations of individuals from decades and centuries ago were somewhat favorites of the penitents, and I winced at the thought that violence seemed to be integral in their imaginations. But what the hell, that's why they were enclosed in a locked ward. If I tried to endure more than five a week, my name would adorn one of the doors on the ward.

CHAPTER 5

One particular Sunday rendered a chance encounter with a night-mare revisited. A patient who attended infrequently, never spoke a word, and sat as far from me as he could. He approached me after the liturgy for very first encounter.

"Can I talk with you?"

"I'm Fr. Tom. I see you here once in a while, but we've never met. Your name?"

"James."

"What do you want to talk about, James?"

"I'm not religious. I only come to get the white thing you pass out."

"It's called communion."

"Whatever."

"How long have you been here, James?"

"Two years."

"Are you from the area?"

"No, Omaha."

"So am I. What part?"

"Lived with my mother, around Seventy-Second and L street."

"Your parents, are they still alive?"

"My father died years ago and my...ma last year."

"Sorry to hear that."

"No big deal."

"You make it sound like you weren't very close to either one."

"My father wuz a drunk. He jus' beat me. I wuz glad to see him go.

"What about your mother?"

"That tub of lard wuz worthless too."

"James, I'm sorry to hear you had such a difficult home life. Is that what you want to talk about?"

"Naw. This religion stuff, God and angels and saints, you seem to know a lot about this stuff."

"Well, it goes with the job."

"I'm not educated like you. My schoolin' wuz—well, there wuz n't much to it. I'm not a reader like mos' these wackos. I jus' fend for myself. Pick up what I can, ask questions sometimes. You know?"

"What do you want to know about God, angels, and saints?"

"The eye-patch lady said you know about gettin' rid of voices."

"Whose voices?"

"Don't know names, but they look like snakes."

"You see them?"

"Sometimes."

"Has anybody else seen them?"

"Naw. They disappear when someone comes."

"What do they say?"

"Lots a stuff."

"Like what?"

"Ohh....they here to help me. Do what they say. That kind of stuff."

"How long have you been hearing them?"

"Since I was a kid."

"Do you remember the very first time?"

"Yeah. My father wuz kickin' my ass, and they jus' showed up."

"What did they say?"

"They'd help me get the bastard."

"Get him?"

"Yeah, payback. Teach him a lesson."

"Did they do something?"

"Not right 'way. Later on they killed him."

"How?"

"Heart attack. Deader than a doornail."

"The snakes caused the heart attack?"

"That's what they said."

"You believe them?"

"Why not? They promised."

"You've been here two years. What have the doctor's done to help?"

"Doctors don't know shit. They jus' give me more drugs."

"Don't the drugs work?"

"Well…they put me on my ass, but the voices are there when I wake up."

"What do the doctors say about them?"

"Told me they're a fig'ent of imagination. Not real, somethin' I invented. Believe that shit?"

"You're sure they're real?"

"Damn right! If I made 'em up, why can't I make 'em go away?"

"I don't know, James."

"What about the eye-patch lady? She said priests have some shit that gets rid of 'em. Right?"

"James, she's probably referring to exorcism."

"What's that?"

"An ancient church ritual expelling demons from someone possessed. Didn't you see the movie?"

"I don't watch movies in here."

"It came out years ago, James. Long before you came here."

"Hell, I've been locked up seventeen years now. Is it older than that?"

"I thought you said you were here only two years?"

"'Fore here, I wuz twelve years in the Omaha joint, max'mum security and shit. Doctors said I wuz makin' progress so they moved me here. Less 'strictions and all."

"So you've been a patient for fourteen years?"

"Yeah, sucks don't it. Mos' my life been locked up and caged like a fuckin' animal or somethin'."

"James, it seems after all those years of treatment, some progress had to be made with the voices."

"I told you, doctors ain't worth a shit. The only thing working is the white stuff you pass out. What'd you call it?"

"Communion. James, if you get some relief from communion, why don't you come here every week?"

"I'd like to. I always says to myself I'm goin' to. But some mornings, the war gets heated up pretty good. The voices start screamin' real loud, and I gots to get pills pronto. Some 'em pills do a number on me, they knock me to the ground. No way I can move."

"Have you ever tried ignoring the voices?"

"Ohhh, you don't understan'. These fuckers are powerful. You don't talk back to 'em. They'll get you. Believe me, they're nothin' you want to fuck with at'll."

"Okay, when the voices began, you were a child and your father beat you. Right?"

"Yeah. My father came home drunker than a hoot owl and jus' pound the shit out of me. No reason needed. I wuz pretty small, so he'd wallop my ass. After the whoopin', the voices would come and we'd plan revenge. You know, shit to get back at 'im."

"What did they suggest?"

"Oh, I'd hide stuff from 'im, steal money from 'im. Put stuff in his food to kill 'im. Shit like that."

"My god, what did you put in his food?"

"Oh, jus' junk from the garage. You know, stuff in cans with X's on 'em."

"James, you said he died of a heart attack?"

"Hell, I never put enough in. Always scared he'd find out, so only put drops in. Found out later had to pour lots in. 'Nown then, he'd a died long, long time ago."

"Where was your mother while all of this happened?"

"That fat ass did nothin' 'cept eat herself to death. Good riddance. She wuz one fuckin' piece of garbage. Hated her almost as much as my father."

"She did nothing while your father beat you?"

"Sometimes she join'd 'im."

"Did you poison her food too?"

"Sometimes. I only drop the shit when no one wuz lookin'. She ate, so yeah I did. I never when the stuff wuz in there, and she got suspectin'."

"Did she see you?"

"Nope, jus' wondered why I wuz n't eatin'. Mos' times she was busy fightin' and drinkin'. Never notice."

"Did the court system send you to the ward after they died?"

"No. My father wuz dead but mother still alive when I sent to the ward."

"James, what did you do?"

"I raped three girls. Well, really…jus' two, one got away."

"So you got arrested in 1974?"

"Yeah."

"James, did you kill any of the girls?"

"Yeah…one died."

"Do you remember her name?"

"First name was Peggy. Don't remember last."

"Is your full name James Hill?"

"Yeah, I told you in the beginnin'."

"No, you only said your first name."

"What's wrong?"

"I didn't recognize you. It's been a long time, and you look different."

"You know me! Small fuckin' world, ain't it? What, from the news and all?"

"Yeah, James, from the news. Listen…I need to get back to the parish. I…ahhh…got work to do back there."

"Wait a minute! What 'bout 'em voices."

"I'm not sure I can help."

"Fuck. You know what livin' with 'em is like? Jus' try that exor… shit on me! It might work."

"I can't do it. Only certain priests can."

"Well…call one of 'em then."

"Listen, nothing can be done today. Let me think about it."

"Man…you don't hav' to yell. Why you mad all o' sudden? I been nice an' all."

"James, I have to go. We'll talk later."

I lost track of James years ago. He ceased occupying space in my mind and my emotions. He became a nonentity. Twenty two years passed since the murder, and it occupied a cavity in my soul that I didn't want to think about. Now he sat right in front of me spewing out the malaise of my personal nightmare. Repulsed and saddened, I wanted to both wring his fucking neck and help his sorry ass. Getting off the locked ward and breathing fresh air were my only thoughts. God knows I should stay out of this place permanently. I had no business ever coming back.

Returning to the rectory, I employed the solitary coping mechanism that came in a bottle. Scotch was still my elixir of choice, and it provided temporary relief to all my burdens. After a few ounces, burdens magically evaporated. Today's episode might require additional ounces, but it always worked regardless of the tumult faced. Never mind scotch never provided long-term or permanent relief. All I needed was temporary amnesia. Never mind a nagging conscience telling me my drinking had escalated in frequency and amount. After two ounces, even the nagging dulled. I knew shutting down my conscience and dwelling on the need to escape was dangerous ground. What I didn't know, it also cleverly opens the door to snake-infested territory.

CHAPTER 6

James and I met the next week. We continued our conversation following the Sunday liturgy. He decided the white bread would do him some good today, and he wanted to find out if I would help quiet the angry mob in his head.

"James, the night you killed Peggy, was it the voices commanding you or the drugs you were on?"

"That drug shit was jus' my lawyer's idea. He said I should use it. Would help keep me out of the electric chair."

"You weren't high on LSD?"

"Nope, hell, I never used the shit."

"Were you drinking?"

"Nope. What's the matter?"

"I don't know. I guess I wanted to believe no one would be capable of doing what you did if they weren't on some kind of drug."

"Did you know her family or somethin'?"

"No, I didn't. Did you ever come into the Baskin Robbins ice cream store on Seventy-Eight and Pacific? Is that where you first saw her?"

"Nooo, never been there."

"In court, you said the night of the murder was the first time you saw her. Was that a lie too?"

"No, that's true. I was jus' wanderin' around lookin' for a house to break into. Quiet neighborhood, decent houses, that's it."

"So you saw her and decided to kill her, just like that?"

"Wait a minute, I never wanted to kill her. It jus' happened."

"You mean the knife stabbed her thirty one times by mistake? Come on, James."

"C'mon nothin'. I wasn't going to kill her."

"In court, you said the voices made you do it. Right?"

"They was talkin', that's for sure."

"Telling you to murder her?"

"No, jus' rape her. That's all I was goin' to do."

"Okay, so you raped her. Why in the hell did you stab her so many times?"

"Well, when I was gettin' ready to rape her, she seemed to disappear. She was there and she wasn't it was spooky. I raped her anyways, but the voices got mad as hell. They wuz screamin' and hollerin' that the bitch didn't care. 'Fore I knew it, there's blood all over the damn place and I's holdin' the knife."

"Why did you have a knife if you only wanted to rape her?"

"I was tryin' to find a fucking scissors. Couldn't find one."

"What did you need a scissors for?"

"To cut off the bra and panties."

"Why didn't you just take them off?"

"Ohh, it's harder than that. 'Member, I'm fightin' her and got to watch out. She already kicked me once. I had to be careful."

"So the knife was only to remove her underwear. Why the hell did you stab her?"

"Voices said do it so I could be powerful."

"You never killed anybody else. Didn't the voices tell you to kill again?"

"Lots a times. I jus' never did it."

"If you didn't obey them afterward, why did you obey them with Peggy?"

"I...don't know. Jus' happened. Didn't want to."

"Hard to believe, James. It's really hard to believe."

"Have you thought about those special prayers, the ones the eye-patch lady talked about?"

"I'm still thinking."

"I wish you'd hurry up. The fuckers are gettin' riled up."

"When did this start?"

"After I started talkin' to you."

"That's interesting, James. Listen, I have to go."

As I sat in my room in the rectory after enduring what James told me, I turned to my favorite coping mechanism, a glass of scotch on the rocks. I knew this was not going to be my only serving. My mind went back to a vision of myself sitting on a curb four or five blocks from Peggy's house with tears streaming down my face. The sight of the blood on the carpet of the living room both traumatized me and angered me. Her body was gone and I would never see her alive again. The tenderness of her embrace and the softness of her kisses had been brutally taken away from me.

I ran from George, Martha, and the neighbors because I had nothing to offer them. Any words I could muster would have been empty vessels of consolation. After all, what in the hell could a fifteen- year old kid offer anybody in this situation. I looked up to God and prayed that I could find the son of bitch who killed Peggy. With a baseball bat as my weapon I would crack his scull open and let him bleed out on the floor. Correct retribution would be him writhing and flailing on the floor before he would die. What the hell, I would plead justifiable homicide to both the judge and the jury.

After fixing another drink, my mind went back to the James I just left. This pathetic creature had just told me a detailed account of the rape and murder. It was a vivid and grotesque summary of that night twenty years- ago. What precipitated the murder was that Peggy did not pay any attention to him while he was raping her. He claimed that her indifference prompted the snakes in his head to scream KILL HER. From all his history with these snakes he knew that if he followed their orders they would calm down. Since he had never killed someone he believed doing it might give him some new power in his life. The rape was unfulfilling so maybe the murder would be.

Fr Sherman had told us in freshman religion class that St. Augustine said, "the eyes are the mirrors of the soul". I didn't understand it then but two decades later I recognized how factual this statement can be. James had black eyes, not from getting punched, but there was not any light visible to my naked eyes. He was devoid of any-life giving spirituality. I viewed him as a barely functioning quasi-human. Maybe an infrared microscope could spot a flicker in his eyes but I don't carry one of those in my Mass kit. Maybe he was simply hopeless.

After finishing God only knows how many drinks I had the thought that my consumption of alcohol was becoming alarming. The episode with James fully rationalized this drinking binge but they were happening far too often and I could not justify the rest of them. Plus, consequences from drinking were mounting faster and faster. I felt myself descending quicker than I could lower my expectations. As my tolerance for alcohol increased, the discipline with my prayer life proportionately decreased. I wanted to fix this somehow but every measure I tried had failed so far. I was becoming a mess.

Above my sofa was a picture of one of Michelangelo's painting from the Sistine Chapel. It depicts God towering over Adam with his arm stretched out and his index finger reaching out to him. Adam is prostrate with his hand reaching up to God with his index finger close to God's. I thought that the small space between both their fingers was the artist's representation of free will. Adam had a choice to either reach up further in faith or pull back in fear. This was a depiction that we all have free will choices in life. For me, I had a choice. I could bring a baseball bat to my next trip to the locked ward and bash James or I could try to find out if there was any glimmer of light left in his eyes. I certainly did not have any grandiose notion of somehow helping him spiritually because I was barely able to even take care of myself.

What I decided to do that night was to trudge through my ministry on the locked ward with all the residents and just maybe I might have a positive impact on James. If trudge is a laborious walk, then I was setting out on one of my most difficult journeys. Isn't it ironic that King David said in the Psalms that a wink of God's eye equals a thousand years. It only took God twenty years to put me face to face with the murderer of Peggy. Watch out what you pray for.

The Virgin Mary offered numerous tidbits of information to all her clients on a regular basis. Her practice remained engaged 365 days of the year. There's no downtime or vacations for mystics or animists. They're services are always on call, especially on locked wards in psychiatric hospitals. Her advice to seek the rite of exorcism was a decent consult. Who knew what else to do with his malaise.

She observed my sessions with James from a safe distance. I allowed it because I couldn't see how it could harm. Eventually, she offered me a tidbit of her expertise. You needed some level of proficiency with scripture when conversing with the Virgin Mary. The patch on her eye never served as an impediment to reading scripture. The Bible was her credit card, and she never left the room without it.

As I left James, she approached and whispered Matthew 12: 43–45. The eye-patch Mary may have been wacky, but I looked it up immediately.

"When an unclean spirit goes out of someone it wanders through water less country looking for a place to rest, and cannot find one. Then it says, 'I will return to the home I came from'. But on arrival, finding it unoccupied, swept, and tidied, it goes off and collects seven other spirits more wicked than itself, and they go in and set up house there, so that person ends up worse off than before. This is what will happen to this wicked generation." (Matt. 12:43–45)

When I returned the next week, I asked her why she chose the passage. Looking around to make sure no one else could hear, she said: "Unclean spirits take the path of least resistance. If James recovers with your help, then be careful, priest, sin and darkness could be crouching at your door. Refer to a passage in Genesis 4, verses 7 to 8."

If you do well, will you not be accepted? And if you do not do well, sin is crouching at the door; its desire is for you, but you must master it. I'd be lying if I said this crazy woman warranted only superficial attention. Her consult scared the shit out of me. Clothed in generality, it still hit a nerve. I wish she had the gift to offer more, but I also knew it was way beyond her grasp. She lived on a locked ward for good reason.

Working with James became an obsession, and I don't know why. I felt compelled to learn more about the voices and what they were saying. The mystery sucked me in, and I rationalized it by claiming priestly ministry. Knowing the obvious dangers of treading in locales beyond my ability only heightened my curiosity. I began to descend somewhere down, and the fall appeared steep.

"James, can you read?"

"Fuck yes. I'm not retarded."

"I didn't imply you were. Relax, remember I'm trying to help. Here, read this for me would you?"

"Which one?"

"That one."

"Re...joice, O young man, whi...le you are young and let... you he...art be glad in the...days of your you...th. See I can read fine."

"Keep going."

"Fol...low the...ways of your he...art, the vi...sion of your... eyes. Yet un...der...stand that...as...re...ga...rds all this God...will br...ing you to...jud...ment."

"Judgment."

"That's what I said. What's with this bullshit? Readin' won't rid the snakes."

"You're right, it won't."

"So why you makin' me do this?"

"I needed to know, James. Reading is just one of the steps we take. It won't get rid of the snakes by itself, but with other steps, we got a chance."

"What other ones?"

"Reading, learning, and prayer are what you're going to do."

"Forget the prayer shit. Nev'r done it, and doubt if I can."

"Ohhh, you can, James. Believe me, you can."

"It'd be a...what you call those?"

"What word are you looking for?"

"Mir...a...les?"

"Miracles."

"That's it. One of 'em if I pray."

"Well, James, they happen all the time. Why not with you?"

"My kind don' get 'em. God gave up on me years ago. Sometimes I thinks God ne'er cared at all."

"James, what if you're wrong? What if you find out God's been there all the time, waiting for you to just invite him in? Wouldn't that be shocking?"

"Fuckin' A it'd be shockin'. Do you know this…or you jus' guessin'?"

"Let's find out. Reading, learning, and praying will provide the answer."

"Where's it start?"

"I'm going to send you a coach for a while. A woman from my parish will come here three days a week to coach you. She taught in a school for thirty years then retired. I asked her if she would volunteer for this, and she agreed. Will you work with her?"

"Did you tell her 'bout the voices?"

"Yes."

"She still'll do it?"

"Yes."

"Why?"

"She wants to help you."

"She mus' be loony. Who'd want to come here?"

"I do, James."

"But you hav' to. That's diff'ent."

James needed help. Going by the seat of my pants on this one, I decided to broaden his life with literature, knowledge, and eventually prayer. Maybe if he saw other vistas in life, the snakes would become tiresome. They fed off his limited vision of life and were probably the only companions he ever knew. Opening new doors might make them believe James was less attractive as a target.

Catherine worked like a trooper, teaching James to read. He made progress, so we raised the ante. Getting a GED became the new goal. Somewhat grandiose and lofty, we pushed on with stubborn perseverance. James benefited from our efforts in small incremental steps. He changed over the next four years, regardless of whether he wanted to or not. Catherine shared my dictatorial resolve, and James was never offered the option to decline.

CHAPTER 7

I brought James a rosary and began teaching him how to strum the beads. Through arduous memorization and regurgitation he got everything down with the exception of the Apostles' Creed and the fifteen mysteries. With the help of a cue card that had the prayers written out, he mastered the recitation of the rosary.

In spite of being locked up on a mental ward, he asked the same questions about the rosary that most people do. Why is there so much repetition? I told James prayer is repetitious because it clears our mind of all the junk we walk around with until we can focus entirely on God. The junk he needed to dispel were the voices from the snakes.

James then asked why the bulk of the prayers were centered on the eye-patch lady not on God. His insight into this matter took me by surprise. It was a good question. I told him Mary was viewed by the church as an intercessor to God. Her role as mother of Jesus placed her in select company in the history of revelation, and we could appeal to her for special graces bestowed by God. Mary's prayer was a mantra we used to place us in the spirit of God and allowed us to seek a deeper relationship with God. She was the mother image we could use to help us feel nurtured and loved by a God who wanted to see us grow spiritually healthy and alive. My explanation fell on deaf ears.

James was teaching me an invaluable lesson. In order for me to reach him, I had to always filter what I said to him through his own experience and background. Using Mary as a mother figure or God as a father figure only works if someone has a positive experience of those parenting figures. James had been treated like shit by his parents. The voices he heard came into his life because of this treatment, so I had to always be aware of this when I offered a new direction for him to follow.

Through holy cards and statues in his room, I gave James plenty of time to allow him the opportunity to separate the Blessed Virgin Mary from his own mother and from the eye-patch lady. His education was enhanced by the fact that he became a quasi-celebrity on the locked ward. The other residents were curious about his new trinkets and admired his new way of talking. The prayers mitigated his profanity, and he slowly began acquiring a personal demeanor that was less threatening. James was making strides at becoming human.

CHAPTER 8

"James, I'm proud of your progress. You've made incredible strides these last few years."

"Scary, isn't it? I hardly believe it myself."

"So many new doors are now open, and you have more choices in life."

"The best part, Fr. Tom, it might even mean a release some day. I ne'er thought it possible, but now who knows?"

"Sound out all your words, James."

"Yeah, I try to."

"Miracles. Remember what I said years ago? Anybody can be a recipient. Even you?"

"I thought you were full of shit then. Well, I thought everybody was full of shit."

"You're down to two sections for your GED."

"Yeah. Catherine thinks I'll be ready for the next one in three weeks."

"Remember, James, the first try is only a warm up. A low score means you work harder for the next attempt. Don't forget where you came from."

"How could I? This joint won't let me."

"I'm sure it doesn't. Hopefully, even that will change someday. Never give up hope, James."

"I'll try, Father, I'll try."

"Still praying?"

"Every day. At first, I thought the rosary you taught me wuz loony. Mus' admit, Father, I had doubts 'bout you."

"James, it made you a celebrity here. All the others wanted one after watching you with those beads."

"Sure did, didn't it? Everybody 'cept the eye-patch lady."

"I offered her one, but she said it was rude to pray to yourself.

"She's somethin', Father. Somethin' else."

"Catherine would scream right now. Finish your words, James."

"Okay. All right."

"Seen any snakes lately?"

"That's the most amazing thing. Haven't seen them in a year. Only hear them once in a while. Fr. Tom, how did you know what to do? Gettin' rid of 'em like you did."

"Honestly?"

"Yeah."

"James, I didn't have a clue what to do. Every move was a hunch at best."

"You seemed so sure."

"I faked it."

"So telling me this wuz going to change from a curse to a blessing was BS too?"

"James, I wanted it to work so bad that I pretended it would work. Blind faith. Plain and simple. I just made sure you never found out."

"Fr. Tom, you wuz convincing."

"Were convincing."

"Yeah."

"That's all I had, James. A convincing demeanor. A hope and a prayer is all I worked with."

"Well…it certainly works on snakes, doesn't it?"

"It did with you, James."

"Fr. Tom, I do have one thing to ask."

"Go ahead."

"You told me you heard of me in the first time we talked. Remember?"

"I do."

"Well…every time I ask you 'bout it…you change the subject or go back to church. Why?"

"I was curious, that's all."

"Did you know the family?"

"I did, James."

"Real well?"

"I met them only months before the murder."

"How?"

"I worked with Peggy at an ice cream store."

"Were you two close?"

"James, we slung ice cream together. I only knew her for a short time."

"See, Father, you're gettin' angry."

"No, I'm not."

"Father…I can tell. If you wuz close and all, why did you want to hear the 'hole deal? You know…the murder and everythin'."

"It….seemed important to me at the time, James. That's all."

"Hearin' all of it had'a hurt, didn't it?"

"It was rough."

"Fr. Tom, I'm sorry it hurt you. I wuz nothin' but a bastard to do that. She'll be with me forever. Makin' the snakes go away is one thing. No prayer will make her go 'way."

"You've come further than I thought, James. Forgiveness is a bitch."

"Father…did you love her?"

"Yes…I did."

"A lot?"

"Yes…James. A lot."

"I am so sorry, Father. Can I give you a hug?"

"Yes, James, you can."

James embraced me with fervor, and tears came streaming down his cheeks. Here was the man who had inflicted utter terror in my life crying in sorrow for the sin of his past. I had moved beyond hate years ago while working with him. The hate had been replaced by pity, and now the pity had finally morphed into actual love. How in the world can such a thing happen? It was my first epiphany of a divine mystery coming true in my life. Unfortunately, when I returned to the rectory, it required a lot of scotch to reach amnesia. I remember saying a foxhole prayer prior to amnesia, "God, please help me." What I quickly discovered was to be careful what you pray for; it just might be given to you.

James remained a work in progress. God only knew his next destination. There were further steps I needed to introduce in his recovery, but my time in Norfolk was drawing to a close. Assignments normally last only three years, and I just finished my fifth. An announcement loomed in the near future.

CHAPTER 9

The archbishop called to inform me of an appointment in his office. He scheduled it for 10:00 a.m. the next morning. Since it was news to me, alarm bells sounded. The nature of the appointment did not surface in our brief conversation. Unexpected calls from the archbishop demanded immediate suspicion. Even though I was due for a change in assignment, this never required a personal meeting. Normally, a simple phone call told me where to report next.

Left in the dark and having no one to consult produced terror. All priests who have skeletons in their closet dread a phone call from the bishop. Secrets demand an inconspicuous presence. The closet must be cloaked in secrecy and guarded perpetually. Those who desire more prominence and visibility clamor for elevated positions in the hierarchy. They figure it's better to be the caller instead of the recipient of the call. My skeleton was obviously alcohol. I knew it but didn't think anyone else had a clue. As I later discovered, an alcoholic is always the last to know. We're not as clever as we think.

Walking into his office, the presence of other priests with the archbishop confirmed immediately the gig was up. The most telling presence of those in the room was Fr. Jim. I privately always called him the liquor vicar, so I knew immediately that alcohol would be the topic of this meeting. After a few cursory remarks of welcome, the archbishop dived straight to the agenda.

"Fr. Tom, it's come to my attention you have a problem with alcohol. I decided it would be in your best interest to undergo an evaluation. I'm sending you to a treatment facility in Minnesota. Here's your airline ticket. The flight leaves at twelve thirty this afternoon. Fr. James will drive you to the airport. I pray you will receive the help and assistance you need. That's all."

The archbishop was a man of few words, and he'd been well coached. Still, I couldn't allow a travesty of injustice to be inflicted on me without some response. I needed to say something in my defense.

"Archbishop, with all due respect, isn't alcoholism a medical illness?"

"Yes."

"Would it be possible then to get a second opinion on this matter before I venture to Minnesota?"

"Fr. Tom, if you are not on that plane this afternoon, dire consequences regarding your future in the church will come into play. Need I say more? Have a safe trip."

The matter was handled quickly. We reached a modus vivendi, a temporary arrangement between parties pending settlement of a particular debate. The archbishop handed me the plane ticket, and I departed for Minnesota. Some kind of an evaluation would take place there. At least I was going back to familiar territory. Maybe I could look up some old classmates after the evaluation. My promise to be obedient necessitated boarding the flight, but I damn well intended to do everything possible to pass the evaluation. With head bowed low in a show of resignation, I exited the office. My confidence remained hidden as my resolve to return shortly increased.

Fr. James escorted me to the airport. Any luggage required would be shipped to the treatment center. A treatment center sounded foreboding. It became even more frightening when I looked at my ticket, a one-way flight with no return listed. Jesus, they didn't give me enough credit. I'm confident this whole thing can be handled in two or three days. They didn't know me as well as I thought they did.

The flight to Minnesota lasted an hour. When I arrived, a man met me at the gate and identified himself. He worked for the treatment center. Amiable and cordial, he obviously encountered all types of drunks from his years of shuttling patients. I purposely declined any alcoholic beverages on the flight. Sober and serene would be my image during the course of this evaluation. Once I passed with flying colors, I could return home and celebrate.

After loading up another passenger, the driver headed north on the interstate. When I asked where we were going, he responded Center City. Eight years in the Twin Cities and never once did I hear of a place called by that name. My quizzical look didn't last long. He said it was a forty-minute drive north of St. Paul. Christ, I thought, we're heading to Duluth. So much for familiar territory.

Entering the gates of the facility, a large lake adorned the border of the property. Minnesota, the Land of 10,000 Lakes, lived up to its claim once again. The modern architecture consisted of a central hub with numerous arms leading to large enclosures. Resembling an airport, we exited the van and were greeted by nurses.

The central hub contained a hospital. All drunks required detoxification regardless of their blood alcohol level. We checked into a ward bordering the nurses' station. I presumed the hallways adjoining the hospital led to wards that housed the unfortunate saps who failed their evaluations. I had no interest investigating those hallways; I would be leaving shortly. All I needed was a competent physician who would render a clean bill of health. Once I got that, I was outta here.

The fellow companion who joined our van ride was severely intoxicated. The airline employees poured him out of the plane in Minneapolis. After voraciously consuming numerous bottles of vodka on his flight from Montana, his speech and gait confirmed his condition. Using a clever story about a relative tragically dying in a car accident, people on the plane showered him with drinks. The stewards demonstrated compassion by handing him four bottles as he exited. They were cleverly hidden in the slightly torn lining of his sport coat. Upon arrival in his new digs, he intended to continue drinking. This guy had no idea where he was or why he was sent here.

I was grateful for his presence. Next to him, I looked like a poster boy for sobriety.

Placed in the same room, a battery of tests were administered by nurses. As she took my vital signs, I glanced at the numbers recorded, and they confirmed my good health. Blood pressure, pulse, weight, and body temperature were all normal for someone my age. I got the first perfect score in this evaluation business.

My companion was doomed. As the blood pressure cuff wrapped around his arm, his hands began to twitch. He told the nurse a shot of vodka would produce instant calm and hands like a surgeon. She smiled and shook her head as his blood pressure was recorded. It apparently exceeded the normal range because she motioned to another nurse the need for medication. This guy would definitely be going down one of those hallways. Hopefully, this treatment center attracted lots of drunks and open beds were scarce. No room at the inn sounded great to me right then.

In between the tests, my new buddy decided a drink was in order. He retired to the bathroom and quickly downed two of the bottles hidden in the lining of his coat. It never occurred to him the nurses had seen every trick in the book. Drunks only think they are clever when intoxicated. Most of the time, drunks are probably predictable. The nurses knew immediately and confiscated his remaining stash. Caught red-handed, any thoughts for a brief stay evaporated like the vodka residue pervading his tissues and organs. That was Lucky Louie's last drink in this place, and I felt sorry for him.

Lucky Louie and myself were led to a lounge and told to watch television. The set was on, but the screen only showed a podium sitting on an empty stage. If someone intended to speak, they hadn't shown up yet.

"Louie, feeling any better?"

"Oh god, am I grateful I had that last nip before they searched me. What's the deal with this joint? Is it really necessary to frisk a person? My lord, you'd think I was a prisoner."

"Louie, they frown on people bringing in alcohol. It goes against the creed of a treatment center."

"What the hell, it was only a few dinky airline bottles. Who'd get excited by such a puny amount like that?"

"You going to be okay tonight, you know—without any more alcohol?"

"The nurse said they were going to give me some medication. Imagine that, I come here with a drinking problem and now they want to make a dope fiend out of me. You figure it out."

"I don't have a clue, Louie. I'm as lost as you."

"Say, what's your name again?"

"Tom."

"Oh yeah, that's right. What the hell was I going to say. Let's see—oh hey, you don't look like you should be here, Tom. Hell, you look great. What's the deal?"

"Long story, Louie."

"Was it your wife? Whooo baby, women get nasty when it comes to husbands drinking."

"No, it was my boss."

"What a prick. You're boss sent you here?"

"Yep, he sure did."

"What business you in?"

"I'm a Catholic priest."

"Say what? You're joking, aren't you?"

"No, that's what I do, Louie. The archbishop told me I had to come for an evaluation."

"The bishop did?"

"Yes."

"Hey, Father, sorry about calling him a prick. I had no idea."

"It's okay, Louie."

"Jesus, Mary, and Joseph. I already got nurses terrorizing me, I don't need God haunting me too."

"Louie, I'm sure God understands."

"You think so, Father?"

"I'm sure."

As the speaker approached the podium, I prayed the staff would share Louie's evaluation of me. Never mind that Louie's hands trembled, his nose burst in veins of reddish-purple, and his blood pressure registered a 7 on the Richter Scale, the man had excellent observation skills.

The speaker was a woman. For twenty minutes, she gave a blow-by-blow description of the horrors of prescription-drug abuse. All the doctors in a three-county area refused any further requests for prescriptions. The only option she could think of was extracting her teeth with a pliers. Her arrival for treatment came after two bicuspids and one molar bit the dust. Lucky Louie and I squirmed in our seats. Louie commented when she finished, "I'll be damned if this place is going to get me hooked on those son of a bitches. Where I live, the nearest dentist is fifty miles away. I'd bleed to death. I'll stick to vodka. It don't hurt as bad as that sounded."

This was our first exposure to "sharing your story." The nurse told us there were different speakers every night of the week. Attendance was mandatory for all residents. For now, we would watch in the lounge, but later we viewed it live from the auditorium. Once we got assigned units, our schedule would change. I was glad I would ace the evaluation. A week of those stories could give you nightmares.

It was now time for bed. I wanted to get a good night sleep because the physician would be examining me in the morning. If I presented a healthy appearance, I could catch a flight back home. A day or two of this stuff wasn't too much of an inconvenience. Based on Louie's condition and the horror story we heard, there was no way I would be a candidate to stay. My chances for release were looking better all the time.

The person responsible for inventing hospital beds had to be a sadist. They're the worst excuse for comfort imaginable. Ironically, they're designed for severely ill people who need a good night rest. How do hospitals justify their existence?

Lucky Louie refused medication. When the nurse showed him the pills and patiently explained the necessity of taking them, she didn't stand a chance. All Louie could see was a pair of pliers to pull his teeth. Those pills weren't going down his throat. Satisfied with winning a battle against the nurse, he laid on his bed and fell asleep.

The bloodcurdling scream shot me out of my bed. The clock said 4:15 a.m. The nurse ran in the room, switched on the light, and blinded my eyes. When I could focus, I saw Louie shaking in bed while staring down at his chest. The stare conveyed stark, living fright. Perspiration poured through his pores as his eyes riveted to his chest. I presumed a cardiac arrest. What I could not see was the cobra snake coiled on Louie's chest. It was real as hell to him and poised to strike. The nurse assured me he was only suffering from a hallucination. Too bad she failed to convince Louie.

Nurses congregated around his bed and administered a hypodermic. The medication worked quickly, and Louie's snake disappeared. The terror in his eyes scared the shit out of me and negated any further sleep. I couldn't imagine what the snake looked like. Poor Louie would never refuse medication again. A pliers is tame compared to a cobra ready to strike.

Lucky Louie required a week of detoxification. His physiological system demanded constant alcohol ingestion, or it would revolt. Since Louie never depleted his body of alcohol since the age of fifteen, he never knew or heard about delirium tremens. What an awful way to be introduced.

Apparently, the staff had witnessed events like this before. They administered a steady dose of pharmacological substances into poor Louie. It rendered him oblivious to everything. Any further conversation with him proved pointless. At least it gave him a temporary respite from the lectures on the television screen. The pair of pliers and the cobra snake slipped from memory as he wandered aimlessly around the ward. Lucky Louie had run out of luck.

Purgatory continued for me. Marshaled into a room, I was given a bevy of psychological tests. One instrument called the MMPI, acronym for Minnesota Multiphasic Personality Inventory, contained over five hundred questions. All of them demanded a simple true or false reply. The questions were simple and concise and dealt with a wide variety of mental and physical disturbances. "Do you enjoy torturing animals," "do you spend an inordinate amount of time examining your feces," "is there a symphony of voices playing in your head" were just a few of the ludicrous inquiries. The instrument measured your state of wackiness. A little wacky was okay. Major League wacky got you another ride in the van to a different facility.

Reaching the final question, I was confident my flight home would be departing soon. Surely, I aced this one too.

The next hoop was the exam by a physician. The doctor asked a few questions about my health and probed into all my major orifices. Finished in minutes, he complimented me on my physical condition. The only reference to alcohol regarded my decision to seek treatment before the disease ravaged major organs. When I told him about coming for an evaluation, he smiled and left the room. It appeared he knew something I didn't know, but I never had the opportunity to ask him.

I sincerely believed the evaluation had concluded. What I found out later, the evaluation concluded when I boarded the plane in Omaha. My detox lasted forty-eight hours, and my new destination didn't require an airplane. An employee walked in and said, "Tom, you have been assigned a room in the Silkworth unit. If you will follow me, I'll take you there."

"What do you mean? I'm still waiting for the results of my evaluation. You must have the wrong person."

"No, you're the one on the form. A counselor will answer any questions you have regarding your evaluation."

"Why can't the counselor talk to me here?"

"Their offices are on the unit. Just follow me, and we'll clear everything up."

"Okay, but there's been a mistake. I'm certain of it."

"Don't worry, Tom. We'll clear it up. Just follow me."

My line of defense rested on the absence of an alcoholic deportment. I could function, my health was good, detox didn't require pharmaceuticals, all my teeth were secure, and cobra snakes weren't on my chest. Wait till I got ahold of the counselor. He would definitely get an earful.

"Tom, I'm Maureen. I'll be your counselor during the course of your treatment. I see here from the forms you're a Catholic priest. I was in the Sacred Heart order for twelve years. I left the order in 1975 and pursued work in chemical dependency. I've been here for twelve years. Welcome to Silkworth."

"Nice to meet you, Maureen. Maybe you could clear up a misunderstanding. I came to this facility for an evaluation. So far, no one has told me any results."

"Tom, addiction is life or death, not pass or fail. You are not in graduate studies. This is a place of recovery. Recovery from an illness so insidious that the person slowly dying from it doesn't even know it. Denial is the weapon it uses with proficient acumen. It's your choice whether or not you desire remission. No one can make that choice for you. It would behoove you to pay attention. Once you get settled, we'll talk some more."

It was a damn good thing the conversation ended because I didn't have a clue what to say anyway. Not only was she charming, polite, and professional, she possessed intelligence. I needed time to regroup. If this was going to be a fair fight, then I better get a game plan. The ex-nun just registered an impressive opening barrage. Three jabs to the chin and a left hook to the sternum were my estimated punch count. In the past, I always got a punch in somewhere, but today I left her office a vanquished fighter. Slithering off to my room, I vowed to show up for round 2.

There was nothing to unpack since my luggage hadn't arrived. I looked around the room and saw four single beds, four desks, and four closets. My three roommates were elsewhere, probably in the auditorium listening to horror stories about someone's drinking. On my desk was a book with a blue cover. In bold letters, the cover read *Alcoholics Anonymous*. If this was the ex-nun's blueprint, then I better get acquainted with it. I lay on my bed and began to read.

It contained commandments, but there were twelve instead of ten. God's name was invoked in four of the commandments and referred in two others by the terms *power* and *him*. With God in the picture, I stood a chance. My theological education would work to my advantage. Somehow, I needed to figure out a way to apply my training and background to extrapolate the correct analysis regarding early release. Whatever homework it required, I wanted to breeze through it as fast as possible. This was going to be a difficult test. It required my full attention.

"Hello. My name is Emerson. Welcome to the unit."

"Hi. I'm Tom."

"How was your stay on Ignatia?"

"The detox joint?"

"Yes."

"Oh, it was eventful."

"How long were you there?"

"Two and a half days."

"Not much detox time."

"Well, I came here in pretty good shape. Physically, at least. I thought there would be an evaluation, then I would go back home. Unfortunately, it doesn't work that way."

"Some people come here thinking just the same thing, Tom. You're not alone there."

"So this evaluation thing is a ruse?"

"It is."

"That's crap. Deceiving people into treatment facilities."

"Tom, who the heck would volunteer to come?"

"Well...I don't know. Maybe people who realize they have a major problem."

"It's going to be fun watching you in here. You're in for an education, my son."

"I sound that naive?"

"You may or may not be. But one thing's certain, denial is rampant."

"Emerson, I really don't belong here."

"Like I said, Tom, it's going to be fun watching you."

"How long have you been here, Emerson?"

"Ten days."

"Where are you from?"

"New York City. Born and raised. How about you?"

"Omaha, Nebraska. You can save any hick jokes for later. What's the unit like?"

"It's regimented. Lectures, group meetings, sessions with your counselor, some free time for recreation. It's a full day. After a day or two, you'll get used to the ritual. What work do you do?"

"Ahh...I'm a Catholic priest."

"When were you ordained?"

"In 1986. What about you, Emerson?"

"I'm also in the church."

"Really! A priest in New York?"

"Well...yes. Tom, I'm a bishop."

"You're...a bishop?"

"Yes. In this place, though, I'm simply another alcoholic. Nothing more and nothing less."

"You really caught me off guard. I didn't expect...well...it's..."

"Get used to it. This place thrives on catching people off guard. It's a necessary tool when working with alcoholics. We're masters of command performances, but a little lacking in the reality department. Especially when it comes to evaluating our own lives. We make rationalizations an art form."

"Emerson, have you done this before? You sound fluent?"

"This is my second treatment."

"Here?"

"No. The other one was in Rochester."

"New York?"

"No, Minnesota."

"Tom, this state is the birthplace of treatment. They have as many facilities as they have lakes."

"I never knew that, and I spent eight years in the Twin Cities."

"Well, it's not something most people inquire about. Usually, we come because someone else did the research for us."

"I got to tell you, Emerson, this place is eerie. My counselor's an ex-nun, and now my roommate is a bishop. Coincidence or is God trying to tell me something here?"

"So you've got Maureen too. She's tough. Be prepared for an inquiry you'll not soon forget. She cuts to the chase, Tom. And, she does it with remarkable precision. Her scalpel tears bullshit to threads."

"I already received minor surgery."

"Thomas, you are in for an education. I don't want to sound redundant, but it will be interesting watching you."

Returning to the book *Alcoholics Anonymous*, my first read of the opening chapters was only cursory. I definitely needed more information. If I could collate, synthesize, and analyze their creedal statements, then maybe I could present a good case to Maureen. Damn, I forgot to ask what's the common length of captivity in this joint. I'll ask her when we meet again.

"Maureen, the treatment process, how long is it?"

"Goddamn, Tom, you just got here. Why in the world is your mind focused on when you get out?"

"Wait a minute, I'm just asking a simple question. There's no reason to get so excited."

"Right. It's also a question you need not concern yourself with."

"What do you mean? All I want to know is how long the process is. It's my life. How long does this take?"

"Is there some anger there, Tom?"

"Yeah. I ask a simple question, and you scold me instead of providing a simple answer. Come on!"

"You don't want to be here, do you?"

"Honestly, no."

"Then pack your bags and go. Nobody is holding you against your will."

"I have no bags because I was put on a plane immediately after finding out I had to come here. Anyway, my bishop sent me here. It was not my choice."

"So he was obviously wrong. Fly home and tell him."

"I can't."

"Why not?"

"I was told to come here and abide by the advice this facility gives me, plus I was only given a one-way ticket."

"That's a smart bishop. By the way, what advice have I given you so far?"

"Not much."

"Have I told you anything dangerous or too difficult to abide by?"

"Maureen, all I'm asking is the common length of stay. A very simple question. I still haven't received an answer."

"Here's some more advice, Tom. Don't ask any more questions. Just listen."

If the whole purpose of counseling sessions is to piss someone off over the minutest trivial crap, then Maureen runs an excellent session. Imagine, I'm sent to a facility and they won't tell me how long I'm required to stay. Common decency demands an answer. How fucking long is treatment? Will somebody please answer me?

"Tom, how was your session with Maureen?"

"Emerson, this place is nuts. I ask her one simple question, and she jumps all over my case."

"Get used to it. What did you ask her?"

"How long treatment is?

"Common rookie error. Never express thoughts conveying an inkling to return home. Present moment, my man, stay only in the present moment. Thoughts of time, place, or people outside this facility are ammunition for counselors. They riddle your case file with remarks about being uncooperative. Get enough of those remarks, and you'll spend the rest of your life here. The church has excellent insurance coverage, never forget that. Your treatment plan is not based solely on insurance, but you'd be an idiot not to see it comes into play."

"Emerson, what's the common time frame?"

"Thirty days."

"What? A month!"

"That's pretty typical."

"My god, an entire month with an ex-nun."

"That's if you pay attention. There's another unit on these grounds called Jellinek. It's set slightly apart from the other units. Minimum time at Jellinek is four months."

"Four months? One hundred and twenty days of this?"

"You got it."

"Who are the sorry saps who get sent there?"

"They come from all the thirty-day units. People who have difficulty staying in the present moment. Uncooperative ones."

"Whoa, thanks for the warning. I'll never ask the nun another damn question. Oops, sorry about the language, Bishop."

"Forget it Tom. A week in this unit and we all begin to talk like drunken sailors."

I continued with *Alcoholics Anonymous*. I read eleven chapters and moved into a section called Personal Stories. The first story was "Doctor Bob's Nightmare." Initially, I thought it was another pliers-extraction or cobra-snake adventure. I discovered he held the title of original apostle. His epiphany experience began AA on June 10, 1935. He was the rock on which the AA foundation originated. Even I had to admit, his story inspired me.

Setting down the book, I unpacked the luggage that arrived from Omaha. No one is capable of packing a suitcase for another human being. Married couples probably never attempt such an endeavor. Other people don't know what constitutes personal effects for someone else. They end up packing clothes you're least likely to wear. Oh well, another encumbrance of treatment. How many more could I expect?

From treatment jargon, I picked up the meeting in the archbishop's office was called an intervention. Many residents in the unit suffered the same experience. The term and method employed probably originated in the church. When any institution exists for almost two thousand years, similarities naturally abound. I linked intervention with the Inquisition. They shared certain vowels and consonants, and both words elicited painful memories. My intervention was tame compared to stories narrated by other drunks in the unit. Some endured interventions where the spirit of Tomas de Torquemada had to be present and nodding approval.

Interventions provide excellent horror stories to share as residents gather at night. They also serve as ice breakers when new drunks check into the unit. Mine was too short and lacked brutality to warrant any distinctions. One drunk called it a fart. After hearing his experience, I understood immediately why he used that term. His intervention sounded like a full bowel retraction. Believe me, I didn't feel slighted in the least.

My blueprint showed me still in control and calling the shots. Based on the book, *Alcoholics Anonymous*, my attitude conflicted with AA philosophy. Holding onto this mind-set would be hazardous with Maureen. The book suggested surrender, but I didn't know how. Also, the term didn't sit well in my vocabulary. Fight on became my battle cry and attitude.

AA philosophy is grounded on principles, not personalities. In order to receive, I had to let go. Since letting go meant no control, it sounded too much like a free fall. This thought scared the shit out of me. AA also claims alcoholics have difficulty recognizing the pattern of insanity in their lives. They tend to repeat the same behavior over and over while always expecting a different result. Alcoholics aren't stupid, but the book claimed their judgment becomes suspended by the power of addiction. I wasn't sure about this insanity business, so I decided to listen more closely in the lectures and with the speakers. The answer would come in time.

"Emerson, how did you end up here?"

"It's a long story, Tom. A sorry diatribe. I'm painfully qualified to be here. There's no debate required there."

"Would it be too intrusive to ask for a summary?"

"Not at all. The question is, are you ready to hear it?"

"It can't be any more shocking than what I've heard from the speakers at the podium."

"Don't count on it, Tom. Alcohol is not what brought me here. I was never a drinker."

"Was it prescription medication?"

"What I took didn't require a prescription. I became addicted to crack cocaine. How's that for a zinger?"

"How in the world did you get mixed up with that stuff?"

"I started smoking two years ago. It didn't take long for complete debilitation to occur. The drug reduces all victims to complete helplessness rather swiftly. The unabridged definition I give crack is 'evil incarnate.' It has the power to extricate and extinguish the forces of life. If you want to meet Lucifer, this drug will provide your introduction. Pretty sad commentary, isn't it?"

"Sad and unbelievable. Once again, it's not what I expected."

"Tom, three years ago, I didn't either. I would have roared in laughter if you told me this would be my fate someday. Heard enough?"

"How did it start?"

"Cloaked in innocence. Isn't sin cunning, baffling, and powerful?

"The book defined alcoholism with those terms, but I like your inclusion of sin."

"It fits, Tom. Fits perfectly."

"So it was innocent. In what way?"

"I'm an auxiliary bishop of Harlem. It's my domain and residence. My ministry to the people revealed numerous horror stories involving crack. It ravaged the community like a plague. When an invitation was offered to try the drug, I viewed it as an experiment—a research project. Like my days at Columbia University so many years ago. How arrogant, stupid, and grandiose I'd become."

"One time did it, Emerson?"

"Tom, I flicked the lighter, inhaled the toxic chemical, and sanity flew out the window. It seduced me. No gun to my head, no blackmail, and no lure of wealth. It enticed me to the tree, and I ate the fruit."

"How's your diocese handled all this?"

"As you can suspect, they're alarmed, shocked, scandalized, and deeply embarrassed. Trying to keep it quiet is the major task facing them. So far, they've achieved success, but eventually it's bound to leak. Absence is more difficult to conceal when you're a bishop. Especially, a black bishop from Harlem."

"Wow."

"I warned you."

"You certainly did, Emerson."

My burden of being in treatment immediately paled in comparison. The bombshell he dropped on me imploded. As I viewed this serene and compassionate man, I saw intelligence, warmth, and humor. Among those gifts was excruciating pain and torment. Contrition and sorrow waged a battle with his sins, and only time would render a final verdict. Tragic beyond belief, yet he wasn't requesting sympathy. He only sought a small degree of understanding.

Emerson is an instructed soul who tragically went astray. Architecturally, luminosity of his soul occurred since conception. His parents nurtured the gift God infused as he passed through childhood and adolescence. They handed off the baton to the church when he reached adulthood and spiritual growth continued. Standing 6'4", weighing 230 pounds, and facially resembling Sidney Poitier, he was ordained a priest in the line of Melchizedek.

We shared the same profession, the same disease, and the same room in treatment, but the similarities end there. Emerson integrated the AA message into his life, while I vacillated on a fence post stuck in denial and unwilling to fully surrender. Maureen saw it tattooed on my forehead and addressed the issue every time we met.

"Tom, how am I going to crack your wall of defense? It looks to be impenetrable."

"I don't know, Maureen. If I say something, you tell me it is addictive logic. Even when I listen to what you say, it is processed within the framework of addiction. It sounds hopeless."

"Don't you see, Tom? Addiction revolts against recovery on all levels. The term *hopeless* gives credence to a continuation of the disease. If you are hopeless, then why not drink? It makes perfect sense. What you have to do is completely revamp your thought process. For a significant period of time, you cannot trust your judgment. The answers will be addictive. You have to rely on others. This is a fundamental maxim of the program. It may sound simple, but alcoholics rarely have a history trusting others. Do you?"

"No."

"Could you?"

"I'll try."

"Trying is not good enough, Tom. I can't be any more emphatic about this step. The recovery rate from this disease is abysmally low. The vast majority don't make it. They end up in dry drunks, insane asylums, or morgues. Given those options, you better do more than try."

"What's a dry drunk, Maureen? If being sober is the goal, how can you be sober and drunk simultaneously?"

"Sobriety is only one facet of recovery. It's the initial step, and all the others hinge on it. But it's only the beginning. Removing alcohol from your bloodstream opens the door. Being sober allows you to hear the AA message. Drunks only hear their own voice. Dry drunks hear other voices but refuse to pay attention to them. They may be sober, but there's no recovery taking place."

"The AA message is what?"

"You have to change everything. The way you think, act, and respond. You change the totality of your existence to date."

"Sure, Maureen. In thirty days, we become new people. Get real."

"Don't be an idiot, Tom. You're more intelligent than that. The cynicism you just projected is an appendage of addiction. Remarks like it provide ammunition to the disease. It keeps it alive and vibrant. Changing everything is a lifetime process. Willingness to stick with it is all we ask for in treatment. If you want to recover, your days as a cynic better be numbered. Try instead to be teachable."

"So a dry drunk is a sober cynic?"

"Yeah, that's accurate. Tom, have you ever spent time with someone who is perpetually sarcastic, someone who sneers at life and sees only the shit floating in a toilet bowl?"

"I try to avoid people like that."

"Well, stay sober for a period of time but never venture into recovery and you'll become one. Just as people slowly check out of your life when you drink, they'll exit here too. Doesn't sound appealing, does it?"

"Nope. It doesn't."

"Dry drunks barely hold on. It's doubtful you'd last more than a few months."

"So, Maureen, you're going to make a new man out of me?"

"Not me, Thomas. That's your responsibility. This place provides the tools. The rest is up to you. God knows you've got lots of work. But believe me, She's seen worse."

How do you go about changing the totality of your life? As I exited my session, early release wasn't a predominant thought anymore. She introduced new material and information for consideration. Everything she said made sense. Even the speakers at the podium were becoming less troublesome. The other day, I heard someone tell a story that sounded ominously like my own. My attention was captured for a brief moment in treatment, so I prayed to

God for the perseverance to keep listening. Prayer was mandatory because I knew perseverance wasn't one of my strong suits.

*****

"Athanasia, back to these demons. If the Creator won't destroy them, why can't tragedy, pain, and suffering be reduced or lessened? Can't we still make choices in a world with a little less torture?"

"Suffering has many levels and degrees. It's not the sole commodity of evil. On one level, it can extinguish light. On another level, suffering can induce growth. It serves as an impetus to challenge and coax. Change demands rigorous effort, and tutorial angels often employ times of suffering as stimulus directing a soul to a higher level of knowledge. The fulfillment of one's destiny demands change, and suffering can help a person move toward conversion."

"Each soul has a destiny?"

"Yes. Each is unique yet in communion with the Creator."

"Suffering helps and hurts simultaneously?"

"It's one of life's ironies."

"Then a lot of suffering indicates souls are either deeply confused or lost in evil?"

"Yes, it can be either."

"Athanasia, there's many distractions in life."

"That's true."

"So destiny is rarely attained by any soul, right?"

"Correct."

"What happens to them?"

"As long as a connection to the Creator is sustained, another opportunity is granted. The light is omnipresent and eternal, and each soul shares this connection."

"As long as light is visible there's hope, right?"

"Correct."

"Even when sin chews and devours light, if a glint of light can be seen there's hope. Is this true?"

"The mere spark of light warrants hope. Only complete extinction renders a sentence of abject hopelessness."

"Athanasia, religions sometimes focus a lot of attention on sins and meager amounts on recovery from the sin. Why?"

"The message doesn't endorse this belief. It's centered on uplifting the soul. Bringing souls to the goal of creation is the beatific vision. Sin has to be acknowledged, recognized, and verbally admitted to the Creator. Dwelling on sin will only keep a person in the sin."

"I need more help with this beatific vision. I'm not tracking with you here."

"Beatific vision is unabated communion with the Creator. Obsession with sinfulness is energy misspent. As one prophet, Ramakrishina, said, 'If all you think of are your sins, then you are a sinner.' Dwelling on sin produces servility. The goal is not dependency. It's spiritual maturity attained through disciplines which foster self-actualization."

"Why do some religions breed dependency if it's contrary to the goal?"

"Mainly for purposes of control."

"The Creator doesn't advocate control?"

"Never. The message is not about dependency and revelation throughout history amply confirms it. Religions are ministers of promulgation. They bring the message to generations of souls. Dependency employs fear as a weapon for control. Fear impedes growth instead of encouraging it. Obstacles need to be overcome not adopted. When religions impose fear in their teaching curriculum, they no longer function as inspired messengers."

"Athanasia, if religions are confused and wander in error, then no wonder so many souls become lost."

"Control and ownership are difficult vices, Peggy. Religions become ensnared by them and begin practicing containment through tyranny. Contrary to their origin and mission, this despotic abuse wreaks havoc in demonic proportions. When the message is contaminated by those entrusted to safeguard and teach it, evil dances with glee."

"I still think the Creator should wipe the demons out."

"You're persistent with this, aren't you, my dear Peggy? Believe me, there are moments where the notion garners majority appeal even here."

CHAPTER 10

The twelve steps of Alcoholics Anonymous have a designed order. Like the Ten Commandments, they lay out a course for anyone to follow. Fortunately, the author of the twelve steps refrained from using any *thous*, *shalts*, or *shoulds*. He emphasized the notion of suggestion rather than a command. Being an alcoholic himself, he understood the disease and a drunk's repulsion to being told what to do. I was taught that the most important word of all twelve steps is *we*. Alcoholics tend to be on familiar ground only with the word *I*. As one counselor said in a lecture, "Everyone here overdosed on vitamin I."

A shift from *I* to *we* sounds simple. All it requires is a decrease in selfishness and self-centeredness. Just a modicum of altruism. How difficult can that be?

"Tom, cognitively you've mastered the program. You've read and analyzed all the material I assigned. You are able to speak clearly and concisely about the program. My question and concern is, have you integrated any of it into your life?"

"I'm living it day by day."

"Sure you are, so is every other schmuck in here. This is a god-damn treatment center, you're doing what you're told to do. Big deal!

Are you doing it to get out of here, or are you doing it because you recognize there's no other way? That's my question."

"Maureen, I wish I knew the answer. Sometimes I want out of here, and once in a while, I see the need to live the program."

"Which one's stronger?"

"It depends."

"That's what scares me. Tom, I'm sure you remember the article 'Compliance versus Acceptance.' For alcoholics, this is a critical question they wrestle with for years. In order to wrestle, it's mandatory to show up. AA meetings have to become holy hours of obligation. Granted, you can attend meetings because you're forced to, but it will never last if that's your primary motivation. Over time, people will not watch closely to see if you are doing what you're supposed to do. Showing up is crucial, and you have to practice the discipline for as long as it takes to move from compliance to acceptance. It might take years, Tom."

"Maureen, I know that. My problem is, I don't know from day to day how willing I am. Some days it's clear, and on others it's foggy as hell."

"Tom, the insidious nature of this disease makes one thing crystal clear. On the day you think it's clear, that's the day you need to fear the most. Recovery is a lifetime process, and you are in your infancy narrative. Don't expect swift progress—you are still a baby in recovery. Babies only know how to cry and excrete bodily fluids. Saying you know the program is the height of grandiosity. You know nothing! Remember the Chinese proverb, 'He who thinks he knows doesn't know. And he who knows he doesn't know knows.' Do you remember who said that?"

"Tao Te Ching."

"Tom, your knowledge can be a liability. You remember the author, but you have difficulty paying attention to the message. Instead of practicing mental masturbation by looking for alternative answers, trust, accept, and follow what we teach you. We're not here to deceive you. The disease emits an inexhaustible quantity of deception. Someone sent you here because they loved you enough and couldn't stand watching you languish in the deception. You have to rely on others in AA. This is why we recommend sponsorship. Asking for help from someone who learned over time how to crawl and eventually walk in recovery is a gift not a burden. Not only does this sponsor put up with all your bullshit, he patiently guides you through the twelve steps. My god, Tom, he does all this for no charge. The gift is free. Deception always charges for services rendered. You damn well know, Tom, sometimes the fee is astronomical. Can you do all this?"

"Yes, Maureen, I intend to."

"Damn, Tom. It's not about intention. The morgues are littered with drunks who intended to get well. Good intentions are nothing but half-measures. They get us nowhere. Remember, this disease is cunning, baffling, and powerful. It is so powerful you don't even have a 25 percent chance at recovery. The vast majority simply don't make it. Those odds are dismal so it's going to take everything you got. If not, it will take everything you have."

Sister Maureen could close. She always sent me out of our sessions with a rip-roaring conclusion. Leaving the church years ago didn't negate her ministry. She flourished as chemical dependency became her chosen field. She wasn't a fortune-teller of the future but a forth-teller of one's soul. From an architectural standpoint, she was fast approaching prophet status.

CHAPTER 11

Emerson and I retired to a communal room called the library during recreation periods in the schedule. We engaged in writing letters, reading literature, and conversation. Occasionally, another member of our priestly fraternity joined us.

Bernard was a Jesuit priest from Boston. He arrived two weeks before Emerson, so his release date was nearing. Since he was assigned to another unit, we weren't allowed to communicate with him. No fraternizing was one of the cardinal rules of the facility. There were four units for men and two for women. Besides taking meals, listening to lectures or personal stories, and enjoying recreation time outside or in the gym, the remainder of our schedule was confined to the units. Even during the shared activities, it was anathema to converse with residents from other units. It was a cardinal rule for a reason. Any mixing of the sexes invited trouble. After all, the entire facility housed nothing but drunks and addicts. Without rules, there would only be chaos. Emerson and I trespassed on this rule and rationalized our sin by claiming ecclesiastical privilege. It would have been inconsiderate to ignore Bernard. Besides, what he offered was worth the penalty of trespassing. We kept our voices low out of deference to our deception and because we were in a library.

Bernard was an instructed soul whose intellectual acumen exceeded all bounds of normative levels. Armed with two doctorates and a litany of distinguished academic achievements, he epitomized a life devoted to the search for empirical truth. His list of published works was exhaustive and impressive. In seminary, we read some of his books. Difficult to read, yet they always provided a keen awareness and synthesis of the subject we were studying. Bernard was a genius in the fields of theology and philosophy.

With chemical dependency, he lacked even minimal comprehension. The church demanded all clerics to remain celibate, but Bernard reneged. Dewar's scotch became his wife and mistress years ago. Now this marriage culminated into a sabbatical in a treatment center.

Viewing Bernard, most people noticed his gaunt facial features and slender frame. He stood six feet tall and weighed 160 pounds. Anemic fit would be the best description. Ingesting food only out of pure necessity, he paid the price physically. When the mind is engaged twenty-four hours a day, eating must seem trivial. With hollowed cheeks and a smattering of disheveled hair, he always looked preoccupied. His distant glaze warned people not to trespass.

Given his propensity to scrutinize all material he encountered, Bernard used the days of treatment as an opportunity to rewrite the first eleven chapters of Alcoholics Anonymous. He claimed the grammar and sentence structure were horrific. Bernard was appalled the treatment center endorsed a textbook so flawed and in need of repair. It required immediate attention, and he would perform the reedition.

As we talked in the library one day, Bernard contemplated taking his manuscript to the president of the facility. Obviously, he possessed the qualifications necessary to review his text. A president naturally had more degrees than the counselor he was assigned. The counselor informed Bernard the Big Book contained inspired writing available to anyone who struggled with addiction. It did not need to be rewritten. Bernard despised labeling the text as the Big Book. He saw nothing written that elevated it to such largesse. This became another remark by the counselor added to the list notating deficiencies in the clinical practice of this treatment center. He informed us the list was becoming copious.

We listened to Bernard's diatribe and attempted once again to inform him he wasn't here for scholarly pursuit, being sent to treatment centered on consumption of scotch not research. Like numerous attempts in the past, our message fell on deaf ears. The best we could do was talk him into taking the manuscript back to Boston. There he could mull over a future course of action with the manuscript and his copious list of complaints. Our logic pertained to his upcoming release date. An appointment with the president might delay or defer his release. Bernard, like most of the residents, feared any mention of the four-month unit. It sounded ominously like a penitentiary, and no one wanted to investigate.

The president of the treatment center was a former Dominican priest. He would be familiar with Bernard's scholastic work and reputation. What Bernard failed to grasp was the concept of recovery. Step one still eluded him. Fortunately, he trusted us and heeded our advice. The manuscript and list of deficiencies took up residence in his luggage.

Bernard wanted to go home, back to the familiar academic environment in Boston. Prior to departure, he gave both of us a copy of his AA manuscript. We didn't dare ask how he got copies made because we were better off not knowing. Bundled in two notebooks, the handwritten entries characterized a man on a mission. Totally misguided yet written with obvious fervor. Bernard was convinced his expansive revision clearly depicted the issue. We could only marvel at his obsession.

The first few pages of chapter five in *Alcoholics Anonymous* are the Nicene Creed of AA. It contains a summary of the dogmas intrinsic to recovery from alcoholism. These are the tenets of the program and the solution for recovery. The first three pages of chapter five are read at most AA meetings. The first paragraph reads,

> Rarely have we seen a person fail who has thoroughly followed our path. Those who do not recover are people who cannot or will not com-

pletely give themselves to this simple program, usually men and women who are constitutionally incapable of being honest with themselves. There are such unfortunates. They are not at fault; they seem to have been born that way. They are naturally incapable of grasping and developing a manner of living which demands rigorous honesty. Their chances are less than average. (*Alcoholics Anonymous* 5:58)

Bernard's version of the same passage:

Extrapolation from previous studies have correlated an index suggesting success when a person applies the virtue of honesty to the pursuit of sobriety. Difficulties arise when deviation from norm diffuses intent and purpose. The paradigm concurs a consistent gradient measure for those genetically predisposed to inculcate the virtue in a consistent pattern of behavioral adaptation. Abnormalities occur when a condition precludes the probability distribution of two variables or more. The given value of a second variable offsets the benefit derived from an identical variable. Justification belies an intrinsic sociopathic anomaly which requires further investigation. (Bernard's revision 5.73)

Alcoholics Anonymous was written in language most people could understand. The version Bernard wrote required an act of God to decipher. With alcoholics, it's mandatory to stay simple and concise when dealing with the disease. Specific IQ scores aren't required. Almost anyone, if they were willing to work at it, could grasp the program from the AA book.

Bernard's version was steeped in jargon that precluded a sizable segment of the population. Most alcoholics, if forced to read his account, would quickly scurry to their favorite cocktail lounge and order a double. Bernard defended his revision by stating he was not seeking any compensation and would translate it into nine other languages. We didn't have the heart to tell Bernard alcoholics who spoke only Latin, Aramaic, or Sanskrit were probably nonexistent.

Bernard presumed most people held at least one doctorate and spoke two or three classical languages. Being a product of the ivory tower of intelligentsia, he rarely strolled far from the tower. Emerson and I believed his revision was complete and astute. God knows his intentions were always to elucidate. Unfortunately, Bernard's concepts of alcoholism and his solution for recovery would never rehabilitate any drunks we knew. Misguided to the nth degree, he remained so damn lovable that you wanted to help him. Sadly, we both doubted our assistance was possible.

Emerson and I discussed the merits of recommending Bernard for a longer stay. Possibly, the four-month unit would provide an opportunity for a glimmer of realization. We weighed the pros and cons for weeks and decided not to interfere. The treatment center needed to make this call. Besides, four months, or even four years, may never crack through Bernard's intellect. He was a program enigma, an inexplicable, perplexing riddle of intellectual prowess that didn't allow simple programs to penetrate. Bernard did not live in a world of simple concepts. He chose to reside in opaque and obscure territory. It's unfortunate the territory also allowed imbibing scotch. Down deep, we knew it would probably be his demise.

CHAPTER 12

The treatment center housed a variety of drunks. Men and women who all shared the same disease yet individually possessed a wide array of talents. Bowery urchins were not present because of the prohibitive cost. The disease can inflict itself on anyone, it doesn't discriminate. In varying degrees, all of us had some position, title, achievement, wealth, prestige, and intellect. Why we were so fortunate to be here while street dwellers did not share the privilege should have been a lesson of humility. Emerson and I broached the subject occasionally, but I was still too screwed up to comprehend it. Humility was the one virtue I needed most. As a typical common drunk, I thought living sober could be achieved through my own volition. Stupidity wears many masks and deceives best when worn by an arrogant schmuck who thinks he knows, and I was one of those schmucks.

Humor uplifts the soul as it bonds individuals into a community. Our stories were gut-wrenching, painful, and filled with anguish. Living in the addiction eventually brings everyone to the agony in the garden. Stay out there long enough, and you'll even share the sweating of blood. Bonded by common despair, we also ascended to hilarious frivolity. Most exploits experienced in active addiction require a contrite act of contrition, but you can't dwell in steps four and five permanently. A sense of humor sometimes abets recovery with the same force as a good confession. One story shared by a resident is inculcated in my memory and ranks at the top of my practical-joke list.

A member of our unit drank heavily at a wedding reception. He surpassed intoxication hours before the reception ended. Like a good alcoholic, he continued to drink. Eventually, his body assumed the fetal position on the floor in the coatroom. Unconsciousness set in as both alcohol and valium were consumed. Thoughts regarding the lethal nature of this combination of chemicals never merited a mention.

His friends found him and failed to rile him from slumber so they carried him to the car. During the course of the ride home, an innocent comment by one of the passengers ignited everyone's imaginations. They removed articles of clothing leaving him only with his pants, socks, and shoes. Then they cut his pant legs slightly above the knee. The fabric was duct-taped to his thigh while the remaining part of his trousers were tossed on the floor. With taped pant legs, socks, shoes, and a winter coat that hung below his knees, he was driven to the airport. With the help of airline personnel, who were deceived by a fictional tale about a stag party celebrating this man's upcoming wedding, he was wheeled to the plane and plopped in a seat. The flight was bound for Cleveland, and arrival time was in about an hour and a half.

Two factors were mandatory. One, the airline would board an unconscious passenger. And two, the passenger would remain unconscious until the plane lifted off. Both factors were successfully achieved. He awoke as the captain made his final descent into Cleveland. As brain neurons reawakened, he quickly took inventory of his location and the duct tape pulling on the hairs of his legs. Any thoughts about how this happened were negated by what the hell he was going to do next.

An examination of the pockets of the coat rendered a solitary dime. Any illusions of discovering his wallet or a wad of cash evaporated into the fog permeating his brain. The only logical move was rubbing his thighs to insure the tape would remain secure. Heading to the bathroom also disappeared as the stewardess made her final round to check for seat belt and tray-table violations. She sweetly assured him they would have him home for his wedding tomorrow. As she moved down the aisle, she whispered a comment about the rigors of bachelor parties. He nodded his head in agreement because it seemed like the right thing to do.

Arriving in the airport terminal, he found the pay phones and called his parents' collect with the solitary dime. After relating to his father the current predicament he faced, a long period of silence was followed by an eruption of rage. Holding the phone some distance from his ear, the tirade lasted almost a minute. When his father's anger subsided, a plan was concocted to get him on the next flight home. The next flight was six hours away at 6:15 a.m. Keeping the duct tape securely attached to his thighs became his only concern. Slinking off to a secluded area of the airport, he sat upright and rigid, waiting for the hours to pass. Shortly before five o'clock, his lips turned upward for the first time since he awoke. A grin evolved into a smile as his anger abated. Recognition of the creative brilliance displayed by this prank demanded commendation. Revenge was utterly pointless. How could he ever even the score for this one anyway?

CHAPTER 13

"Emerson, why do you have to go to the hospital every other week? Is there a health problem you're not sharing?"

"There is."

"Why the curtain of secrecy?"

"It's the second chapter of the Emerson story, and it's worse than the first."

"Cancer?"

"Worse."

"What's more dreadful than that?"

"Try this, Tom. AIDS."

"What?"

"You heard it."

"From a blood transfusion?"

"I wish."

"Crack cocaine is only smoked, isn't it?"

"It wasn't IV use."

"How?"

"It happened one night, Tom. One lurid evening gave me a death sentence."

"A woman?"

"Yes. Chaste for all the years of my priesthood and out of nowhere I followed an allure one evening and savored the fruit. Biting the fruit is the first transgression, savoring it is a cardinal sin."

"I assume you were smoking with her?"

"I was."

"Wow…just one time?"

"That's right. One cataclysmic orgasm."

"How did you discover it was AIDS?"

"About a year later, I began having health problems, so I went to my doctor and he ran a series of tests. Testing for AIDS only came about because certain factors pointed in that direction. He told me it was a shot in the dark. The results shocked him almost as much as me."

"The doctor was a friend?"

"Known him for years. We go way back."

"What came next?"

"HIV positive required treatment, and I knew the cardinal would eventually find out because of the insurance claims. I figured it was better to tell him personally."

"Emerson…what a bombshell to drop."

"It certainly was."

"How'd the cardinal handle it?"

"After heart fibrillation returned to normal, he converted into an administrative mode and began searching for steps to be taken. If he had composed a list of possible topics before the meeting, trying to guess what I wanted to talk to him about, HIV positive would not be on it. Shock tends to be contagious with this illness."

"Who would ever suspect it?"

"Remember, Tom, he caught all of it in one large dose. Crack cocaine and HIV combined. How he managed to function reinforces my belief that he possessed awesome ministerial gifts."

"Where did you go from there?"

"Rochester."

"For a month?"

"Four months."

"Ohhh…was it like this?"

"Treatment wise, yes. Living wise no. It's for priests only and has more of a church flavor. Mass every morning and many opportunities for prayer. Besides desperately needing what they offered, I reconnected my life with God. Amazingly, I had no idea we drifted so far from each other."

"Kind of sneaky how it happens, isn't it? The daily discipline of prayer gets sacrificed in tiny increments."

"Yeah, one day you wake up and discover it's gone and it's been gone for some time."

"Did you go back to New York?"

"I returned to Harlem for a year."

"Then what?"

"They sent me here. HIV turned into AIDS. They had a dual concern—my health and public scandal if the press found out. The mess I created exceeds the bounds of my imagination. Believe me, it's an epic I never intended to write."

"Emerson...I don't know what to say."

"I warned you. Shock is contagious."

Emerson had gone astray. Crack cocaine and one romp under the sheets were serious sins. Like Adam and Eve, he bit the fruit and awakened to consequences of enormous proportions. In Harlem as in Eden, the transgression renders a death sentence. Unfortunately, Emerson's death decree was akin to the snake's interpretation. He would give anything in trade to receive the interpretation God handed Adam and Eve. How he maintained dignity and grace in light of this tragedy baffled me. Regarded on the unit a model of humility, the other residents only knew about the cocaine use. The treatment center staff granted permission to keep the AIDS issue mute. Apparently, the cardinal requested this injunction prior to Emerson's admission. New York wanted him cared for, but they feared public scandal if the story leaked. Trusting twenty-four drunks in the unit to remain close-mouthed was beyond even the cardinal's deposit of faith. Who could blame the man? I searched Genesis for some inspiration.

> That same night he rose, and taking his two wives
> and his two slave-girls and his eleven children he

crossed the ford of the Jabbok. He took them and sent them across the stream and sent all his possessions over too. And Jacob was left alone. And there was one that wrestled with him until daybreak who, seeing that he could not master him, struck him in the socket of the hip, and Jacob's hip was dislocated as he wrestled with him. (Gen. 32:23–27)

Emerson stared death square in the face, yet he wasn't seeking pity. His resolve centered on amending for his sins. The past severance in dialogue with God showed signs of repair through daily prayer. As one resident so aptly stated, "Emerson carries himself in a manner I'm unaccustomed. His movement and speech can be defined only one way. He appears to be growing in holiness. When I see him, I marvel at his stature and envy his serenity."

The man making the observation is the founder and president of a Fortune 500 corporation. He possessed an incredible business acumen and proficient observational skills. I concurred most assuredly with his appraisal of Emerson. He was a man hard not to love.

CHAPTER 14

I trotted to Maureen's office for our final session.

"Tom, there's not much else to tell you. You've been given the tools for recovery. Now put them into practice. Here's a copy of my aftercare recommendations. As you can see, the list is short. None of these items should be altered or amended. As an alcoholic, you'll look for shortcuts. Treat them with dogmatic reverence.

"They are proven means to recovery, so analysis and synthesis isn't required. Spend your time following them, instead of investigating their merit. In recovery, they have attained the status of infallibility. When strictly followed, active addiction matriculates into full remission. Accepting them requires a leap of faith. This should not be foreign ground for you. Now, read them to me."

"Abstain from all mood-altering chemicals, attend a minimum of five AA meetings per week, contact the alumnus listed below within twenty-four hours of your release, invite him to serve as your temporary sponsor, daily prayer and meditation, weekly reading from the Big Book and Twelve and Twelve.

"You have a long road ahead. Surround yourself with people in the program. Rely on others for a while. Vulnerability is new territory for you. Go slowly. You'll come to find out the disease can be transformed from a curse to a blessing. That realization could be years away, but you get there how? How do you get there, Tom?"

"A day at a time."

"Myyy, spoken with bloody dejection."

"Maureen, these slogans. They're pithy."

"Ah, you know some better ones. Share them with me, wise master of sobriety. I yearn for your wisdom."

"Okay, okay, I deserved that, but it was honest."

"Well, I'll be goddamned, Tom. You make honesty sound like it's a rare event in your life. You know what? It is. Deception, manipulation, dishonesty are your modus operandi. They're ingrained in the fabric of your soul. It's taken you years to do it, but you've succeeded. Your soul is cloaked with a destructive cloth. It can't be stripped with one fell swoop. You peel it off incrementally, slowly, over time. Beware though, destructive cloth has the power to permeate the core. It consumes with steady daily doses of selfishness and being self-centered. Practiced long enough and your spirit is obliterated.

"Want to know what hell's like, Tom? It's simple. Obliterate your spirit, and you're there. All alone in abject hopelessness. You're *only* thought is 'How do I cease to exist?' It's not 'Do I live or die?' The disease is much more insidious than that. It's 'How do I cease to *exist*.' Alcoholism will take you there. The cunning, baffling, and powerful aspect of the disease is the trip to hell. Alcoholics get there via parties, festive gatherings, bar-room banter, weekend binges, rock concerts, solitary drinking, nipping from cleverly hidden bottles, orgies, and dark alleyways. The invitation list goes on to infinity. Stay in the throes of the disease long enough, and a plethora of enticing locales and people will be added to your resume. It's cunning because when you finally discover the pungent odor is coming from the bowels of hell, you'll ask, 'How did I get here?'

"And most wickedly, it's powerful. Abject hopelessness can't be pardoned. When your only thought is 'How do I cease to *exist*,' you've arrived at the sin of the Holy Spirit, the unforgivable one. Remember that one, Tom?"

I chose to ignore her question.

"Damn you, stay with me!" A simple response is all I ask."

"Yes, Maureen. I remember the sin."

"Tom, you can leave this office and mutter a host of profanities in my direction. Like, 'The bitch makes me angry,' 'The ex-nun is crazy,' 'How dare this bastard speak to me this way!' 'Who does she—'"

"Maureen, that's enough. You made your point."

"The point is, you're going to hear this whether you like it or not. I'm telling you because it's my ministry—I'm obligated. Stay in recovery and it'll never surface or require your attention. But feed your addiction long enough and someday out of the bowels of hell, you'll recall this lecture. Then you can appropriately say, 'Goddamn it, the bitch knew what she was talking about.' Hear me, Thomas?"

"Loud and clear."

"Here's the rub. Wanna hear it?"

"Do I have a choice?"

"No."

"Okay then. What's the rub?"

"Robert Frost wrote great poetry. I only take issue with one metaphor he used. Remember the two paths?"

"Yeah."

"Tom, there's only one path. That's it—just one. There are two destinations, and the path leads to both. We choose the destination. Alcoholics dance along mesmerized by neon lights, billboards, exotic clubs, and snake-oil salesmen enticing them to simply go a little further. There's excitement with every step. Once in a while, you'll peer over your shoulder to glimpse back to where you began. You'll consider turning around, but the lights and the noise will dispel the thought quickly. Going to the bowels of hell is easier, more colorful, alluring. Mileage markers aren't posted. Progress is measured by the layers of destructive cloth adorning your soul. Go far enough and you'll eliminate everyone who nags, rants, or raves about your behavior. Acquisition of vices tends to gradually eliminate anybody who loves you. They figured out where the path leads.

"A few might share their insight with you, but why listen to them? Snake-oil salesmen scoff and ridicule anyone telling you to turn around. Flashing a devious smirk, they say, 'Wait till you see what's coming up next.' Any of this sound familiar Tom?"

"It's certainly creative imagery, Maureen."

"Do you even consider the notion that addiction will ultimately take you to hell?"

"It probably could when you throw in all those other sins. I'm struggling with how a priest simply drinking scotch ever gets to the places you describe. In Nebraska, those enticements simply aren't offered."

"Don't ever minimize the power of addiction, Tom. It ensnares people who do because they never see it coming."

"So, Maureen, the other destination is what, heaven?"

"We call it that."

"Abstaining from scotch takes me there?"

"You arrogant asshole! Don't play that shit on me. 'The ex-nun says if you don't drink you'll go to heaven.' Ha ha ha. You know goddamn well what it takes to go the other way. It's a bitch. Slower, more difficult, tedious, and sometimes downright boring. We dance and skip to hell, but you trudge the path to heaven. You know that. Don't talk like an idiot."

"Sorry. I was out of line."

"Tom, alcoholics disdain trudging. Who wants to plod when you can run from one adventure to another? Drunks want euphoria—massive amounts of it. AA looks redundant, cumbersome, and too disciplined. Fuck the trudge, I want to have fun. And oh, it's fun for a while. But where it ultimately leads you is diabolical. You'll see the snakes and realize they've been the voices you were listening to all along. I pity the soul who gets to that point. Even my vivid imagination wouldn't dare trespass into that magnitude of desperation. I abhor the power of addiction, and I'm careful about treating it lightly. I hope to God you'll never recall this lecture. The only ones that do are souls smothered by destructive cloth and tormented by the sound of hissing. Well, Tom, any comments?"

"You speak with authority, Maureen. I've been listening."

"I wish it was more than that, but I'll settle for listening. Later, it may sink in."

"Maureen, how long have you been sober?"

"Twelve years."

"The path to hell, did you venture far?"

"Far enough, Tom. My soul wore destructive cloth, and it took time to undress."

"Do you ever get tired of trudging?"

"Initially, yes. It's a bitch at first. I looked over my shoulder a lot."

"Do you still look?"

"Rarely. The scenery today is too serene and tranquil. I wouldn't trade this view for anything in my past."

"Did you have a spiritual awakening?"

"I did. Everyone in recovery does. They're the point in your life when you turn around. That's it. Glancing over your shoulder doesn't diminish the awakening as long as you don't turn back around."

"What lead you to turn around?"

"It wasn't me. The gift came totally from God. I simply asked for it and assented to do everything I could to protect it. The AA program showed me how."

"Sounds too simple."

"Asking is a no brainer. Receiving is the most difficult task you'll ever face. Many people ask, but only a few have the courage to receive."

"What does the path look like for you today?"

"It's uphill the whole way. The billboards, neon lights, and snake-oil salesmen are distant entities. At some point, the scenery clears and the horizon becomes more expansive. I'm trudging toward a mountain. Even though I'm still navigating foothills, each day the mountain becomes more visible. God is it majestic Tom. The climb appears rigorous but inviting. It's beauty far out ways the toil of getting there. Just the sight invigorates me. Oh and, Tom, the aroma is delectable, a scent so pleasing to the senses. It's authentic, genuine, and pristine. Frolicking to the bowels of hell eventually reeks. As the descent to those bowels gets closer, you'll gag and vomit in the odor.

"Worse of all, there's a chill—a bone-chattering chill which invades every fiber of your being. Adorn your soul with enough destructive cloth and the precious warmth of life extinguishes. The chill confirms demonic possession. Your soul sleeps with the snakes. Don't go there, young man. Very few ever come back."

"Maureen, I hope I never do."

"Let's close our final session with the last paragraph from chapter 11, 'A Vision for You.' Read it, Thomas."

"Abandon yourself to God as you understand God. Admit your faults to God and to your fellow human beings. Clear away the wreckage of your past. Give freely of what you find and join us. We shall be with you in the fellowship of the Spirit, and you will surely meet some of us as you trudge the *road of happy destiny*. May God bless you and keep you. Until then."

"Good-bye, Thomas. Trudge gracefully with God."

I exited her office and retired to my quarters. This session exceeded all others combined. Hearing it and integrating it into my life sounded arduous. She presented so much that I began writing it down. My memory couldn't be trusted on this one. Intuition screamed importance. Why it was important remained to be seen.

When she mentioned snakes and a chill, alarm bells rang. I never told her about the murder scene or James and his experience with these critters. Her knowledge came from other sources. Obviously, these experiences haunted others. I made a vow to avoid trespassing into snake-infested territory.

CHAPTER 15

Only one exercise remained before my release, the fourth and fifth steps of the program. These steps are (1) "Made a searching and fearless moral inventory of ourselves" and (2) "Admitted to God, to ourselves, and to another human being the exact nature of our wrongs."

Initially, the resemblance to confession diminished any anxiety of working them. Cognitively, I understood why they were critical for recovery. Curiously, it had been two years since my last confession in spite of the fact I needed the sacrament more than ever. Maureen knew me well. My head and heart were not in tandem.

Entering the room for my confession, I felt contrite, sorrowful, and repentant. Needing grace to restore my broken relationship with God compelled me to practice honesty to the best of my ability. Maureen inspired me. She had reached prophet status in the addiction field, and I was attempting my first venture as her disciple. I just wished I had the fortitude to get really honest about the murder and the demons.

*****

"Athanasia, what stage am I in?"
"Stage 3."

"What happened to stage 2?"

"You went through it already."

"When?"

"With Benjamin."

"I had no idea."

"Good. You're assimilating knowledge at a comfortable pace."

"Benjamin returned to a new corporal existence. Why hasn't it happened to me?"

"Do you want to return, Peggy?"

"Well…no. I don't."

"That's why you haven't."

"What if I had said yes?"

"I don't know. No one who reached stage 3 ever said yes."

"No one?"

"Not to my knowledge."

"Why is that, Athanasia?"

"You should know. You've decided to stay."

"I want to stay because this is where I belong. It's only a sense, but I don't feel compelled to return."

"Exactly. Trust your instincts, Peggy. They are genuine guides to follow."

"So Benjamin, my father, and all the others who returned felt compelled to do so?"

"Yes. Their destiny called them back. They still had a ministry to fulfill."

"Will they attain their destiny this time?"

"I don't know. It lies in their hands."

"What am I now, Athanasia?"

"An angel in process."

"What's that mean?"

"You'll see. Like I've said, the answer will be revealed."

"Can I whisper yet?"

"You have already—to your mom and Tom."

"Tom, do as Maureen told you. There's so much awaiting you, but evil lurks patiently. Don't let it consume you."

"Peggy, you whisper well."

*****

As I exited from my confession, I felt cleansed. Burdens released and departed to locales unknown. I rejoiced as they flew away. Out of the blue, a soft whisper became faintly audible. It sounded like Peggy, a voice I hadn't heard since my ordination. All I deciphered was to do what Maureen told me. The word *evil* got garbled by the conversation two others were having as they passed me in the hallway. I loved hearing Peggy's voice, I just wish she spoke more clearly. I also wished the blood and chalk line weren't so vivid every time she whispered.

PART IV

1997

CHAPTER 1

I was forty-five years old and incapable of even knowing what innocence was anymore. I left dry drunk years ago and was swiftly moving into what appeared to me to be terminal alcoholism. Instead of fighting this predilection, I was now trying to flee from it. My flight was on Route 66. Three 6s designate demonic so two of them are appropriate to register where my life is currently based. I'm far from my physical destination, but I am really close to my evil state of being. There may be a glint of light in my soul, but it has only the frequency of a firefly. It goes on and off. I'm in deep shit.

> If you ever plan to motor west
> Travel my way, take the highway that's the best.
> Get your kicks on Route 66.
> It winds from Chicago to LA.
> More than two thousand miles all the way.
> Get your kicks on Route 66.
> Now, you go thru Saint Looey and Joplin, Missouri
> And Oklahoma City is mighty pretty;
> You'll see Amarillo; Gallup, New Mexico; Flagstaff, Arizona;
> Don't forget Winona, Kingman, Barstow, and San Bernadino.
> Won't you get hip to this timely tip

When you make that California trip.
Get your kicks on Route 66.
("Route 66," Bobby Troup, Londontown Music)

My path to Los Angeles did not follow the above route. Being in a hurry mandated interstate travel. It's less scenic and definitely monotonous, but when demons are breathing down your back it's best to be in the fast lane. Fuck the trudge, I'm on the run.

The years since treatment have rendered abysmal adherence to the principles of AA. The only consistent thing I did was to relapse quite often. There were too many to tally, so I gave up counting years ago. I had one dresser drawer loaded with thirty-, sixty, and ninety-day medallions given to me in the meeting rooms of AA. My stockpile rivaled in quantity the inventory kept at the AA Central Headquarters in Omaha.

I never observed the aftercare recommendations Maureen outlined for me. The brief interludes of sobriety I experienced were all attained by going to speaker meeting, where I could sit rigidly on a folding chair next to the exit door. As I grew impatient with the beginning of meetings, where four articles were always read, I solved the problem by simply arriving fifteen minutes late. Gradually, I became impatient with the speakers also. I ended up giving them only fifteen minutes to either engross me or send me out the door for my car.

My thought process was primarily aimed at comparing myself out of the room. I listened for any information given by the speaker that confirmed he or she should definitely be in this meeting, but it didn't apply to me. DUIs, legal difficulties, divorce, bankruptcy, daily drinking, and taking a nip in the morning were all the ammunition I needed to politely disengage. They were not part of my resume, so it justified my belief that I didn't belong there. After a while, I quit going altogether. I wasn't missed because no one knew me anyway. I hadn't gotten around to introducing myself, and I certainly wasn't paying any dues for membership.

No meetings, no sponsor, and not working the Twelve Steps of AA culminated into liters of vodka because I believed it was easier to hide than scotch. That switch was the only primary change I made since treatment. Going to treatment just once made me a marked man in the diocese. All the priests knew I wasn't supposed to be drinking, so it took a full-scale effort to hide my consumption. This effort centered on the practice of professional manipulation and rigorous dishonesty. I became an exquisite manipulator but lacked the photographic memory to be an expert liar.

Scotch is difficult to disguise. The aroma of the elixir tends to seep out of your pores for days after a binge. Anyone with a functioning sense of smell and an inquiring mind can pick up the scent in a second. There were quite a few bloodhounds in the clergy, and they all had access to the archbishop's phone number. I had to practice stealth, and the energy it commanded was wearing me out.

As my vehicle left Omaha, I'm sure the archbishop was sad about my perpetual malaise, but he also had to feel relief that I was taking it to some other locale. I was ushered out of the diocese on four tires and a prayer. The wing would hopefully land in Los Angeles, the City of Angels.

Boy did I need angels. My last foray in drunken malaise was a doozy. Nothing even comes close in comparison to any earlier escapades I committed. It began with a phone call at 3:15 a.m. from Veteran's Hospital. A man was in the throes of death, and his family needed a priest to administer last rites. I had phone duty that night, so only my telephone rang. There were two other priests in the rectory, so every third night, I had my phone on. One of my cardinal rules had been never to drink the night of phone duty. Initially, I had twelve cardinal rules, but I had already violated ten of them. This was one of the two remaining ones that I had not disobeyed. At least, I had not up until this night.

Still in the repulsive residues of vodka-induced trauma, I got dressed in my black clothes attire and headed to the hospital. My destination was room 412, where I would try to disguise my condition and preside at a going-away ritual for a man close to death. I was so sick at the time that the thought of a foxhole prayer did not even cross my mind. Looking back, it most likely would have not made any difference anyway.

As I parked my car in the space reserved for clergy, I reached in the glove box to fetch my purple stole, oil, holy water, and the ritual book. In room 412 was Harold (which the family called Harry), his ex-wife, two sons, and a daughter. Harry was dying of sclerosis of the liver, which is commonly a disease precipitated by a lifetime of alcoholism. His family greeted me and thanked me for coming at this untimely hour. I stood over Harry and recognized he was in a semicoma state. Getting all my sacred implements on the hospital tray table, I began the ritual.

I sprinkled the room with holy water, along with all the family members. Then I put the water on Harry's forehead, his lips, his hands, and his feet while I read prayers out of the ritual book. This was a way to denote his thoughts, his speech, his work, and his travels were now being blessed as he prepared to leave this world. I also blessed the same places with the oil that had been consecrated for this sacrament. Sometime during the Litany of the Saints (I think it was St. Anthony), Harry emitted a muffled groan, and the medical machine flatlined. Nurses came in, and we were all invited to the hallway outside. I thought, *Thank God this was over*, and now I could stay with the family for a while and then go back home. Boy, was I wrong.

About a year ago, I began hiding vodka in my holy-water containers in my room and in the glove box of my car. At the time, I thought it was a brilliant move because I suspected that my room and my car were being checked for alcohol. I figured no one would bother to check the holy-water decanters. My glove box had two of them. The one with vodka had a black mark on the bottom, while the other had the real liquid.

Harry's oldest son came up to me in the hallway and asked for a private moment. "My dad was a drunk. That's why my mom divorced him, and my brother and sister and I avoided him as much as possible. He has not been in church for probably forty years with the exception of two weddings. He asked me three days ago to please call a priest if he was close to death. He said it couldn't hurt to at least leave this world with a sacrament. Isn't it ironic that a drunk priest shows up to minister to a dying drunk? And how fitting was it that the priest saturates the room, all of us, and my father with vodka instead of holy water. You are an embarrassment to my family and probably a fitting end to my father's life. You should be ashamed of yourself. Please leave."

He finished and walked away. I had finally sunk to the level of the snakes that were hounding me. I slithered to the nurses' station and did what was the only sane move I was capable of making at the time. I asked the nurse to please give me the name, address, and phone number of Harry's contact list. She wrote it down, handed it to me, and I slithered out of the hospital. I had finally reached the stage that Maureen had described at the treatment center.—abject hopelessness.

California dreaming took root a few months ago. Wrapped in delusion, the state shone like a beacon promising refuge from the insanity of my behavior. Some people view the state, more specifically the city of Los Angeles, as a haven for insanity. Here I was driving there in search of serenity and tranquility. What the hell, at least it was well over a thousand miles from Omaha, and if I drove fast enough, maybe I could outrun the demons who were nipping at my heels.

The demons had already convinced me to trade the priesthood in for more liters of scotch. Now they wanted me to go further. The crazy part of our dialogue is that I was listening to them. Sometimes I even asked them to repeat themselves or provide further clarification. These pests were driving me insane, and I was doing nothing to shut them up. I figured a good long road trip might sever my relationship with them and get them out of my life. I didn't have a clue how insane I'd become.

What I failed to take into account with the demons was they like to take road trips too. Usually, they ride shotgun. As I periodically checked the rear-view mirror for any sign of the critters, I didn't realize they were sitting beside me. They don't bring any luggage, they remain quiet when it suits they're purposes, and they don't chip in any money for gas. As travel companions, you barely know they're there. I may have my foot on the gas pedal and my hands on the steering wheel, but they knew who was really in control. And they were in control because I allowed it.

In California, I wanted to link up with my old college roommate. He lived in Santa Monica for the last ten years and had just celebrated his second year of sobriety in the AA program. His venture into the realm of recovery from alcohol gave me hope, and I was attracted to his new way of life. I had heard quite a few times at meetings that this was a program of attraction rather than promotion. My miserable behavior the last few years was open to any invitation promising hope. I was sick and tired of living the way I had but I didn't have a clue how insane I had become.

Santa Monica was enticing on another level. St. Augustine was one of the great theological doctors of the church. Even though he drifted aimlessly in debauchery for many years of his early adult life, a conversion experience turned him completely around. Church lore attributed a portion of this spiritual transformation to the incessant prayers of his mother, Monica. My destination was named after his mother, and I was speeding there, hoping to receive a dose of conversion. Grandiosity had become one of my character defects, but I still had some semblance of boundaries regarding reality. I would never be a saint, and I had no chance of ever coming close to the intellect and impact of Augustine, I just wanted to stop drinking and quit listening to the demons. My journey was a complete shot in the dark, but my life had been reduced to very few options. This was the best I could see.

CHAPTER 2

Michael, my college roommate, is an instructed soul attempting to rechannel the energy spent in active addiction into long-term recovery. He grew tired of going astray. Practicing a list of steps identical to those Maureen gave me years ago, he trudged the road to recovery.

Growing sick and tired of being insane, the AA invitation sounded like a better way of life for him. He tried other approaches over the years, but they all ended up with the same scenario—debilitating hangovers and credit-card receipts for evening activities he couldn't recall. The key to his newfound success rested in a willingness to listen and abide to the advice offered by another human being who had been there and done that. His initial reluctance to follow directions offered by someone else was overcome when he ran into in the rooms of AA, and slowly and painstakingly, it diminished because he kept showing up and he didn't consume a drink. Infancy in any endeavor is difficult at best. In recovery, he was learning it might be the most difficult journey he ever had to take.

Unlike the Catholic church, the AA program contains very few dogmas. Michael told me he was abstaining from all mood-altering chemicals, showing up for meetings, talking to a sponsor daily, and working the twelve steps in his life. The program says, without equivocation, these are the tenets for recovery. Any maneuvers that deviate from these norms are called half-measures, and they eventually avail us nothing. Even though the language is cloaked as a list of suggestions, there is a need to be emphatic about certain dogmas. Alcoholics and addicts are notorious when it comes to maneuvers. They are capable of going to extreme bounds of creative imagination in order to find an easier, softer way. Like the tree in the garden of Eden, enticements and allures come in many sizes and colors. But the fruit they offer is the same as it was in the garden—it's lethal.

Bernard was addicted to the fruit, and he bit the dust in the spring of 1995. Intellectually, he didn't suffer from scholastic pursuits, but pathologically, sclerosis did him in. Dewar's scotch and Bernard's liver came to an impasse. As more scotch got ingested after he left Minnesota, ligature of the cell walls of his liver increased proportionately. The liver hardened into one large mass and said, "Okay, Bernard, the gig is up." Bernard's soul headed for the cosmos that had enraptured his mental acumen all those years, and he came face-to-face with the transcendent mystery that he attempted to define. Sadly, he left behind mountains of unfinished work. The disease that killed him abhorred the completion of his academic pursuits. The only consolation was he probably discovered after death that so much needed to be revised, anyway.

Emerson tragically died also. Confined to treatment facilities in Minnesota for years, the cardinal of New York granted him one final wish. He wanted to die at home in the company of his family. In the fall of 1996, a final breath was taken from a body racked and ravaged by AIDS. Following his funeral, the *New York Times* ran a story with the facts of his malaise. The archdiocese provided Emerson with excellent medical care and achieved, for a while, their goal to keep the story under wraps. The article in the newspaper, despite the tragedy of addiction and AIDS, captured a glimpse of the man's dignity, intellect, and grace. I could only hypothesize that releasing the information sooner may have been an opportunity for Emerson to be a witness and a spokesperson for the trials of life, a testimony to the diabolical nature of evil, and the possibility for reconciliation and redemption. Who knows what may have happened? With God's grace, he at least died sober and at peace.

Bernard's and Emerson's deaths were tragic. Even though their results met the same fate, my conversations with both of them in the years prior to their deaths gave me a profound glimpse at a nagging reality. Emerson's final years were somehow different than Bernard's in spite of his tremendous battle with AIDS. Over the phone, he transmitted a sense of tranquility about his life and his medical condition. Bernard always sounded irritable and discontent. Obviously, there are so many factors that could come into play regarding their differences, but my mind kept returning to the promises mentioned in AA. They read as follows:

> If we are painstaking about this phase of our development, we will be amazed before we are half way through. We are going to know a new freedom and a new happiness. We will not regret the past nor wish to shut the door on it. We will comprehend the word serenity and we will know peace. No matter how far down the scale we have gone, we will see how our experiences can benefit others. That feeling of uselessness and self-pity will disappear. We will lose interest in selfish things and gain interest in our fellows. Self-seeking will slip away. Our whole attitude and outlook upon life will change. Fear of people and economic insecurity will change. We will intuitively know how to handle situations which used to baffle us. We will suddenly realize that God is doing for us what we could not do for ourselves.
> (*Alcoholics Anonymous* 6:83–84)

All spiritual programs have to offer promises. As a wise philosopher once said, "Without the bunny, the old dog won't run." The difficulty with promises can be reduced to the fourth word of the above quote. *Painstaking* is an ugly word for all human beings. It conjures up images of toil, energy, and change. Since these were part of the message God gave Adam and Eve when they were banished from the Garden, we tend to view them as a curse. We'd much rather be in the garden.

Alcoholics and addicts are especially prone to aversion from being painstaking about anything apart from their drug of choice. Our mind-set is geared to quick release and the bullets we choose to bite are laced with amphetamines and barbiturates. A rigorous, disciplined approach to anything holds as much enticement as a rectal enema. The easier, softer way is so enticing. Give us a solution and list of promises, and we'll begin calculating how to condense the time frame and constrict the steps with ways to get to the promises by another route altogether. Like obsessive, compulsive, self-centered saps, we want it all and we want it right now.

Michael went to ninety meetings in ninety days when he began his journey into the program. He suggested I do the same when I arrived at his home with a couple suitcases in my hands. To say he felt leery of what I was about to face would be a gross understatement. He knew my track record with this disease, and he had ample respect for the power of addiction. If he was a betting man, the odds did not warrant a wager on success. How long I could stay sober favored a bet taking the under rather than the over.

He knew the glamour of LA. Its cultural diversity, enormous opportunity, and the stargazing potential were all matched by an equal proportion of decadence. Hollywood can allow you to reach to the heavens and take you down to levels unimaginable. It's avant-garde in both respects. Running away from demons is tough duty in LA because there are snake denizens galore. Michael could only hope that if I got bit, I'd have enough sense to find antitoxins. He knew the venom there was toxic if it's ingested in massive doses.

My financial resources prohibited massive doses of anything. They were meager at best. As I stood in his doorway with suitcases in hand, cash wasn't in my luggage. All my money occupied space in one pant pocket, and it didn't have much of a bulge. Priesthood sort of negates building up a large economic surplus because the pay is fairly puny. It doesn't take long for active addiction to wipe out the meager resources a priest can accumulate. I stood before my college roommate poor, unemployed, and only a few days sober. He would have been wise not to answer the door.

The unemployment issue was addressed immediately. The exterior of his house needed a coat of paint, and I at least had the talent and the time to perform that task. We agreed on an hourly wage, which would provide me a little walking-around money. He figured it was best I stayed in the immediate neighborhood so the wage reflected short walks.

Sobriety was addressed next. Because our relationship went back many years, Michael offered to introduce me to the AA meetings he attended, get me a directory of the meetings in the area, and put me in touch with certain people in the program. The rest would be up to me. There would be no lectures from him or investigations concerning my whereabouts. I was free to come and go as I pleased. If I wanted to recover, then it was my responsibility to take the appropriate actions. Michael is a true friend, and I appreciated the dignity and respect he showed me that day.

CHAPTER 3

I met some people in AA, and I met some people who weren't in the rooms. Far be it from me to make any judgments regarding an inventory on someone's drinking, but I did find the group outside the rooms more enticing. They held court every night in the backyard of a home owned by a couple who had hospitality down to an art form. The ability to be socially engaging was my last tangible resource. Being a Catholic priest, even one in exile, added to my mystique and charm. The group was always in search of new blood, and I had all the qualifications necessary to receive an invitation.

On one evening when I decided to abstain from AA and nurse a glass or two of white wine (my attendance in the group was beginning to exceed my attendance at meetings), a vivacious redhead made an elegant appearance into the courtyard. The man of the house rose to greet her, and after pecking her cheek with a kiss, he walked her directly to my chair and made the introduction, "Fr. Tom, I'd like you to meet Rev. Patricia."

I stood up and touched her hand. With a nod of my head, I directed her to the chair next to me. Pulling the chair back in a show of proper etiquette, I invited her to rest comfortably. She sent me a luscious smile on lips that radiated a soft crimson color. Beautiful sunsets on the ocean didn't hold a candle to those lips. I was beguiled from the onset as my mind silently intoned a poem from India that had laid dormant in my memory banks for years, "We must have loved each other long before this life, for when I first saw you my heart leaped for joy."

It was most likely the two glasses of wine, my raging addiction, a little Hollywood glamour, her floriferous dress, and the fact I was currently exiled from Holy Mother Church that brought out the saying from India. Who knows? I fell in love.

"Patricia, are you really a reverend, or is he just playing a little joke?"

"I am an ordained minister, and I've got to be honest he told me about you earlier today on the phone. This was sort of a setup. He wanted me to meet you."

"Well, I'm glad he did. So you know I'm a Catholic priest?"

"I do. He said you're from Omaha, is that correct?"

"I am, but don't hold that against me, okay?"

"Don't worry, Thomas, I'm originally from Minnesota, so I know the Midwest very well."

"When did you make the move to LA?"

"Fifteen years ago."

"What area of Minnesota were you from?"

"Minneapolis. You're familiar with the Twin Cities?"

"I spent many years there. College, seminary, and graduate school were all spent in St. Paul."

"So you were born in Omaha and educated in St. Paul?"

"Actually, I was born in a town in Iowa, but my family moved to Omaha when I was fourteen."

"I was told Michael was your reason for coming to Santa Monica."

"Yeah, we've been friends for many years. Have you ever met him?"

"Only briefly. I've shopped in his store a few times, and we exchanged pleasantries a couple times. That's all. He isn't here tonight, is he?"

"No. Michael quit drinking two years ago, so gatherings featuring alcohol no longer appeal to him. He's not uncomfortable around drinking, but he has other interests that occupy his time. Retail in anything is very time consuming."

"How long have you been a priest?"

"Fifteen years. How about you?"

"I've been ordained four years, but I've been a member of the church for twelve years."

"The church is called?"

"The Church of Inner Light. It's not affiliated with any denomination. We hold services every Sunday morning at ten."

"Patricia, is the congregation large, medium, or somewhere in between?"

"It's small Tom. We have about fifty people who regularly attend. Once in a while, maybe twenty or more might make a visit. For what we offer, it's best the numbers stay somewhere in that range."

"You minister full time there?"

"Heavens, no. I'd starve to death. Ministry is my passion, but acting pays the bills."

"You're an actress?"

"Yep, that's what brought me to Tinseltown."

"Theater, screen, what?"

"Both. I started in theater in Minnesota, and I've done some work here also, but the bulk of my time now is television and movies. You look surprised, Thomas. Did that startle you?"

"Well, a little. You see, I'm just this country priest from the Midwest. I'm not used to the glamour and the lights of Hollywood. I'm way out of my element here."

"Yeah right, Father. You don't look lost in the least. In fact, you look very comfortable right now. Country priest, my, you know what."

"Reverend Patricia, are you being a little cynical?"

"More than a little, Father. What sights have you seen in LA so far?"

"I haven't been out of Santa Monica since I got here."

"What? You've been here almost what?

"Two weeks."

"What's Michael doing, keeping you a prisoner?"

"No, not hardly. I'm painting his house while I'm here. It pretty much consumes my day, and he has things to do most evenings."

"Thomas, you need a new guide. LA has so much to offer. Do you like the theater?"

"Love it."

"Do you like to listen to jazz live?"

"Love it."

"Well, I know places to go to see both."

"How do I hire a guide? Is there a yellow page I can consult?"

"I don't know, Father. Guides are pretty expensive in this town. You're not in Omaha anymore."

"Patricia, just off the top of your head, do you possibly know anyone who might be interested in showing a priest around LA? Someone knowledgeable yet affordable?"

"You're lucky you didn't say cheap."

"Sometimes I do get lucky."

"I'll bet you do, Thomas."

"So do you know someone?"

"I might. You know, I just might."

We talked for hours. Conversation flowed in short rhythmic statements without anxiety or much concern for what was spoken. Even though we were in the information gathering stage of interaction, it seemed easy rather than a struggle. Both of us had a sense there was some chemistry present, and we wanted to find out why and how many chemicals were present. I could sense Patricia and I would be spending time in each other's company.

She shared at length about her stage and film career, while I offered morsels about the current level of frustration I was having with the church. After hearing the list of her screen credits, it was obvious she had carved out a comfortable niche in Hollywood. Nothing in the megastar galaxy but definitely a resume to be admired. I was impressed, infatuated, and beguiled. Sensually, she had activated a lot of dormant hormones.

"So, Thomas, can I book you in for the Sunday services at the church this week?"

"I'll fit it into my busy social calendar."

"You're sure? Remember this isn't a Catholic number. We offer a little wider array of spiritual suggestions than you might be used to.

"I think I'll be able to handle it as long as my only responsibility is just to sit there and soak up everything that's offered."

"Ah, you never know. Maybe you'll receive a calling in this ministry. Another route to take perhaps."

"Who knows, Patricia. LA appears to be filled with lots of mystery. I might just encounter some in your presence."

"Are you ready for mystery, Thomas?"

"We'll have to wait and see, won't we?"

Our first formal date came two nights later. She got tickets to the performance of *Swan Lake* and escorted me to my first theater experience in LA. The performance was both impressive and odd because this adaptation featured an all-male cast. Patricia had warned me on our way to the theater that some of the critics had renamed the production *Gay Lake*.

"Well, what were your impressions, Tom?"

"Our seats were excellent."

"What about the ballet, silly?"

"The choreography was good. Of course, I know little about that subject."

"What did you think of the adaptation?"

"The all-male ensemble?"

"Yes. It's like pulling teeth with you."

"I don't know. I guess it was okay."

"Did the blatant homosexual overtones offend you?"

"Not in the least. It's theater. What's the story with this line of questioning?"

"I just wondered what you thought. The Catholic church is rather emphatic on the sinfulness regarding homosexuality, and I wondered what your views were."

"Now that's a loaded entrée, Patricia. I really don't know where to go with this one."

"It's not that complicated, Thomas. Are you with the church on this one, or are you reserving your judgment?"

"I'll opt for the B answer."

"The safe route, huh?"

"Patricia, I have trouble with the whole concept of homosexuality. Frankly, it baffles me because I can't understand or comprehend the attraction. So I'm reluctant to pass judgment on something I just plain don't get."

"Good answer, priest."

"Is this some kind of test?"

"Yeah, there's a tape recorder in the stereo, and I'm sending a transcript to the Vatican."

"Give them my regards, will you? Although I seriously doubt they even have a clue who I am. What are your views, Patricia?"

"About the ballet?"

"Very coy, my dear. No, about the sexual orientation."

"I've received an education since coming here to LA. In the theater, the gay lifestyle abounds. You simply run into it everywhere. I made a decision years ago to allow people their own discretion regarding their private personal lives. I think it's their spiritual decision, not mine. Haven't you had to deal with it in your ministry?"

"Not very often. Church doctrine tends to speak on the subject in words that do not sound very inviting to the gay community. They either find a more hospitable worshiping community or just remain silent about the issue."

"What about priests who are gay? In LA, there are some. I've met a few.

"I'm from Nebraska, Patricia. Remember?"

"Your entire life was spent there? Born there, raised there, and will die there?"

"No. I was born in Iowa, lived in Omaha, and received my education in Minnesota."

"No gay priests in the Midwest, Thomas?"

"I'm sure there are. Friends have told me there has been an increase over the years of gay men coming into the priesthood."

"Is it creating any problems?"

"Not that I know about. The biggest problem the church has is with an entirely other group."

"Pedophiles?"

"Exactly. It's created a horrendous amount of publicity and deeply hurt so many really innocent kids. I shudder when I think of the damage, and I'm about as far from a saint in the church as someone can get without that affliction."

"Oh, so Father has been a bit of a rebel?"

"My archbishop might use a little different terminology than *rebel*, but it conveys roughly the situation."

"And pray tell, what has the good Father done to warrant the status of a rebel?"

"I have brought mental anguish to my bishop by continually straying from the fold. He's the shepherd, and I'm definitely a lost sheep."

"Here I just thought you were out in LA on a vacation."

"Not entirely correct. Patricia, it would be more accurate to say I'm on the run."

"My god, I'm on a date with a fugitive priest?"

"Renegade priest, my dear. It sounds better and would make good copy."

Patricia and I became a couple. When I wasn't applying brush strokes to the exterior walls of Michael's house, I basked in her presence and loved every minute of it. She enjoyed dropping teasers about the church and the priesthood while I countered with snippets about Hollywood and the mega ego business of stardom. Both of us had ample ammunition to draw from and banter about.

Patricia is an instructed soul who would have difficulty going too far astray. Her moral grounds are bounded by a fence that is so far out in the horizon there are acres of room for about any behavior, lifestyle, or attitude to find a home. She practiced bountiful tolerance when it came to what others might do or believe. The only commandment in her repository was a refrain from malicious conduct or language. Her moral ranch transcended black and white because she updated to the cinematic inclusion of color years ago. She believed black-and-white morality was only practiced by people horribly aligned to the past or heavily steeped in ignorance.

Even though she had two marriages and divorces in her resume, she continued to hold herself open to new relationships and possibilities for intimacy. The creatures who roamed her ranch were peacocks because of their adorning plume. It sounded like a logical choice to me because she always dreamed about starring in a television sitcom. If meditating on peacocks could somehow move NBC to call her, then so much the better. This was her mind-set, and I began to grow a little more comfortable with it because Sunday was drawing near.

CHAPTER 4

The Church of Inner Light conducted worship services in a Masonic lodge. They rented by the month. Since Masons and Catholics have years of bad blood, this marked my first lodge experience. It was impressive.

I had been in Elks and Moose lodges before, and I had a feeling when I walked into the Masonic temple that this place did not have the designation of a critter in the wild. For the Church of Inner Light to transform this locale into a worship space was an easy transformation. Mystery was inherent in the ambiance of the setting. They adopted the minimalist approach and settled for rows of folding chairs all facing the large window to the east. Whether or not this was out of deference to Allah or some other deity, I'm sure I would eventually find out. At least they were punctual, the service began exactly at ten o'clock, and I was sitting in the front row of chairs. I wanted to remain more conspicuous by being in back, but Patricia insisted. Following her directive was the first encumbrance I endured in our relationship. I knew it wouldn't be the last; I just had no experience with these things.

A young woman strummed the harp (she resembled a flower child from the sixties), an olive-skinned man who looked either Indian or Pakistani played the chords on an electronic keyboard, and an older gray-haired woman softly nursed a flute. Patricia was the cantor as she led the congregation in a song of celebration. All of us stood, and everyone except me sang along. The song was obviously their main hymn of praise because they all knew it and there were no worship aids that I could see. This only bolstered my feeling of being out of place. The feeling had begun when Patricia picked me up that morning.

We all sat down after the final verse mercifully ended. Then a man in his early thirties with short black hair left the folding chair section and headed to the main window. He began to softly intone the words, "Freedom to dare". He kept repeating the phrase over and over while everyone gradually joined in. Applying a rhythmic cadence and periodically fluctuating the decibel level, people around me closed their eyes as if they were in a trance. This was definitely their mantra of choice, and I had a brief temptation to stand up and ask them, "Dare to do what?" Using better judgment, I remained seated and silent until the thought passed.

After God only knows how many repetitive recitations they did, an older woman took center stage. She was five by five—five feet tall and five feet wide. Barking out short terse statements with a heavy Germanic accent, she made it clearly known she was the church's founder and guru. She gave a state of the church address and made it clear this talk was only given once a year. After detailing the financial condition of the worshiping community, she exhorted everyone to be more generous with their contributions. Leave it to me, out of fifty-two Sunday's of the year, I show up and get the money talk.

When the guru finished shaming everyone to kick more in the collection plate, a beautiful young woman in her early thirties came forward, scanned the room, and began pronouncing prophecies that applied to specific people in the congregation. I was damn lucky she couldn't read my thoughts because I was dwelling on the fact the church had a hymn, a mantra, a guru, and now an animist. If you added a shaman to this show, then you'd have a full occult orchestra. I prayed to God a shaman wouldn't ascend because it was doubtful I could restrain my laughter.

The animist moved around the room to selected targets with bits of general crap about relationships, job opportunities, and the favorite "seer subject," general angst about conditions in life. Phrased with some specificity to make it alluring, it was obvious she could have gleaned most of her information from a minute of polite conversation with these people before the service. I was disappointed. She probably knew everyone in here and had known them for some time, so she could have been much more revealing. Nothing was generated at Patricia or me, so she obviously hadn't heard we were now a number. By next Sunday, the word would definitely be out, and I, most likely, would be the topic or a recipient of a spiritual message. My frustration had to be visibly apparent. If you're going to run a scam, at least have the fortitude to do it well. A smile crossed my face as I thought of a perfect role for the animist today. She should have publicly identified all the lax contributors in the church so the guru would know who to go after for more money. The thought was at least entertaining.

My hope was a final recessional hymn following the prophecies. I wanted to gracefully exit this joint. This was my hope until Patricia moved from the music section to center stage and she announced a special time for healing. When she called herself a licensed shaman, I almost fell off my chair. Supporting her ministry this day were two young women in their twenties, and they were introduced as shamans in training. They must have been in the internship stage of training because they gathered next to Patricia and formed a circle. I wondered what texts comprised the curriculum of shaman training and how many course credits someone needed to get licensed. Obviously, I could ask Patricia after the service, but I was kind of scared to find out. We were in the infancy stage of our relationship and sometimes too much information can be dangerous. It's better I wait on that one.

When the three women formed a circle, individuals left their folding chairs and came forward to be personally prayed over. Once a person got in the circle, hands moved all about and phrases were chanted. I had no clue what the phrases were because they could have been spoken in Swahili for all I knew. This led me to surmise that healing doesn't respond well to English. One by one, the people came forward, and nobody was in a wheelchair or showed visible signs of any physical afflictions. This led me to believe the relief they sought was more geared to mental illness. If they were regular weekly attendees to this hocus-pocus, then this assumption made sense.

The final whacko received treatment, and I was looking forward to blowing this pop stand. All of a sudden, my worst fear began to materialize. I felt forty pairs of eyes burning a hole in my back and another ten looking straight at me. As I slowly moved my head to peer behind me, it became obvious immediately, I was the only one in the joint who had not come forward for healing. Glancing toward Patricia only confirmed my fear. She beckoned me forward with a nod of her head, and I rose like a fatigued fighter and stepped to the front. I had no chance of conveying dignity; it was beyond my power to manufacture that look. I positioned myself in the middle of the circle, closed my eyes, and started to silently intone Hail Marys. They are a great rote prayer to say when you find yourself in situations where you are powerless to change anything but you know it will pass eventually. By the fourth or fifth one, the madness was over, and I slithered back to my seat. They broke into song, and I thanked God this service at the asylum was finally over. The only "inner light" I wanted to ever see again was the bulb illuminating the exit sign out of this place.

What I experienced at Inner Light did not totally reflect my views on the totality of independent spiritual worship communities. I was sure there were many authentic expressions of peoples need to discover their relationship with a higher power. I also knew that any one's search for a transcendent being was the most arduous task a human can undertake. Besides, Patricia would have a field day dissecting a typical Catholic liturgy. It was my current frame of mind that produced prodigious amounts of cynicism.

CHAPTER 5

I immediately went back to what I could recall from Genesis. I really needed Fr. Sherman's help on this one, but suddenly I remembered a captivating verse.

> Dinah, who was Jacob's daughter by Leah, went out to visit the women of that region. Shechem, the son of Hamor the Hivite, who was the ruler of that region, saw her, carried her off and raped her, and so dishonored her. But he was captivated by Dinah, the daughter of Jacob; he fell in love with the woman and comforted her. Accordingly, Shechem said to his father Hamor, "Get me this girl, I want to marry her." (Gen. 34:1–5)

Where this verse was taking me, I did not have a clue, but it came to me when nothing else even registered. Obviously, I chose not to recite it. And the sexual theme that ran through it cogitated with the sex I was receiving.

After enduring the Masonic moment filled with inner light, Patricia drove me to her apartment in Santa Monica. From a biblical point of view, I knew my first shaman. It wasn't a rape like Dinah, but it still was a severance of an ordination vow. I now batted three for three in vows broken, and I knew from a Vatican perspective this was grounds for expulsion from the plate.

Undressed with tenderness, kissed voraciously by succulent lips, my claims to chastity since ordination dissolved in exaltation under the sheets of her bed. The sexual encounter was good, and it confirmed that all my physical equipment still functioned despite a lengthy sabbatical. The only real surprise I encountered were Patricia's breasts. My first caress identified the presence of a plastic surgeon somewhere back in her past.

In California, the possibility of earthquakes mandate that certain buildings undergo a process called retrofitting. In Hollywood, some women apparently borrow this architectural revamping when they see a surgeon for a little structural adaptation. They simply call it reconstruction, and Patricia was only following the mantra of her church when she opted for the procedure. She had the freedom to dare for bigger tits.

A woman's breasts are God's mysterious appendages. Even though their physiological function is obvious, they elicit many curious responses from men. Some males are fixated on breasts. Since their function is to feed infants, maybe they stir up a wanton desire to return to a time when someone nursed and cared for us. Then again, breasts are also viewed by some males as cute playthings to fondle for sexual arousal. Since men have an abnormal propensity to want big toys, breasts sometimes get lumped into the fray and sizes, firmness and buoyancy are constant subjects for debate. Breasts are an anatomical anomaly that will obsess and feed the sensual desires of men for all time. As long as evolution allows women to have breasts, men will never be able to dismiss them completely. These babies compete and pulverize all competition. Sports, politics, finances, and yes, even religion can always be interrupted or suspended by a great set of tits. They win hands down.

I lit a cigarette and asked Patricia, "Is this a normal ending to your weekly services?"

She giggled like a child and seductively informed me there would be more to come. At this point, I was a puppet. and she could have pulled any strings she wished. For a brief interlude, I felt swayed to the notion that chastity and celibacy were totally nonsensical disciplines in the church and I was a fool for observing their practice. For the first time, I completely empathized with all the men who left the priesthood over the years after they had partaken with what the seminary called "the forbidden fruit." The avalanche of guilt I fully expected to cascade down on me never surfaced, and I couldn't figure out why.

It was way too early for any signs of intimacy, so we had no business being in bed. Chalk this decision up to lust. I knew we had to begin with honesty and then move into the other virtues before our sexual union could even approach the level of bliss. This would demand that I navigate areas like vulnerability, exclusivity, and selflessness. They all appeared to be so distant and unattainable. Hell, I was in mortal combat with honesty alone because I just didn't want her, or anyone else, to know me intimately. I decided to simply wallow in lust, even though I knew this obsession usually has a fairly short shelf life in any relationship it inhabits. Once again, I was giving those damn demons too much control.

One topic of honesty I could never dream of disclosing were the brief thoughts that resurrected while Patricia and I had sex. Peggy made her entrance into my fantasy world. Patricia was eleven years older than me, yet at times, a sixteen-year-old was the recipient of my kisses and affection. I had sexual intercourse with Patricia, but I made love to Peggy. She remained in a secret treasure chest in my heart, and it was dangerous to open that chest very often. If I even mentioned this to Patricia, then she would have had grounds for justifiable castration.

*****

"Athanasia, I'm confused."
"About what, Peggy?"
"The glamour of evil."
"Glamour's a fitting description. Tell more about your confusion."

Well, as I look on Tom, I see the civil war raging in his soul. How can I reach him? What can I whisper to him?"

"It's hard to observe, isn't it?"

"More difficult than I could ever imagine."

"Peggy, you've been whispering good counsel. Everything you've conveyed is excellent advice."

"If it's so excellent, why isn't he listening?"

"That's his choice."

"*Choice*. What choice? The demons are shouting, and my whispers get drowned out by their clamor. This is not a fair fight here because they seem to have more impact solely based on the noise level."

"The decibel level Tom's experiencing is purely based on the fabric of his soul. When a person's soul is clothed in radiance, our whispers are clearly audible. The decisions a person makes are as clear as the light of day. We furnish exhortations to the soul to choose the decision that illumines one's life, and then we observe free will at work. Souls clouded in darkness for long periods of time simply reduce the volume level of our exhortations. Remember, Peggy, a whisper is easy to hear only if you are what?"

"Close to the source."

"Correct."

"Athanasia, don't you ever get frustrated when you observe someone sliding toward evil and all your power is simply reduced to a faint whisper?"

"Peggy, you've reached an important awareness. Yes, it can be frustrating. You have a personal relationship invested with certain people, and observing them from this dimension is difficult. But remember your father. As you witnessed his regeneration, your frustration level diminished. He has another opportunity to attain his destiny. What he experienced and, to some degree what you are going through, is called purgatory. The purging process of rising to a higher level of wisdom."

"The highest level is the beatific vision?"

"That's correct, Peggy."

"So purgatory is both of the world and in this dimension?"

"It is."

"Athanasia, you witness countless souls making their movement through life and into this dimension. How do you handle it with so much grace?"

"Remember the stage you are in, Peggy. More will be revealed. My role with you is to guide you through the stages of wisdom. It is your decision to accept them. Free will dominates the entire landscape of the Creator. All beings have the gift."

"So as I go through the stages, I detach from those I knew in life?"

"Detachment is a partial comprehension of what occurs. Higher levels of wisdom provides a new perspective, like what you have already experienced with your father."

"Athanasia, I wish to reach your level of serenity. You are at peace with your being."

"Patience, Peggy. The journey continues."

CHAPTER 6

Living in Santa Monica required cash, and painting Michael's house wasn't cutting it. I needed another source of income to augment my hourly wage job. The answer to my dilemma shot like a lightning bolt from the sky, but I also knew it wasn't divinely inspired. Out of desperation, I decided to enter the occult world. The Inner Light junk wasn't a viable meal ticket, but I did discover an area that offered lots of potential and was definitely doable. Being a lifelong fan of the *Twilight Zone*, I was approaching it's gates with increasing speed.

The animist at the church had a full-time gig as a channel for spirits from the past. Once a week, she held court in a ballroom of an LA hotel where approximately 150 patrons shelled out fifty bucks a head to hear her prophecies and oracles. She had physical beauty going for her, but the message I heard at the church was not that hot. When Patricia took me to see her perform as Meiserius, an ancient Egyptian princess, I knew immediately that with a little practice and a few alterations, I was capable of putting on a much better show.

One of the talents I honed during the years of priesthood was public speaking. I acquired the techniques through lots of practice and constructive criticism from many parishioners. The homiletics professor at the seminary gave us one piece of great advice and one superlative suggestion. The advice was as follows: "Don't rely solely on your parishioners comments about your homily as they exit the doors of the church after Mass. They'll tell you what they think you want to hear, and you need to hear what many will not want to say to you in person. In order to become a good homilist, you have to coax the missing information from them."

The suggestion he gave was a single piece of paper with three questions on the front and three on the back. The front three addressed public-speaking techniques, while the back asked about the content of the message delivered. He encouraged us to present this paper to our parishioners and invite them to fill one out on a weekly basis. Besides a critique of our homily, the only personal information they needed to divulge was the date and time of the mass. No names or signatures were required—anonymity was the key component. During the week following the liturgy or in the collection basket the next week, they could drop the sheets off, and they would be compiled by the secretary or volunteers in the parish. The priest would then receive a compilation of all the sheets regarding the sterling message he had preached. It required some work, but the payoff would be invaluable because the people now had the opportunity to lay it straight on the line without personal retaliations. All of us nodded our heads to the wisdom of this suggestion, but I have no clue how many decided to implement it when they got ordained and began their ministerial lives. All I'm sure of is that both Mark and I did it for a three-year period, and we benefited immensely from the instrument.

As Meiserius sat in her chair, clothed in a white robe and adorned in sparkling jewelry, her prophecies flowed like water from the Nile as she viewed the gathering throng who paid good money for their seat. I sat there and began devising a scheme that would render me some of the milk and honey that this gig could offer. This stuff was right up my alley. All I needed was a name, some flighty material, and a good costume. Being male, I decided to skip the jewelry. Besides, after the performance ended, Patricia told me it was fake, anyway. What the hell, the prophecy was bullshit so what did it matter if the jewelry was cosmetic.

Choosing the right name was crucial. People had to be enticed to come and plop fifty bucks down on the table for a seat. In the past, the book of Genesis had always provided needed answers to difficult questions so I consulted the text. The name came quickly. I decided to use Melchizedek. It dated back over three thousand years, and he had the lofty status of high priest. This was good enough for me. I could only hope the punishment for my current transgressions wouldn't last long. I knew they'd be coming; of this I was completely sure.

To find the right costume, I let my fingers do the walking through the yellow pages. I found a religious goods store on Sunset Boulevard and chose a white alb and a violet stole as my vestments for prophecy. For two hundred dollars, I was outfitted to work a scam that could bring in thousands.

While finalizing my purchase at the counter, two priests walked in. I lowered my head in shame while paying out the cash for the purchase. Patricia engaged the woman clerk in banal conversation, while all I wanted to do was slither out the door. As we left the store, I could swear I heard the loud hiss of a snake in the general vicinity. When I peered about looking for the rattler, Patricia shot me a quizzical stare.

"Thomas, what are you looking for?"

"Oh nothing. I thought I heard a familiar noise."

"What noise?"

"It's nothing, Patricia, never mind."

Some things are just best left unsaid.

Melchizedek made his appearance in a ballroom at the Westminster Hotel on a Monday night in May. Monday wasn't my choice; it was the only night available. Prophetic entities face strong competition in LA. There's a lot of unemployed actors and actresses who just happen to experience a calling for spiritual revelation. The calling has more to do with their meager bank funds than it does with a message from above.

Patricia took care of publicity. A professional photo shoot rendered a slick head-and-neck shot that gave me an air of distinction. It didn't hurt that I had my clergy shirt and collar on. She put together a poster with my picture and a short bio below my name. Advertised as a former priest from the Midwest with graduate degrees in philosophy and theology, I was offering a spiritually informative message through the psychic channeling of a high priest, Melchizedek. I wanted to add that this message was available to any schmuck who'd fork out fifty bucks to hear it, but I choose to bite my tongue. I had no idea where Patricia passed out these posters, and I never bothered to ask. As I was beginning to meet more of her friends and getting introduced to the network of this occult crap, I became aware that most of these people were looney. I kept my association with them on a very superficial level and practiced active detachment whenever I could. Besides, Melchizedek needed plenty of isolation so he could meditate and memorize his script.

Prior to my entrance on my big night in show business, Patricia came back stage and informed me the crowd was over seventy people. I was flabbergasted. Twenty-five people would have been overly optimistic, I thought. How the hell Patricia managed to do this was way beyond me. She once again marveled me with her creativity and resourcefulness. In spite of all the guilt I had associated with this scam, she continued to beguile me with her charm. Now it was my turn to perform.

Patricia introduced me in words that flowed poetically from her lips. I stood back stage and listened. My memorization of the beginning text of this scam was complete, and I felt confident. I borrowed from the Kabbalah, an ancient Hebrew text. The material I took came from between the third and eighth centuries, although it didn't get officially documented until the second half of the twelfth century by Rabbi Nehunya ben HaKanah. I'm sure the rabbi could explain what this material meant very clearly, and I was comfortable with the text also. My whole purpose was to present these people with something both familiar and obscure. I wanted my audience receptive but also in my control. One thought crept into my mind as I prepared to walk on stage. Thank God, there was a two-hour time difference between LA and Omaha. And, thank God, my archbishop wasn't clairvoyant. Right now he would probably be resting comfortably in bed. If he had the gift and knew what I was up to, it could have provoked a cardiac arrest. When it comes to renegade priests, bishops are damn lucky *not* to have ESP.

New age music softly played throughout the ballroom as I entered in my vestments and portable clip-on microphone. I sat on a throne positioned in the middle of the stage, and I slowly twitched and turned for about ten seconds. Then I placed my hands on the side of my face and went into a meditative trance. Actually, I just counted to sixty because that's when Patricia turned down the volume of the music. Making the patrons wait to hear my message was theatrics. It served as another ploy emphasizing the fact that tonight they were getting Melchizedek, a high priest, not some flunky Egyptian princess.

Remembering the necessity to use voice inflection and periodic pauses for emphasis I began my shtick. After this obscure introduction, I would take questions from the audience and then deliver a heart-warming message of hope. I wanted to send the faithful out of the hotel and back onto the streets of LA with a memorable evening in the presence of a biblical high priest.

The Holy One, be blessed, saw it was necessary to put into the world all things so as to make sure of permanence and of having a brain surrounded by membranes. The whole world, upper and lower, is organized on this principle, from the primary mystical center to the very outermost of all the layers. All are coverings, the one to the other, brain within brain, spirit inside spirit, shell within shell.

The primal center is the innermost light, of a translucence, subtlety, and purity beyond comprehension. That inner point extended becomes a "palace" which acts as an enclosure for the center, and is also of a brilliant radiance beyond the power to know it. And God said, "Let there be light, and there was light." This is the primal

light which God made. It is the light of the eye.
This light God showed to Adam, and by means
of it he was enabled to see from end to end of the
world. This light God showed to David, and he,
beholding it, sang forth his praise, saying, "Oh
how abundant is your goodness which you have
laid up for them that fear You." Light is shown
for the righteous, then will the worlds be in harmony and all will be united into one. (Kabbalah,
p. 144)

The material went on further, but this was a good representation of where I intended to go. I practiced a memorization technique that Patricia taught me, and I had plenty of time to rehearse
as I continued painting Michael's house. Fortunately, he and all his
neighbors had jobs outside the home because they might have locked
me up if they heard me reciting this stuff with a paintbrush in my
hand. The only ones who heard Melchizedek pontificating were the
Hispanic maids, pool cleaners, and lawn workers who ventured into
the neighborhood periodically. From what I could tell, English had
not yet become their language of choice, so they probably wrote me
off as "el loco." If they had been in LA for any length of time, then I
was just another crazy gringo they encountered.

After my initial address, Patricia walked the floor with a
microphone asking for questions from the audience. We previously
rehearsed the first two questions by planting a man and a woman in
the audience. They didn't pay admission, and after the gig was up,
I would give them each one hundred dollars. They both aspired to
work in the film industry, but they were having trouble finding full-
time work. Patricia told me people like this were easy to find in LA.

"Melchizedek, I've been working as an extra for two years now.
I'm tired and becoming disillusioned. Do I have a future here, or
should I go back home and work in a different profession?"

Taking my hands off the regal throne Patricia borrowed from
the Paramount Studios prop room, I bowed my head and rubbed
my fingers across my temple. Trying my best not to look hokey, I sat

FOUR DECADES IN GENESIS

engaged in thought till I counted to fifteen. Then I raised my head slowly and asked him, "You're from the Midwest, aren't you?"

"I am."

"What would you do if you went back there?"

"I…don't know."

"Working in the film industry has been your dream for quite a few years, hasn't it?"

"Most of my life."

"When you came out here from the Midwest, did you have a time frame?"

"I don't know what you mean."

"Did you say to yourself, 'I'll give it two years and that's it'?"

"No, not really. I moved here for good. This is where I wanted to live."

"Are you currently working in the film industry?"

"Yes, as an extra."

"I take it the work's not steady."

"Not steady at all."

"I have a sense you don't live alone. Is there someone else in your life right now?"

"There is."

"Another man?"

"Yes, how did you know?"

"It's unimportant. The man you live with, you are in a relationship with him, correct?"

"We are."

"You met him out here and he works in the film industry also, right?"

"He does."

"His work though is more intensive than yours and is more regular?"

"He has a better position than I do."

"If you left LA and went back to the Midwest, what's the chance he would come with you?"

"Ah…a…a…he probably wouldn't."

"So you're willing to give up the relationship and your current career to move back to where you grew up. Do you have a profession to go back to in the Midwest?"

"Not really, but I know some people."

"What about the relationship, are you ready to give that up?"

"I don't know. Right now I'm really confused."

"Is anyone else in the audience tonight sharing this young man's dilemma? Or has anyone else here ever gone through what he is currently struggling with? By a simple show of hands, raise them if you can identify with what he's going through." I turned back to the actor. "Turn around and look. See all those hands in the air? Those people are your kindred spirits. They have been there or are currently in the same malaise you are in. It's quite a few people isn't it?"

"It is. It's more than I expected."

"Now, the difficulty of your current dilemma is twofold. First, there is jealousy in your relationship, and second, there is frustration in your career. Individually, each one causes immense strain and stress in our lives. Collectively, they are triggers for terrible decisions to be made because you'll make your decision from the throes of utter confusion. Making a good decision when you are in this state is like playing the lottery. The odds don't favor you making even a stab at a healthy decision, and it usually comes back to haunt you later. I recommend that you stay in the film industry as an extra for now and work extremely hard at the jealousy factor in your relationship."

"How do I do that?"

"You said there's periods of downtime as an extra, right?"

"There are."

"Take that time and rechannel your energy into productive labor. Instead of sitting at home commiserating over the lack of work while the person you love and live with is at work, volunteer at a place where people are far less fortunate than you are. Find the address of an AIDS clinic, and find out what you can offer in terms of time and assistance. Or volunteer to work at the food pantry or one of the many missions for the homeless. It doesn't really matter where you go as long as you do it. The effort you expend in this direction will return a hundredfold in other areas of your life."

The young woman we had rehearsed was next, followed by six others who I dealt with by the seat of my pants. I was adaptable and quick on my feet with the patrons that were random, but it made little difference because my credibility was cemented with the first two. The customers were convinced I knew my shit even though all of it came from a bull.

CHAPTER 7

Patricia announced in the car, as we drove from the hotel, that she had a surprise for me. I was only half-paying attention because I was busy counting the cash in my hands. The crew who put this prophetic business on paid me $1,800 for this gig. After paying off the extras who were planted in the crowd, giving Patricia her cut for services rendered and the prop from the studio, I still had numerous hundred dollar bills to pocket. Where else but in LA could someone do this crap? The agency took care of ballroom rental and always paid the prophets in cash. No receipts were tendered, and no taxes were deducted. I had an inkling that if you went back and investigated the family lineage of the crew who put on these performances, you would eventually discover a hoard of gypsies in their background somewhere.

"Oh, Thomas! Thomas, are you with me?"

"I'm sorry, Patricia. What were you saying?"

"My surprise. I have a surprise for you. Do you want to hear it?"

"Sorry, dear, sure I do."

"While we were at the hotel, Annie and one of her friends were doing us a favor. They went over to Michael's house and gathered all your possessions, along with your car and moved you into my—our apartment. We have now become a couple. How's that for a surprise, dear?"

I didn't say anything.

"Well, aren't you going to say anything?"

"I'm...flabbergasted Patricia...I don't know what to say."

Flabbergasted was mild compared to what I really thought. If I got rigorously honest with Patricia at this moment, then it would have been a long walk back to my car and my clothes would have been out on the curb. We were miles from Santa Monica.

"Tom, talk to me. Say something. Say anything."

"Patricia you...caught me off guard. I had no idea this was coming."

"Well, do you want to move in with me or not?"

"Of course, I do, dear. It's just so...sudden. I didn't expect this to happen so quickly."

"Okay...that does it. I'll have Annie move everything back to Michael's tonight."

"No...no, I didn't mean it like that. Listen...I love being with you. Tonight was a blast, and you're responsible for putting this whole thing together. You've been great. You just caught me by surprise. That's all, Patricia."

"I was really hurt. I want you to know that. Here I put all this effort into making tonight a success and giving you this beautiful present as a gift of my love for you, and then you sounded like it wasn't what you wanted at all."

"Patricia, I wasn't rejecting your gift or your love. I was just simply shocked. Honey, let's go home and celebrate the success we had tonight and the love we have for each other."

"That's sweet. So you are sure you don't want to go back to Michael's?"

"Patricia, I spend more time at your place than I do there, anyway. Why would I want to go back there?"

"Thomas, you really worried me there for a moment."

"All I simply did is hesitate until I could come up for air."

"So...now you're saying I'm drowning you?"

"Patricia, I'm lusciously drowning in a sea of love."

"Melchizedek needs a little loving, doesn't he?"

"He needs lots of lovin', my dear."

"Well, I know just the place he can find it."

"I'm sure you do, Patricia. I'm sure you do."

Patricia's three-bedroom apartment came courtesy of the legislative moves made by Tom Hayden and his wife Jane Fonda. Their digs were more glamorous, but his push for rent control in Santa Monica allowed her to reside five blocks from the Pacific Ocean. Without rent control, she would be residing in the Valley, and the difference between the two is an immeasurable chasm.

Annie occupied one bedroom, while Patricia and I were in the master. The third bedroom served as an office where she could talk to her agent and work on future roles. The relationship with Annie puzzled me. Patricia told me she was a lost soul and had nowhere else to go. Any claims that she helped out with rent went out the window because she was unemployed. I had reasons to be suspicious about her, but at this point I was just tagging along for the ride.

Annie is too fucked up to be an informed soul, and the vibes say she went astray years ago. Intellectually, she is street smart, probably from years of living there. Her drugs of choice are beer and marijuana, and she consumes them in prodigious amounts. With a Native American heritage and hailing from the Northwest, her stout, muscular features are positioned on a five-foot-six frame. Dark complexion and a short cropped cut of her black hair give her an aura of rugged independence and strength. Bodybuilding is in her resume somewhere, and I could only hope it wasn't in prison. She could beat the shit out of me, and she knew it, so I stayed out of her way. Now that we shared the same domicile together, it was going to be tough finding a safe distance. Every time I broached the subject of Annie with Patricia, I received evasive maneuvers. What the hell, I was being a tad bit nonrevealing also, so I didn't venture into that territory often.

Sexual trysts with Patricia were frequent enough to satisfy my libido, and I presumed they sated her desire and thirst. I hated being suspicious because the Melchizedek gig had started out well and there was future promise. Besides, the apartment had all the creature comforts I needed, and it removed me from direct eye contact with Michael. Lately, he was beginning to register facial looks that bordered on stares. He knew I was drinking wine, and he had his doubts about the health of my relationship with Patricia. None of these topics were talked about, but they hovered in the air like a rancid mist covering any time we were together. AA meetings had been completely removed from my social calendar, so our time together was minimal at best.

Regarding Annie, I chose to remain partially blind. My intuition said Patricia and Annie had a sexual history, and she would continue to sneak a little on the side. I should have been pissed off, but embarrassingly, it sounded a bit erotic and alluring. Two men having sex sounded revolting, while two women engaged in the identical behavior offered a completely different perspective. Double standards abound regarding the genders, and this was just one more example. I dealt with Annie by keeping her as distant as possible and privately giving her a new name, the Chinook. Her Northwest heritage and the fact she probably swam upstream all her life were ample grounds for her new title.

My role as a house painter was drawing to a close. Melchizedek drew bigger crowds each week as word got around there was a crazy priest performing on Monday nights at the Westchester on Vine Street. With each increase in attendance, my take-home clams rose proportionately. Besides doing the group performance, I made myself available for private sessions in a room at an Occult Bookstore. For twenty-five bucks someone could get a half hour with Mel. These sessions were a hoot because the clientele went way beyond anything I encountered in my confessional and counseling experience in the church. These people were really whacky.

The income derived increased to levels I was unaccustomed to, and all of it was tax free, so to speak. The absence of federal, state, and FICA taxes I attributed to my ministerial status. I also didn't worry about workmen compensation because as a prophet, I would most likely know when an injury was coming in the future. I knew this was pushing the levels of IRS beneficence, but I also shared a little gypsy magic with my promoters. Just like them, my bags could be packed in a matter of minutes and I would skedaddle down the road.

All the bases looked covered as I applied paint to the last small section of Michael's house. Then he pulled into the driveway one afternoon and told me to call my mother in Omaha.

CHAPTER 8

Phone calls from home in the middle of the afternoon or in the middle of the night emit an odor of concern. Something was amiss; of this I was sure.

"Mom, it's Tom. Michael told me to call. What's wrong?"

"I didn't want to bother you, but I thought you better know— I've got a brain tumor."

"What!"

"I just returned from the Mayo Clinic, and the news is bad, Tom. Very bad."

I slowly sat down on Michael's sofa and tried to catch my breath. "Mom, I don't know what to say. What did the Mayo Clinic say?"

"It's a type 4 malignant tumor. They don't have a type 5. It's the worst."

"What can they do? What kind of treatment is there?"

"Very little, Tom. They suggested radiation, but they offered little hope for any recovery."

She began to sob. All I could hear from the earpiece of the phone was agony and despair. My mom tried to mask this by a resolve to be tough, but it wasn't working. An absolute pillar of strength for all the years, I knew she was facing the ultimate test of her life.

"This is unbelievable, Mom. How could this tumor just suddenly appear?"

"I don't know. The doctors claimed they didn't know what causes these. All I'm left with is to deal with it as best I can."

"There was no warning at all?"

"Not really, Tom. A month ago, I had some numbness in my hand and left side, but it would come and go. Last week, it grew more intense so I went to the hospital for a checkup. They found the tumor, and I went to the Mayo Clinic for a second opinion. It's all been so sudden and quick."

"Listen, Mom, I'll fly home tomorrow. I'll make some calls and get on a flight. Have you called all the other kids?"

"I have. Everyone is coming home shortly."

"I'll be there tomorrow, Mom. God, this is unbelievable!"

"It's the shits, Tom. It really is."

Patricia immediately volunteered to go with me, but I delicately declined her offer. My mother was dying; bringing Patricia home might have sped up her death. I knew I had done enough damage with my addiction and exile from the church. No new material needed to be added at this point.

Thirteen brothers and sisters presents an enormous menu for achievement and dysfunction. Playing the role of a renegade priest lost its luster in my family years ago. For most of my siblings, I graduated into the classification of simply being a royal pain in the ass. Antics and maneuvers based on dishonesty were practiced with stubborn acumen for years as I clung to addiction. Trust had vanished from their eyes and ears. My mother held on to St. Monica's resolve regarding me and prayed her novena daily. Her prayers were coming to an end, and I certainly hadn't shown any change

Arriving in Omaha, I was greeted by my father at the airport. When I got to the house, I received a cordial yet somewhat aloof welcome. My father embraced me, but everyone else was satisfied with simply a cursory greeting. Who could blame them? My entrance through the door was met with as much aplomb as a visit to a proctologist. What could I expect after years of being an asshole?

There was an eighteen-year span between the oldest and youngest children in our family. Fourteen successful pregnancies in eighteen years was my mother's legacy, and she frequently pleaded not guilty by reason of insanity. Physically, psychologically, and spiritually she possessed the gifts conducive to sound child rearing. Behavioral deviations taken by me or any of my siblings were never due to the lack of maternal care and love. We all had the tools to live sane and productive lives, so any of our sins were of our own making.

Dorothy is an instructed soul whose maternal nature never allowed her the opportunity or the time to go astray. Raised by parents who provided the basics and a brother who nurtured her Irish roots and humor, she acquired empathy for others while never becoming obsessive about herself. This mixture allowed her to flourish with fourteen children and a myriad of relationships that highlighted her eclectic tastes. Rarely did she ever encounter a person whom she didn't find some redeeming quality that perked her interest. Curmudgeons even stood a chance with Dorothy because she always gave a person the benefit of the doubt. Her gift would make her an excellent gatekeeper in heaven because you had to be diabolically challenged not to receive her blessing.

I came home to fulfill one mission only—reconciliation to the best of my ability with a mother whom I loved yet continually hurt by my behavior. I prayed for success on the airplane because I knew failure dominated my landscape in this regard.

"Mom, it's good to see you, although I can think of many different circumstances for a visit."

"Thanks for coming, Tom. How was your flight?"

"Mom, that's so typical of you. Here you are battling this illness, and you're worried about my stupid plane trip. You are amazing."

"They cut a lot of umbilical cords from me, Tom, but all of you are still my children. It's my nature to be concerned for you."

"Well, I certainly allowed you to spend an inordinate amount of time in your nature, didn't I?"

"All of you stepped on my toes when you were young, and some of you stepped on my heart when you got older. That's why I initially thought this brain tumor was a misdiagnosis. I should have heart problems instead of this."

"Mom, it shouldn't have taken your illness for me to say this, but I'm truly sorry for stepping on your heart so many times. I've been selfish, self-centered, and arrogant at times, and it hurts to know that I've caused you pain."

"You'll get no argument from me about the pain you've caused, but the important thing is for you to turn around and head in a new direction. I don't know why this tumor came, but I hope to God something positive can happen because of it. God knows I've offered enough prayers on your behalf."

"I thank you for those. Justice would be better served if I had the brain tumor instead of you."

"Tom, I'll gladly give it to you, but we both know that's impossible. Of course, you might sing a different tune if you had this monster for a day or two."

"How bad is it?"

"It's not so much the pain, Tom. It's the debilitating progression that's most difficult. Every morning, I wake up and discover I've lost or am losing another bodily function. My left side is growing numb, and I can barely walk. Pretty soon, I'm destined for a wheelchair. My speech is slurred, and eventually I won't be able to communicate. A hospital bed awaits me eventually, and it will be the last piece of furniture I occupy in this lifetime. Pretty gruesome, isn't it? Still want the tumor?"

"Mom, I know this sounds stupid, but how scared are you of what happens after death?"

"I don't know, Tom. As you well know, I've been going to mass almost every day of my life. God has been good to me in so many ways. But as I get closer, it truly is frightening. So many doubts surface out of the blue, and I start questioning everything. I don't want to leave yet. There's so much more I want to see and do, especially with you kids and with all the grandchildren I love *so* much."

What do you say to a woman who gave birth to you, cared, nurtured and protected you for so many years when you couldn't take care of yourself? The word *love* initiates the response, but the human language doesn't have the capacity to carry it from there.

"Mom, I've been a lousy priest in so many ways, but I have been an excellent observer. What I'm about to say may not be any consolation. You can take it and do with it whatever you want. I've seen many people die, not as many as Grandma, but I've seen my share. Quite often, in fact, more than quite often, the person dying in the last hours or minutes of their life has a vision. It's not spooky or eerie, it's calm and tranquil. They suddenly see a face of someone they knew and loved during their life who has gone before them in death. This person is like an angel sent by God to make the journey more peaceful and less fearful. I have no idea who may come to you, but I'm pretty sure, in fact I'm certain, you'll be getting a visit."

"Thank you, Tom. That helps more than you can imagine."

Emotions were heightened, and nerve endings were frayed for everyone in the family. Impending death of one's mother tends to do that to people. Since I inflicted my share of wounds on most of my siblings, having me physically present served as a reminder and opened old scar tissue. The scent of fresh blood began permeating the household, and a week of its odor created dissension in the ranks.

Mayo Clinic diagnoses of my mother's illness was termed a glioblastoma multiforme tumor. They could offer no explanation for its existence because research had not yet pinpointed a cause for this abnormality. One of my brothers, who possessed no medical training that I'm aware of, claimed to have better research than Mayo's. He declared I was the reason she contracted this tumor, and he invited me to leave for the sake of family peace. I knew the accusation was grounded solely on anger and had no basis, and I also knew there would be no family peace after I left. There were rifts among certain members that transcended me. Instead of striking out with a venomous angry retort myself, I choose to leave and return to LA. After all, I knew my guilt was justified in so many areas besides my mother's tumor, so I slithered out the door and told my mother I'd keep in touch by phone.

If inflicting excruciating pain on another human being is a goal, then timing is critical. My brother's attack had the correct timing and inflicted copious amounts of pain. Massive amounts of blood seeped from my emotional pores on the airplane ride back to LA. When Patricia met me at the airport, I needed a transfusion. I became painfully aware she might be the only psychological caregiver I had left in my life.

For the next month, she nursed me. Intensive care required all her attention and maternal instincts. Occasionally, she lavished in the role, but it was also extracting a toll. Adopting a docile submissive posture, I simply acquiesced to every suggestion she proposed except Melchizedek. I didn't have the esprit de corps to do the performance at this time. And believe me, it required a lot of esprit to get through it. The gypsies recommended I take a sabbatical also. They could see the lethargy that permeated my being since the visit to Omaha. Lethargy is a deadly virus in the scam business. Not only is it a detriment to a person's performance, it can also be contagious with the other prophets.

*****

"Athanasia, I'm not as perplexed about this dimension as I was before."

"Welcome to stage 4, Peggy."

"Is this the beatific vision?"

"No, but you are drawing closer. Peggy, what do you feel called to be?"

"I sense a ministry somewhat like yours—to shepherd souls into this dimension."

"It's a noble ministry of being, Peggy. I'm pleased with your decision."

"That's it. Just voicing it means I get to do it?"

"One of our final lessons, it's not so much what we do. Doing is not really our strict function."

"I'm lost again, Athanasia."

"What you decided is who you want to *be* more than what you want to *do*. Doing is a partial aspect of being. Humans do things hoping to become someone, but being an angel is reaching the totality of your greatness with the Creator. Have you ever heard 'My being proclaims the greatness of the Lord'?"

"It's not familiar, Athanasia."

"It's been said throughout history in many languages, cultures, and religions. Hannah, Astarte, Inana, and Mary all used it as a proclamation of their love for the Creator. Notice their word for the Creator may have been different but they all said 'my being.' If they would have said 'my doing,' then the Creator would have made human doings instead of human beings. And the beatitudes would have been the 'doatitudes.' The important point is that neither of this happened."

"So the message is about being not doing, right?'"

"Correct."

"But, Athanasia, doing something is part of becoming someone, isn't it?"

"It's a vital part, Peggy, but doing is not the goal. When you make the doing your goal, destiny is rarely attained because so much energy is misspent chasing after delusions. A penultimate doer usually wakes up one day and discovers they are completely unfulfilled. Something is missing from the core of their being, and they know it. Unfortunately, they never took the time for prayer and especially meditation to find out what they should have been doing all along. Without proper guidance, all souls usually end up lost, confused, and unfulfilled."

"The world, though, really rewards people who do things well."

"So does the Creator, Peggy, if they are receiving direction and moving in fulfillment of their destiny."

"Athanasia, I've asked this before, but I'll try again anyway. Is the major block to spirituality centered on the concepts of ownership and control?"

"Yes, it is. People are led astray more often by those distractions then by anything else. Without proper guidance and direction from tutorial angels, these concepts ensnare most souls in a web of confusion and doubt. Once confusion and doubt enter the picture, the demons have a field day. That's why the fruit in the garden is such an excellent picture of instruction. The Creator used the story to convey a simple message. The garden of the universe is immense, almost beyond human comprehension. All of it is there for humans and angels to revel in, explore, and partake of. But not one soul controls or has ownership of any of it. The fruit of the garden is the Creator's expressed domain. When angels or humans want direct ownership, all hell breaks out."

"So the terms *heaven, purgatory,* and *hell* all apply, right?"

"Peggy, tell me what you believe those terms mean."

"Heaven is the beatific vision, purgatory is states of searching and striving for destiny, and hell is abject hopelessness."

"Very good. At least for now. Believe me, more will be revealed to you."

"Athanasia, do most souls require multiple lives to attain their destiny?"

"The majority do, yes."

"And I've become an angel completely by my own choice, right?"

"To some degree, yes. You made a free will decision."

"So angels have free will then."

"All living beings in the image of the Creator have free will."

"Is that where the demons came from? A free will decision by angels."

"Yes, that was the initial severance from the Creator."

"Will I learn more about evil?"

"In other stages, you will but now you have a ministry to share. You have a soul to shepherd. Her name is Dorothy. She's Tom's mother. When you appear to her, you will resemble and speak like her brother Robert. I know you are ready."

"Will you be with me, Athanasia?"

"What do you sense right now?"

"That you are leaving me, and I'm not at all comfortable with that sense."

"You have honed your skills well, my dear. I am not leaving because all of us are united integrally with the Creator. But our communion with one another is transforming and changing. You are in ministry, and the soul you are shepherding requires your complete attention."

"Athanasia, my being proclaims the greatness of the Creator, and you have guided me to this vision. We don't say good-bye in this dimension, do we?"

"We are together for all eternity Peggy."

CHAPTER 9

As my mother's condition worsened, I stayed in contact with her by phone and by going to church in prayer. I may have been insane, but I did choose a Catholic church. One day, I needed something from Genesis to help me cope.

> They left Bethel, and while they were still some distance from Ephrath, Rachel began to be in labor, and her pains were severe. But in her difficult delivery the midwife said to her, 'Do not be afraid; you have another son here.' At the moment when she breathed her last, for she was dying, she named him Ben-oni. His father however named him Benjamin. So Rachel died and was buried on the road to Ephrath, at Bethlehem. Jacob raised a monument on her grave, and this is the monument of the tomb of Rachel which is still here today. (Gen. 35: 16–20)

Dorothy mercifully died five weeks after my visit. Unlike Rachel, she survived all her childbirths. But like Rachel, Dorothy's home had a sliver of Bethlehem. A hospital bed was placed in the living room because she wanted to die at home. Hospitals were for bringing children into the world; her home was familiar ground to end her days. Her only sibling, a brother named Bob, who had died years ago from a heart attack, made a return visit to bring his sister into her new world. Their affinity for each other never waned over the course of time since his death, and she glimpsed again his Irish wit and the sparkle in his eyes. It relieved my mother of all her fears, and it was a fitting end to a life well lived.

Priests in exile are allowed to attend their mother's funerals, but their sitting arrangement is altered. They sit with the congregation in the pews. Since Patricia insisted on joining me and I didn't have the resolve to fight it, I donned a gray suit instead of the customary black attire. Needless to say, I felt totally out of place.

The wake and the funeral drifted by me without the energy or power for memory or recollection. Medically, I had lapsed into a self-induced coma. I felt less than, not whole, and insignificant. I couldn't wait for it to end. On the flight back to LA, I pulled a Lucky Louie. I tried to consume all the scotch the airline had on board. Patricia poured me off the plane and guided me to her car. As we were walking in the parking garage at the airport, I had the distinct impression I entered the large intestines of hell. It had nothing to do with where I was, the odor came from my soul. I knew at that very moment the chill would be close behind.

CHAPTER 10

Patricia became combative as I self-destructed. We argued constantly and disagreed about even the most trivial aspects of our daily routines. Where to go, what to eat, and whom to meet were now matters to fight about. Sleeping arrangements began to shift as I spent more nights on the couch in the living room. As my drinking increased, sex lost its luster. Pleasure became the domain of solitary nights in front of the television with a bottle of white wine. The slight weight gain I began to acquire was only a minimal aspect of my unattractive deportment. Even I had brief moments of clarity, and I knew I had become despicable.

The Chinook bid her time and waited patiently in the wings. She celebrated in my self-destruction because it reunited her with Patricia as I slept on the couch. They tried to be sneaky about the late night trysts, but I wasn't that drunk or stupid. Periodically, when I did crawl under the sheets with Patricia, the image of her and the Chinook always invaded my sexual passion and desire. I constantly wondered whether I was the main entrée tonight or just an appetizer. Fuck the trust issue, my pride was decimated.

I became another victim of the "Fagin Factor." Fagin was an old college friend who inadvertently returned home early one afternoon and found his wife in bed with another woman. Both Michael and

I lamented the burden this posed on him and found out he left her immediately. As he told us years ago, he wasn't sure if his wife was bi-, tri-, or quadsexual, but she quickly became his ex. I knew the wise move would be to follow his example, but due to mental illness, I decided to stay and somehow make Patricia pay for this transgression. Insanity was reaching even greater heights in my mind.

Eventually, without Melchizedek, I ran out of money. It doesn't take very long for this to happen in LA. In a fit of desperation, I saw a "Help Wanted" ad somewhere, and it directed me to the doors of a place called Labor Ready. I went there only because they advertised that they paid by the day. Gypsies may govern the occult world, but addicts certainly dominate the temporary (daily) labor market. Walking into the waiting room at six thirty in the morning put me in a world I had never seen before. I just didn't have the sense to leave immediately.

Walking to the desk, I passed rows of folding chairs occupied by men who wore either haggard expressions or euphoric smiles. The difference between the two had to do with who was currently out of drugs and who still had a few left from last night. All of them were looking for work so they could replenish their supplies.

Labor Ready had the nerve to give me a form to fill out. They wanted to ascertain if I had the ability to do menial labor for minimum pay. As I glanced around the room, I thought a pulse would be sufficient documentation. The form they gave me was two pages long, and I was certain most of these guys couldn't navigate a half a page. Immediately, I felt the chill. I was now in the bowels of hell.

I walked to the counter and handed my application to a young man dressed in a white shirt and cheap tie. Without bothering to look at me, he motioned for me to return to my seat. His words and hand gesture conveyed scorn. I went back to the folding-chair section and prayed to God for the courage to drive out of here. A lack of cash was the one impediment that kept me glued to my seat. After an indeterminable period of time, my name was called, and I went to the desk to receive my orders.

My assignment if I chose to accept it was at the International House of Pancakes, familiarly known as IHOP. Along with a man named Henry, we would report for duty as dishwashers. The pay was $7.50 per hour for an eight-hour shift. Labor Ready would give me an extra couple bucks for transporting Henry to and from the assignment. All they needed to see was my driver's license, automobile registration, and proof of insurance card. They photocopied the documents and told me Henry knew how to get there. Henry was handed a slip of paper that we would take to the manager of the IHOP. When we finished washing dishes, this slip got signed and returned to Labor Ready for issuance of our check.

Henry and I washed loads of dishes. We made the progression from pancake syrup to ketchup as our shift moved from breakfast to lunch. After eight hours of cleansing plates, glasses, and silver wear, I began to feel a kindred spiritual link to the Hobart machine. Henry uttered maybe ten words all day, while the dishwashing machine provided a constant cleansing noise. There was a slight chance the Hobart machine had a higher IQ than Henry.

After finishing the shift and getting our paycheck from Labor Ready, Henry spoke his first complete sentence to me. He asked for a lift to the grocery store where most of the labor pool cashed their checks. I was in no hurry to return to Patricia's apartment because all we ever did anymore was fight, so I agreed.

The grocery store was a small neighborhood market. We walked to a cage and presented our checks. When I fumbled in my pockets for ID, Henry indicated with a turn of his head that it wasn't necessary to show identification. The man behind the cage handed me forty-seven dollars for cashing my check. I said to him the check was for more than that, but he made a hand gesture to the sign on the back wall of the cage. It stated that there was a ten-dollar fee for cashing checks. What a rip. Normally, ten dollars was an inconsequential sum of money, but my payroll check only amounted to fifty-seven dollars. Since Henry told me most of the labor pool came here to cash their checks, I thought what scumbags for taking advantage of the semi-destitute and downtrodden. Scams come in many flavors; this just happened to be one that targeted those who had allowed themselves to fall through the cracks. Sadly, I had now entered their midst.

With cash in hand, Henry's demeanor changed radically. He began to talk.

"You goin' anywhere?"

"Back home, Henry."

"You's in a hurry?"

"Not necessarily, why?"

"Ever do drugs?"

"I'm a drinker Henry. Why do you ask?"

"Oh...I wuz jus' wonderin' if yous want to tries some good shit."

"What do you have in mind, Henry?"

"I'll shows you."

I followed Henry's directions as we drove into a neighborhood that should have been condemned. This looked like a gantlet of impoverishment. Drugs invade all socioeconomic neighborhoods, but they definitely flourish among the poor. Downtrodden and haggard people live with a daily propensity for escape, and pharmacology provides the vehicle for flight. Many of them have given up hope for a geographic or financial upgrade, so one of the things they can do is seek short-term amnesia. I could see how snake-oil salesmen would thrive in a ghetto.

When we pulled up to the house, I couldn't believe I would willingly enter such a horrific abode. Like me, it was moving to a point beyond redemption. Meeting the occupants of a crack house requires minimal social skills because conversation rarely evolves beyond short grunts and statements laced with profanity. As a rule, vocabulary is tolerated if it does not frequently exceed two-syllable words. One guy paced the floor and continually peered out the blinds of the windows, while the others huddled in a corner smoking and cleaning glass pipes. The fact that I was the only white person in the room didn't seem to matter. All they wanted to know was how much Henry and I were going to spend. I turned the negotiations over to Henry. For all I knew, he could have been a serial murderer wanted in four states and this house could be busted by the police in a matter of minutes. This information barely registered in conscious thought as I sat there waiting to see what happened next. I was becoming oblivious to the world around me.

When the business transaction ended, Henry handed me a glass pipe and put what looked like a cookie crumb on top of some black glump residing at one end. He flicked a lighter, held the flame on the crumb, told me to inhale slowly, and hold the smoke in my lungs. I followed his orders as my lungs filled up with a rancid vapor. After a few seconds, my head imploded.

Time went into slow motion as objects blurred and sounds became distorted. Whatever sanity I had left flew out the window likes exhaled smoke. This was la-la land, and it felt damn good. Henry occupied a place in some other territory because he transformed into someone else right before my eyes. He wanted to leave the house immediately. Henry became a hyper, rabid creature who acted like he just found out someone was looking for him and intended to do him harm. I barely made it to the car and had no idea how I could drive. The only break I got from this current tension was Henry's offer to drive my car. I found the invitation hilarious. Here was this nutcase, clutching the glass pipe while fidgeting to find some place to stash it in his clothes, offering to drive my car with me in it. The crazy part was that he actually believed he was capable of driving.

Henry was convinced someone was following us and even asked me if I heard noises coming from the trunk. Mercifully, he told me to pull over and let him out after only going a few blocks. I watched as a frightened desperate man walked down the sidewalk constantly looking over his shoulder for signs of danger. My high didn't last long, but I certainly didn't want the reaction Henry experienced to ever invade my life. Why would anyone willingly pay money to go through that?

CHAPTER 11

Alcohol ingestion for someone prone to addiction normally follows a prescribed path. The treatment center used a grid describing the stages of alcoholism. Called the Jellinek Chart, it was named after a doctor who researched the disease, and it depicted a debilitating progressive illness that culminates in either institutionalization, prison, or death. The emphasis of the chart was on slow.

Crack, along with other drugs, adheres to a different time frame. It would best be described as the Jellinek Chart to the tenth power. Emerson had warned me that if I wanted to meet Lucifer in person, then all I had to do was become addicted to crack. Do it long enough, he told me, and there would be a visit.

Washing dishes at IHOP became my daily chore. Labor Ready offered more stimulating work, but the Hobart machine and I were becoming intimate friends. They at least boosted my wages to eight dollars an hour, largely because I showed up every day. Henry didn't share my punctual work ethic and was replaced by a collection of facsimiles all bearing the same MO but with different names. I got on a first-name basis with the regulars at the crack house so I could freely drop in on my own. The only problem centered on cash. My appetite began exceeding the daily pay earned from my labors.

To augment my income, I began extracting money from Patricia's purse. I called it borrowing because I had every intention of paying it back, but she kept asking about a shortage of funds and whether or not I was stealing from her. Like a good addict, I lied and tried to shift the blame on the Chinook. Another rationalization and another move deeper into hell.

A binge loomed on the horizon, and I began plotting a strategy that could render more capital. A personal check surfaced as the scheme I would use to get enough money to really get high. When the opportunity presented itself, I grabbed one of her checks without a moment of hesitation and stuffed it in my shirt. Like removing a piece of fruit from the tree in the garden, I was off and running toward fraud and complete severance in my relationship with Patricia. In the bowels of hell, consequences are meaningless. As I approached the domain of nonexistence, there was no future to consider anyway.

To reach a point lower than a snake's belly, all you have to do is go directly to the end of a binge. A place where there are no more drugs, no more money, and absolutely no one to call because everyone you know has slowly exited out of your life. The enormity of where you are descends like an avalanche in your brain and every neural fiber of your body. Lucifer didn't make a personal visit, but the odor, taste, and chill in the crummy motel room signaled he was lurking in the neighborhood. All I had left was a car with some gas in it and the carbon monoxide that would put an end to this pain. It was not so much that I wanted to commit suicide; that presumes I was capable of having a rational thought. All I wanted was the pain to finally end, and carbon monoxide appeared to be the only option I had left.

CHAPTER 12

Temescal Canyon came to mind as a secluded venue to engage in the last endeavor of my life. I picked my entrance to the canyon by turning right off the Pacific Coast Highway. I needed a secluded off road where I could park my car in a place that would not be visible to the two-way traffic traveling on the canyon road. I had decided that carbon-monoxide poisoning was the fastest and most painless way to go.

Out of the blue, an image of Maureen materialized. It was only her facial features, but her lips moved, and I heard the words coming from her mouth. She was repeating the final lecture she gave me at the treatment center so many years ago. The ex-nun was a prophet because everything she had said did come true. Here I was ready to act on a mission to *cease to exist*. As she had said, I really did not want to die, but I had reached a point of almost total denigration of my moral fiber. The glint of light in my soul did not even have the luminosity of a firebug, and the repetition of the blink had graduated to much longer intervals.

In my car was the hose and duct tape that I had procured at Mike's house. For some unknown reason, I got out of the car and looked in my trunk. Maybe I was trying to ascertain what meager possessions I would be leaving behind when my car and dead body were discovered by someone. There on the left side of the trunk were my Bible, my Big Book from AA, and a couple legal pads that I had purchased to write down ideas I had for Melchizedek to offer the faithful in the hotel ballroom. I picked them all up and returned to the driver's seat. It was time to revisit the book of Genesis maybe for the last time in my life. It had been my spiritual guide since I was fourteen years old sitting in Fr. Sherman's religion class. Now it just might become the last written document I will ever read.

> The Lord was with Joseph, and he became a successful man; and he was in the house of his master the Egyptian, and his master saw that the Lord was with him, and that the Lord caused all that he did to prosper in his hands. So Joseph found favor in his sight and attended him, and he made him overseer of his house and put him in charge of all he had. From the time that he made him overseer in his house and over all that he had the Lord blessed the Egyptian's house for Joseph's sake; the blessing of the Lord was upon all that he had, in house and field. (Gen. 39:2–5)

Why in God's name did I simply open the book of Genesis and this was the page it revealed? Joseph and I have nothing in common. The book should have opened to some deviant who was at his wits end and contemplating suicide. Joseph was a man of integrity and character, like my friend Fr. Mark. As I read these verses further, Joseph is approached by his master's wife, and she pleads with him to lie with her. Joseph declines her offer, and she retaliates by lying about it, and Joseph is thrown in prison. I am running from Patricia, and I basically enticed her. There is not one scintilla of comparison between Joseph and myself.

Call it coincidence, superstition, intuition, or anything else you want, this passage did something to me. For whatever reason, I called for an intermission on suicide. I left my isolated death chamber and drove down to the PCH. I arrived at Mike's house at two fifteen in the morning and parked on the street. I climbed in the backseat of the car and fell asleep. Tomorrow would arrive soon enough, and it was time to ask him for help.

*****

"Dorothy, I'm Peggy."

"Peggy, where am I, or better yet, what am I?"

"Dorothy, let me reassure you, what you are experiencing is normal. Do not be afraid, I'll guide you. Be patient, and everything will be revealed."

"Am I a speck of light?"

"You are more than a speck. You are radiant."

"Where are we?"

"Simply in another dimension."

"What does that mean?"

"Patience, Dorothy. Believe me, it is revealed as you are ready to understand it. For now, let the power of the light refresh and nourish you. You lived a good life, and the Creator welcomes you home."

"Creator. You mean God, don't you?"

"Close enough. I'll tell you more as we go along. Believe me, you are in for an education, Dorothy. A brilliant, resplendent epiphany for all eternity.

"Where's my brother, Bob? He was here before."

"That was me, Dorothy. I looked and talked like him in order to diminish your fear. It makes the transition to this dimension more peaceful."

"Isn't he here also?"

"That will be revealed also. Remember, patience is the key for now."

"Are you an angel?"

"I am."

"You have a soothing presence, Peggy."

"Thank you."

"I'm confused, though. This is so overwhelming."

"So was I, Dorothy, when I arrived."

"What do you mean? You're an angel. Haven't you always been here?"

"No. I once dwelled like you. In fact, I knew one of your sons."

"Which one?"

"Tom."

"My god, are you the girl who was murdered so many years ago?"

"That's right, I am."

"My heart went out to you when I heard what happened. I was out of town when it occurred, and your funeral had already taken place when I returned. I'm so sorry you went through what you did."

"Dorothy, from this vantage point, it is not as tragic. We are blessed to be in this dimension."

"Do you know the future, Peggy? Will Tom, my other children, and my husband be all right?"

"I do not know the future, Dorothy, so it remains to be seen what will happen to your family. As far as Tom goes, he's in serious spiritual trouble."

"Can you help him?"

"I am trying, but I can only whisper to his soul, and right now, he is not listening."

"He's always had trouble listening, believe me. He drove me crazy on more than one occasion. There's nothing more you can do besides whisper?"

"That is all I can do, Dorothy."

"How about a loud yell?"

"It is not allowed."

"Angels don't have the influence I thought they had, Peggy."

"You will be surprised. We have more power than you can imagine. Free will, though, presents a major impediment."

"Free will. What do you mean?"

"The capacity to choose. Angels freely abstain from direct involvement with a person's right to choose what they will do. We observe, offer whispers, and sometimes present suggestions for people to follow. But *they* have to decide what to do with the suggestions."

"Did an angel whisper to me?"

"All your life, Dorothy."

"With fourteen children, I guess there was too much racket for me to hear."

"Oh you heard, Dorothy. You heard more than you can imagine. Your life was a resplendent tapestry radiating light to many souls along the way."

"I wish I could have done more, Peggy."

"Such is the nature of your being, my dear. Bask in the illumination of your being. The beatific vision awaits you."

CHAPTER 13

Michael knocked on my car window, and the *thud* startled me as I sprang from the backseat. Crouched in the fetal position, sleep came intermittently with rigorous effort. Briefly awakened twice due to the lack of a pillow and blanket, I managed to get a few hours of rest. As my eyes began to focus on his face, he wore a look of consternation mixed with disgust. It was evident he expected my eventual demise, but the time frame was sooner than he expected. He knew I was drinking, and he placed little faith in my relationship with Patricia. His eyes saw a friend bent on self-destruction. He had no clue I was destined for hell also.

"Tom, what in god's name are you doing sleeping in my driveway? There's motel rooms all over the area."

"They require cash, Michael."

"Broke?"

"Totally."

"Patricia kicked you out?"

"Not yet, but it's coming."

"Come in the house. We better talk."

The distance to his door only measured several feet, but it was a long walk just the same. Humiliation hung like a drapery over me, and the window treatment wasn't elaborate. The artistry of my paint job went completely unnoticed. Even though it was finished only months ago, it seemed like years. My descent to hell had its beginnings years ago, but the final leg of the trip sped by in the blink of an eye. Whirlpools are like that—they increase in speed as the eddy plunges you into oblivion.

"Tom, as a friend, I'm worried. You look like shit, and you're going nowhere. I have a sense this whole business with Patricia is an escape, and your drinking is simply fueling the trip. You are running from life, and the alternative is death. This is serious, my friend. You've got to stop."

"Michael, you have every reason to be worried. I'm truly lost, and I mean really lost. I don't have a clue what to do."

"You got to get help, Tom, and I don't know anywhere except through AA. You have to stop drinking."

"I've said it before, so my word means nothing. I know what you are saying."

"Any ideas where you can go?"

"No, but maybe they'll surface as I'm driving."

"Did you get your stuff from Patricia's?"

"Yeah, it's in my trunk."

"You're worse off than I think, aren't you, Tom?"

"Yeah, it's bad."

"Do you want to talk about it?"

"I will tell you later, Michael. This I promise from my heart. I need to drive somewhere right now."

"Omaha?"

"Maybe."

"You need money, don't you?"

"Money for gas."

"Listen, I'll give you the money, but what you do with it is your business. Get help, my friend, and I don't mean help from a bottle or a woman. Call me when you get to wherever you have to go."

"I will. Thanks, Michael. Please pray for me."

"What do you think I have been doing for months? I'll keep it up."

"Thanks, you're a great friend."

Filling the gas tank to the brim, I hit the Pacific Coast Highway heading north. I went north only because it was the first sign I saw after leaving the gas station. Random travel was the best option I could think of, and a plan needed to unfold quickly because Michael didn't trust me with very much money. The snakes yelled for me to buy crack, and I told them to fuck off. I wanted to be rid of these demons, and it was time to talk to them in a language they understood. The fuck off got me north of Malibu, which was far enough to override any temptation to turn around.

The thought to stop and visit Patricia also crossed my mind, but it too was overridden. To the best of my knowledge, she had never performed in the production of *Annie Get Your Gun*, but I had a sneaking suspicion that the Chinook was packing heat. God only knows I gave Patricia enough ammunition to allow the Chinook a close-range shot. Given her hatred for men, I also knew where the Chinook would aim. It was best to stay heading north.

When I got to Oxnard, I pulled over into a gas station for some food and water. It had been days since my last ingestion of sustenance. Exiting the store, I saw a steeple adorned with a cross. It looked Catholic, so I drove there and walked in. My sole purpose was prayer until I happened to notice the red light on in the middle door of the confessional. This door was exclusively reserved for priests. Although it was Saturday, which is normally confession day in the church, it was odd to have a priest hearing them in the morning. Usually, most priests hear confessions in the late afternoon. Without a moment of hesitation, I walked over to the penitent's door. I needed time in the box. A brief thought passed my mind. It was a throwback to my first adventure in the confessional at the age of seven. The eighth-grader had warned us that the priest had a lever in his box and he could pull it if he decided we were not being completely honest with him. God knows it wasn't true, but for just a split second, I wish this priest had a lever and I could disappear and rest in peace.

"Bless me, Father, for I have sinned. It has been four years since my last confession, and that confession wasn't totally accurate. Get ready, Father, this is a doozy."

"I'm awake and alert, son, and I have heard many doozies. So go ahead."

"Father, I'm a priest. Well, I was at one time in my life. Today, I'm simply a pathetic, despicable, creature dangerously close to losing my soul. I'm a liar, thief, manipulator, alcoholic, addict, and fornicator. I have asked God for help, then I've spit venom in return. The gifts God gave me have been demonically abused on others. I inflict pain on people I love and wallow in stages of unabated self-centeredness. I'm oblivious of anyone but myself, like a tornado sweeping down on people and leaving a trail of wreckage behind. The carnage is so great that I can't recall the exact numbers today.

"The list includes family members, friends, people who have tried to love me, and many people who just accidentally got in the way. I don't establish relationship—I end up taking hostages. I come here today because I have nowhere else to turn. Last night, I attempted to commit suicide, and I have no idea why I'm still alive today.

"I want to turn around, and I want to live, but I really don't deserve another chance because so many chances have already been given to me. I know today that nothing is possible without the grace of God in my life, so I'm on my knees pleading for forgiveness. Without God's grace I'm sure I'll be doomed. That's all, Father."

"You certainly warned me, and you did for good reason. I'm not going to sugarcoat this, so get ready. Are you with me, son?"

"I am, Father."

"You are in serious condition. If I was placing your soul in a spiritual hospital, then it would go immediately to intensive care. The suicide attempt places you inches away from terminal. The malaise in your life begins in one area and *one area* only. Get off the alcohol and drugs immediately. Get your rear end to AA, and begin working the twelve steps. Coming here and admitting what you've become is an excellent beginning, but it will not alter or change who you've become until you get into the meeting rooms of AA and begin working a program of recovery.

"This confession and absolution will be meaningless if you don't take the next step. This point I'm making is not up for debate nor is it negotiable. You are worthy of redemption, but there comes a time when you have to work in partnership with God. Only God knows why you are not dead yet, but even God can't rescue you forever. The demons will win eventually if you stay out there any longer. Are you still with me, son?"

"Loud and clear, Father. I'm definitely with you."

"Okay, that's a start. Now for the rest of your sins. At some point down the road you will have to make restitution for what you stole and amends to the people you have hurt. The twelve steps will address all of that when you reach that point in your recovery. Find a sponsor immediately because you're incapable of even finding out where to begin. Sponsors are there because people like you walk into the program with brains that are toxic. Let your sponsor lead you. Are you still with me, son?"

"I am, Father. Everything you're telling me I heard from a former nun who worked at a treatment facility. I should have followed what she told me years ago."

"You'll get no argument from me on that point, but keep in mind, the past is history. You can confess it here and in greater detail in your fourth and fifth steps, but it remains a rehash of behavior you have already inflicted on others. Today can be your initial spiritual awakening. You can get the opportunity to turn around one hundred eighty degrees. Do it by going to an AA meeting immediately after you leave this confessional. Can you do that, son?"

"I can. Do you know where a meeting is in Oxnard?"

"Three blocks north and one block west on the left hand side of the street. It's an AA club, and they have meetings throughout the day."

"Father, this might be out of line, but it sounds like you are in the program. Are you?"

"No, I'm not. I've never drank, but I have seen countless miracles come to pass in those rooms, and I regard it as one of the best spiritual programs of the twentieth century. Their message is not new, it's been preached by major religions for centuries. But AA managed to simplify their creed into language that is clear, concise, and Creator-friendly. As you can tell, I'm a big fan of AA."

"Would I be out of line once again to ask for your name, Father?"

"Not at all. I'm Fr. Mark. Go to AA immediately and let the spirits guide you from there."

"Father, I have another problem. After the meeting, I have nowhere to go."

"Where were you a priest? What diocese?

"Omaha, Father."

"Can you go back there?"

"No. The carnage I created there is too immense."

"Is there any place in California you could go?'

"No, there is not."

"Let me make a suggestion. Obviously, it will be your choice to follow it or choose to dismiss it. There is a residential facility in St. Louis, Missouri, for troubled priests. It's run by the Paraclete religious order, and it is called St. Michael's. This saint is especially fitting for you presently because he is an archangel and he rescues souls trapped in the snares of the devil. Your life supremely qualifies you to seek his embrace. Do you have the financial resources to get there?"

"Barely. A friend of mine in LA loaned me money."

"In your current state, barely is probably best. It might preclude you from the temptation to do something else. Do you know what I am referring to?"

"Yes I do, Father. Believe me, I do."

"Your penance will be to make a free will choice regarding my suggestions. Absolution will be given, not today, but by some other priest when you choose the path you are going to take and go to confession when your path reaches its destination. Is all of this clear in your mind?"

"Yes, Father, it is."

"Go in peace, Tom, and may your soul proclaim the greatness of the Lord."

"Thank you, Father."

I left St. Rose Church and headed to the AA meeting. The house was right where Fr. Mark directed me, and a meeting began fifteen minutes after I arrived. When the chairperson asked if there were any newcomers present, I stood up and said, "I'm Tom, alcoholic and addict. This is my first day of sobriety."

The people in the meeting welcomed me and invited me to keep coming back. Sitting down, I noticed a sign hanging on the wall to my left. It read, "Losers do what they want to do. Winners do what they have to do." I felt for the first time in my life this is where I have to be—in the rooms of AA.

After the meeting ended, many men in the room invited me to stay and share a cup of coffee. After an hour and a half meeting and a half hour with the men in the group, I decided to return to St. Rose and simply thank Fr. Mark for his advice and support. The church was empty, so I went to the rectory and rang the doorbell. A young Hispanic priest came to the door.

"Excuse me, Father, I'm sorry to trouble you, but I would like to see Fr. Mark for just a moment. He heard my confession earlier this morning, and I want to thank him for helping me."

"Sir, I'm the only priest here. There is no Fr. Mark in this parish or this town.

"No, Father, there must be some mistake. I came here less than two hours ago, and the light in the confessional was on so I went in. A priest who told me he was Fr. Mark heard my confession. I'm sure of this, Father."

"Sir, what confessional in church had a light on?"

"Let's see. The one on the right hand side as you enter from the front door."

"On the right about halfway down the aisle?"

"Yes, that one."

"You're sure, sir?"

"I'm positive, Father."

"Did you see this priest?"

"No. I never saw him."

"So you have no idea what he looks like?"

"No, Father. I don't have a clue."

"Sir, those confessionals haven't been used for years. I've been here four years, and I always use the reconciliation room by the tabernacle. We usually use those confessionals for storage, but we recently cleaned them out because we're going to remodel shortly. Either someone played a practical joke by pretending to be a priest or you may be in need of some help. Are you sure you're okay?"

"Father, I'm not crazy, on medication, or in need of psychiatric care. Please don't get alarmed or go in that direction. I'm okay, really. I'm sorry for being a bother. There must have been someone in the confessional, and when I entered, they just thought it would be interesting to play along. I guess I got duped, Father."

"Well, I must say you don't look like you are having problems, but I have never had anyone complain of someone in those confessionals before. It is rather strange."

"Thank you, Father, for your time, and once again, I'm terribly sorry to have bothered you."

"Where are you heading?"

"To LA, Father."

"Drive safely, sir."

"I will. Good-bye."

I drove away as quickly as I could. Lying to him about going to LA was rotten, given the fact I just went to confession two hours ago. But I felt scared he might call the highway patrol and report me as some crazy motorist. Heading north on the Pacific Coast Highway, I was totally befuddled by my confession with Fr. Mark. He sounded like a priest not some prankster. He knew the ritual of reconciliation, although there could have been a book with the rite in the box. And he gave me excellent advice to follow, probably the best advice any priest could offer me. I began playing back the tape of the confession to see if anything jumped to mind.

In spite of my current insanity, I still possessed an incredible memory whenever my listening skills were fully employed. It was a trait I honed over the years, and it proved invaluable both in graduate school and in parish ministry. As the tape played, I discovered an eerie recollection. At the end of the confession when he asked me to make a free will decision regarding his suggestion, I think he called me by my *name*. I don't believe I ever stated my name to him. Maybe I did in the beginning when I was introducing myself as a priest. I just could not recall that specific detail.

*****

"Peggy, was that really Fr. Mark in the confessional?"

"No, Dorothy. It was an angel named Athanasia."

"An angel heard Tom's confession?"

"Athanasia is qualified to hear confessions."

"Does this happen often?"

"Hearing confessions, no. But angels make brief visits to people quite often. Remember what I told you about whispering messages and making suggestions."

"Yes."

"This was a suggestion. Tom received a visit."

"So angels visit someone when they are in spiritual danger?"

"They visit everyone, Dorothy. Those in danger and those who simply need to move up another level in spiritual growth. The visits are a more direct approach, but they still do not violate free will. Suggestions were made to Tom. It is still up to him to decide whether or not to follow them."

"Do you think he will?"

"Dorothy, I have no idea. Time will tell us both what that answer will be."

"So angels do not see the future?"

"I certainly do not. The present moment is enough for me."

"I'm still worried about him, Peggy."

"I am too. I will whisper to him, and I will send him your love."

"Do you think he'll hear you?"

"There is a chance. Reconciliation is a powerful medium for grace. The light he received by virtue of his confession might allow him to hear me more clearly. Besides, Athanasia was clever. She used the name Fr. Mark because Tom has a good friend by that name. You see, Dorothy, angels guide people by creating situations where they have the possibility to reach out to them, and they sometimes use a name the person knows or give a vision of someone who died before them that they loved. They did this for you when the vision of your brother, Bob, came to you at the moment of your death."

"Peggy, it made the entire experience more peaceful and soothing. God knows I was as scared as I ever had been in my life."

"Dorothy, that's our ministry."

"Peggy, please tell Tom for me to quit drinking, quit using drugs, and go to AA. If you want, tell him his mother said that."

"I will, Dorothy. I am also going to whisper to him to seek the sanctuary that Athanasia suggested."

"Whisper as loud as you can, Peggy. Tom has difficulty when it comes to receiving counsel."

"Spoken like a true mother, Dorothy. I can see why your soul is so brilliant."

CHAPTER 14

In silence, I motored down the highway heading for God knows where. Suddenly, I heard a whisper in the car, and the words were remarkably clear: *Quit drinking and using, go to AA, and find a sanctuary for recovery*. It sounded like Peggy's voice, but it had been years since I last heard from her. Between this and the confession incident, I decided to exit off the highway. I pulled over in a rest area and shut off the car. The whisper disappeared.

I pulled out the Bible and went to Genesis once again.

> And Pharaoh said to Joseph, "Behold, I have set over all the land of Egypt." Then Pharaoh took his signet ring from his hand, and put it on Joseph's hand, and arrayed him in garments of fine linen, and put a gold chain around his neck." (Gen. 41:41–43)

When I received ordination to the priesthood, I gave my mother a ring. What the heck, I was getting married to Holy Mother Church and where would you put a ring on an institution. For some strange reason, I went to the trunk of my car and took out a legal pad and pen. Sitting in the driver's seat, I decided to write a note of some kind to my mother. I never cried following her death or funeral, and the thought of that haunted me daily. It tore at the fabric of my soul. Since my confession, the pain became more pronounced. Fr. Mark told me I would make amends to the people I hurt as I became ready for it in recovery. I felt ready to say something to my mother.

My mother was a graduate of Indiana University with a BA degree in English. She appreciated the elegance of poetry, but I had little talent in that art. Regardless of my novice status, I composed a piece that was the best I could possibly write. It reads as follows:

A deep breath is taken then I swallow.
Anxious for slumber, but I cannot sleep.
Alone with my thoughts, fears, and passions.
Attempting to reach you for a caress and a kiss.
Where are you today, it's excruciating without you.
Winnowing and tunneling in the recesses of my soul.
When I recall your voice, it is resonant and clear.
What an eclectic message this business of death and rebirth.

Impatiently scrambling through a quandary of emotions.
In a mixture of hellos-good byes, life-death, and love-longing.
Intoning serenity yet simply settling for a semblance of balance.
It becomes my daily ritual to pray for just a little peace.
Positioning myself obliquely in the confines of a bed.
Placing my soul in the embrace of a mother who loved me.
Pouring out the emotions of grief, loss, guilt, and fear.
Pirouetting the edges of a lover lost and an angel gained.
Sanity resides knowing your absence is only temporal.

Signposts signal a faith that reverberates for all
eternity.
Separated this moment, there is always the promise of unity.
Seared by the call to seek reconciliation and
forgiveness.
Rest now God's servant, your destiny has been
attained.
Relationships you formed remain as the diadems
of your crown.
Recognition unlocks the transcendent mystery of
redemption.
Resurrection invites all of us to the faint promise
of tomorrow.

I got out of the car and walked around the rest area as tears rolled out of my eyes. It was the best I could give my mother, yet I knew I waited too long and hurt her too deeply.

I got back in my car and consulted a map. Interstate 80 became my new destination. Catching it at Sacramento, I could stay on it till I hit Wyoming. From there I would drive down to Colorado and take Interstate 70 to St. Louis. It was time to follow some good direction in my life. I put the car in drive and headed east.

A few miles down the road, out of the clear blue, I roared in laughter. An adage Peggy occasionally used registered in my mind for the first time in over thirty years. It best described the current journey I was taking, and it summed up everything that led me here to begin with. I could still hear her voice on the grassy knoll by the football field saying, "Silly not to."

This was the first time *since* the murder that I had an image of her face and didn't see the blood and the white chalk line on the carpet.

CHAPTER 15

The journey continued. Once again I could have taken Route 66 because it ran right through St. Louis, but interstate travel offered speed. I stopped at a Catholic church in Sacramento and filled my holy-water decanter with the actual liquid instead of vodka. The decanter, my Bible, and an AA Big Book occupied the front passenger seat. I did not hear the snakes, but I had doubts that they had left completely. Because of my confession in Oxnard and the powerful tools in the passenger seat, I figured they slithered back to the trunk of my car. There they could wrap around the spare tire and hiss to their hearts content.

The black eye-patch Mary in the locked ward had now risen to the lofty stature as a professional seer. She completely annihilated all those at the Church of the Inner Light, and she even bested old Melchizedek. James had been hounded by a legion of demons; of that there was no doubt. But when they searched for a new target, namely me, they came as a horde. I don't believe that demons have a preference over who they chose to devour because, let's face it, a soul is a soul. But maybe it gives those critters some intoxicating sensation to be invited in by a member of the clergy. Since their sole purpose is to infect and destroy the threads of the tapestry of one's soul, then it may provide some lasciviousness to inflict their damage on someone whose mission is to enlighten and uplift this tapestry for themselves and for others. One thing remained unabashedly certain in my mind: these fuckers are powerful if you are sick enough to invite them in.

Arriving in St. Louis, I had a decision to make. After I researched the location of St. Michael's and found out it wasn't a parish but instead a residential facility run by the Paraclete religious order, I had to decide whether I should call them to see if a bed was available or just drive to their location and walk in unannounced. After checking my wallet and finding out I had only eighty-four dollars left to my name, I opted for just showing up. It's easier to turn down a request on a telephone than it is when you are face-to-face with a desperate priest seeking asylum. I had heard a few times at the AA meeting in Oxnard the phrase "suit up and show up." This was one of the many suggestions that these men flew my way. So I decided to follow their advice.

The Paracletes were a Catholic religious order founded for the sole purpose of providing physical, psychological, and spiritual renewal to wayward Catholic ministers who had gone astray. They had healing centers all over the world, and their two main facilities in the United States were in Missouri and New Mexico. Now New Mexico was a hell of a lot closer to Oxnard than Missouri, but my confessor at St. Rose had specifically suggested I come to St. Louis. I could have saved time and money going southeast rather than coming here, but another suggestion that was offered at the AA meeting was to follow good orderly direction (GOD). I was just beginning to recognize that AA had a plethora of euphemisms.

Parking my vehicle and walking into what looked like the business office was one of the first conscious acknowledgments I had of what my counselor, Maureen, had told me. In recovery, we trudge. With my head bowed down and my voice lowered, I asked the woman at the desk to please see the director of the facility. After responding to her question that I did not have an appointment, she told me to please take a seat. I did not have to give her too much information because I had enough sense to dress in clergy attire. Having the blacks on with the white collar furnished enough information.

Meeting with the director can best be summed up by my opening statement: "Father, I left California on February 15 with a garden hose and duct tape in my car because I fully intended to commit suicide by carbon monoxide. You can call my archbishop in Omaha, and you will find out how sick I have been and still am. My soul is in jeopardy, and I have neither the resources nor the ability to go anywhere else. I am begging you to find in your heart some way to help me."

As I was sitting in the lobby waiting to see the director, I implored something my spiritual director in seminary told me. "Before you have to speak in an important conversation, it would be best to intone a prayer to the Holy Spirit." I could not believe I even thought of that because it was so many decades ago when he told me. Sure enough, the prayer worked by keeping my speech short, concise, and to the point. Why in the world did I ever forget this practice? Needless to say, I got a bed. Thank God.

The daily structured practice at St. Michael's was morning prayer, breakfast, group therapy, mass, lunch, individual counseling, a periodic session with a psychiatrist, recreation, evening prayer, dinner, and an outside AA meeting with the other residents. The composition of all these activities left little time to sit alone and dwell on how screwed up your life had become. Over time, I became aware of how therapeutic this structure was for myself and the other twenty-three residents.

All the residents were priests from areas all over North America. Each of the other residents were sent there by their bishop or provincial, and all of them had some approximate time frame when they would be returning back to their diocese or religious order. I was the glaring exception, a voluntary admission and absolutely no place to return. The initial argument I had with Maureen in Minnesota about how long treatment lasted was now a moot point. I was here, and I was eternally grateful.

On my second day there, I met my savior (small case *s*), my confidant, and my psychiatrist. His name was Dr. Jack. To simply say he transformed my life would be an understatement. He proved to be the perfect ancillary to Maureen. Their styles were incredibly alike, but he was able to provide a missing ingredient that, he explained, was absent from my attempts to remain in recovery. I suffered from chemical dependency; that was seriously evident. But I was also a dual diagnosis, and my psychological makeup required another treatment that required additional therapy. He broke the news on my second session.

"Tom, you have provided me with a thorough self-examination. Everything you shared with me and all the discussions I have had with other people you have allowed me to talk to points very accurately, I believe, to bipolar disorder. This is a serious malady for anyone, but it is extremely important for someone with chemical dependency. Tom, share with me the second step of AA."

"Came to believe that a power greater than ourselves could restore us to sanity."

"Correct. Now in your time of sobriety, did you have distinct periods where you believed sanity was returning?"

"Doctor, it would be hard to say because the mood swings I had while using only increased after I quit. I was told at my treatment in Minnesota that this is a normal reaction for all alcoholics and addicts. But they assured me that those levels would diminish as my brain healed in recovery."

"Did you ever experience some semblance of the mood swings decreasing?"

"No, they actually got progressively worse."

"Tom, part—and I emphasize the word *part*—of your chemical use was your indiscriminate attempt to control the ravages of your mood swings. It is best described as self-medicating. Unfortunately, without prescription medication, the chemicals you chose may have worked for some time, but like a true alcoholic and addict, these chemicals turn on you and will completely debilitate you."

"Indeed this has happened, Doctor."

What Dr. Jack laid out was a complete and thorough summary of my medical condition, and then he proposed a treatment plan that would make it possible for me to enter the human race for maybe the first time in my adult life. After eight weeks of drawing blood from me once a week at a nearby hospital, the correct level of lithium was attained. There were side effects to this new creature being ingested into my system, but they certainly did not have the shelf life that this disease had. Slowly over time, I grew accustomed to the immense change they had in my life. Interestingly, I missed small levels of the mania, even though they never remained small levels before I started this treatment. There were so many examples of creativity, endurance, and even certitude when I was in that state of being. I even remember playing the best rounds of golf I have ever played when I was in that condition. Too bad, those periods were short-lived.

Dr. Jack questioned me at length why I had not brought my symptoms of bi-polar disorder to therapists I encountered in my previous treatment. The best answer to his question is as follows:

> "From the time I was a child, I suspected something was wrong about my mood swings. As I grew older, I suspected something was terribly wrong. My short but livid relationship with Peggy 35 years ago was my first glimpse at Dante's Divine Comedy, specifically Paradiso. Her murder thrust me immediately into Purgatorio. Later in life I descended into Inferno. My role in Peggy's murder required her to go home that evening and get her bathing suit. Lust centered on the hope that her suit was a bikini. If she had not gone home that night James would have simply committed a B&E (breaking and entering). Paltry possessions would have been stolen and a window would have been broken. So what!!! I chose to bury my part of her murder in the recesses of my small intestines. I told no one about this belief and never wanted it to be public. To the best of my knowledge this became my first irrational core belief."

"My second irrational core belief was the haunting terror of my expanding mood swings. Somehow this belief became a mastoid cell that developed into a cancerous tumor. I believed that if I ever told someone how debilitating my disorder was becoming, I would be immediately fitted for a white jacket that straps in the back. Institutionalization would be my permanent location for a lifetime. Who knows, I could have ended up on the locked ward with James and eye patch Mary."

"I told Dr. Jack about the extremes of my mood swings. No one else had ever heard my description so I could never blame anyone else for not picking up on my disorder. Like the pendulum of a grandfather clock my mania swung left and depression swung right. Experiencing middle ground became shorter and shorter as I grew older. The extreme of my manic episodes would be times where I would go for 10- 12 days with only 2 or 3 hours of sleep each night. The extreme of depression would be times where I wanted to be semi-comatose forever. My ascent into mania happened much more frequently and I became addicted to its early stages. As I said before, it was intoxicating because I was so creative and liberated. Too bad it didn't last very long."

"As the manic stage progressed to levels of insanity I discovered that alcohol had the power to curb and sometimes halt my ascent. Depression was an entirely different enigma. Since I loathed my descent into the inferno I found that any amphetamine also curbed or blocked my dark well of misery. I had learned over the years a statement regarding suicide. It was described as a permanent solution to a temporary problem. Any sane person would agree with this statement. Unfortunately, my serious depressions lacked two ingredients, I was not sane and my problem occurred too often to warrant the term temporary."

"Dr. Jack called my efforts misguided self-medicating. They kept me barely alive but they also became toxic. When treatment for chemical dependency entered my life, I lost my only two coping mechanisms for my disorder. I initially threw myself into sobriety praying that the mood swings would stop. My prayers fell on deaf ears. Step 2 of AA's 12 steps claims we would be restored to sanity. Without alcohol and drugs I became horrendously insane."

"I was told by Dr. Jack that both chemical dependency and bi-polar disorder are progressive illnesses. One of them demands complete abstinence and the other requires daily medication. He said my dependency would require daily maintenance but as the years of abstinence increased my compulsions to relapse would become less frequent. Unfortunately, the disorder has the opposite timeframe. As the years go by on the medication, sanity becomes normal and there will be an increase in thoughts that the pills really could be stopped. He said bi-polar patients suffer an affinity to quitting their medication.

What he suggested that I do was to get a journal and keep track of every time I have the compulsion to use or the thought of not taking my pills. Each time I override these two compulsions I need to write them down and date them. They will become my progressive successes. If I put together many of them, I will increase my chances at remission from both my afflictions. Neither can be cured. I only have the opportunity to live life in remission. If I elect to not treat them in tandem then my prognosis will be how many levels will I chose to descend into Dante's Inferno before my family has to select what hymns they want sung at my funeral."

*****

"Peggy, he heard you. He is actually going in the right direction."

"Dorothy, it is not my doing. Athanasia gave him some suggestions, and the Creator poured out grace because Tom took some right actions for a change. Angels can only point to what path a human can take, but it is up to each individual to not only pay attention but to act on it and stay committed."

"What about your whisper? He actually heard it, didn't he?"

"Yes, he did, but, Dorothy, angels whisper all the time. We are taught to have high hopes that someone will listen, but we also have low expectations."

"Are you saying deaf ears reign?

"They sure do. Also, some people really do hear us but quickly dismiss it as an imagination or illusory experience. They blow it off as if it was a wisp of air."

"Don't you get frustrated?"

"Not if you remember what I just said—we have low expectations."

CHAPTER 16

A watershed experience occurred on Easter Sunday. It wasn't a cause for celebration like the resurrection denotes, but it was a sobering lesson on the pitfalls of life. A week before that Sunday, the director asked us if we would go together to their other facility in Dittmer, Missouri. It was about a forty-mile drive from St. Michael's, and it was a residential facility for priests. The difference between these two complexes was that Dittmer was fenced in, and no one could leave the grounds without a Paraclete employee at their side at all times. This was where the sexual abusers were basically imprisoned.

These Paracletes had taken on this ministry because not all transgressions suffered by priests were the Punch and Judy syndrome. Punch served as alcohol consumption, and Judy was womanizing. The sexual-abuse scandal had been with the church for some time now, but it was only recently in Boston where the public got a lurid look into the scope of the problem and the way it had been dealt with by the hierarchy. To say it completely rocked the country would be a misrepresentation. If it could be compared to an earthquake, it probably would register a 10 on the Richter scale. It flatlined the faith and integrity of most of the country in that the church was believed to be sweeping these cases under the rug. This was not my total belief because I would later learn of many cases where there was a supreme effort to take all the right action and the victims were treated with empathy and compassion. Unfortunately, there were other cases where it appeared to me that I wasn't the only cleric hearing the hissing of snakes. The cold chill of evil was definitely present, and decisions that were made indicated it was there. Also, whenever subterfuge is practiced, the demons normally leave a business card.

When all of us walked into the refectory to help prepare the meal and greet the residents, I sensed a penetrating aura. I'm not sure if depression has an aura, but I was not sure what adjective to use to describe it. It became clear from the very start that certain individuals were not pleased we had made the trip. I had the sense they would have preferred that the gates to this facility would remain closed to outsiders. In a way, I could see their point. They were caged in this place for the remaining years of their life, and they didn't want this place to be a zoo where spectators came to see them. Who could blame them for that attitude? Periodically, one of the St. Louis local television stations would camp outside the gate and attempt to film the residents as they walked the grounds. The station began reporting from their new designation of this place—they called it Club Ped.

I wished with all my heart and soul that I had not denigrated the church with my behavior. Visiting on Easter Sunday produced a unique spiritual revelation to me. I had two disorders, but mine were treatable, and I was finally, with Dr. Jack's expert guidance, on a path that Maureen so vividly explained to me in our final conference. I was trudging, but more importantly, I had the freedom to do so. These men could trudge also, but their world had been reduced to a cage. There's not a lot of freedom in a cage. It remained a mystery to me, and it may never be known that most of them, if not all, were sexually abused when they were young. If they were, then I am fairly confident they adopted something that I carried in my psyche for decades. I had an irrational core belief that I somehow participated in Peggy's demise. This does not excuse my behavior or justify my debauchery. But it served as a gateway to sensing I was insignificant, not whole, and not a part of. That is a lethal opening to letting evil find a home.

It must have been the confession at St. Rose along with the poem to my mother that somehow cleared a channel to receiving some dose of divine light. Not a blazing bush or a high wattage illuminate, rather a soft incandescent glow coming from someone or someplace that miraculously removed this core belief. That's why for the first time when I began this trip to St. Louis, I visualized Peggy without the white chalk and the blood on the carpet. It behooved me to say a prayer for the men at Dittmer that this same experience will happen to both them and to all the victims they abused. Silly not to.

CHAPTER 17

This experience at Dittmer exhausted my ability to stay focused on the issue of sexual abuse. I needed to go back to Genesis in order to reside in a different frame of mind.

> All these are the twelve tribes of Israel; and this is
> what their father said to them as he blessed them,
> blessing each with the blessing suitable to them.
> Then he charged them, and said to them, "I am
> to be gathered to my people." (Gen. 49:28–30)

The number 12 shows up in the Bible on occasion, and it is also predominant in AA. There are the twelve steps, the twelve traditions, the twelve principals, and the twelve promises. As best as I know, there is not any conjunction between these entities, and if twelve is some kind of mystical number, I am not aware of it. St. Benedict, in the sixth century, wrote the twelve steps of humility, and even though there are some similarities to AA, I have no idea if the founders of the AA program even knew about them. There was a Jesuit Catholic priest who was a spiritual director for one of the founders, but the Big Book had already been written by the time they initially met.

The number 12 remains an enigma for me, and personally it doesn't really affect my recovery program.

What directly affects my program is my sponsor, attendance at AA meetings, fellowship with the other people in the program, and lastly a daily sustainable prayer life. St. Michael's provided all these recovery ingredients. At some point, though, I was going to have to move on to a new locality, and everyone I trusted provided the advice that it would be best to stay here in St. Louis. One of my therapists recommended that I begin attending an AA meeting not far from the campus, which met every morning at seven. Being open and willing to follow suggestions given to me by people who had a higher level of sanity than I possessed, I began attending. This became another watershed moment in my life.

Allen, my therapist, could not have offered any better advice. Daily morning exposure to AA was just an incredible and critical instrument to having long-term sobriety. I have and will continue to designate this action as one of the fundamental instruments of my now long-term recovery. Just as Maureen, the priest in the confessional, and the men at the AA meeting in Oxnard told me, you have to suit up and show up. In early recovery, it sure was mandatory for me to follow suggestions and get to a meeting every day.

The concept of fellowship with other recovering alcoholics both at the meetings and in activities outside became a supreme blessing in my life. My sponsor had told me not to write my own screenplay for sober life. Follow step 3, "Made a decision to turn our will and our lives over to the care of God as we understand Him—to the best of your ability," was his advice. It was the fact that I heeded this advice, and it led me to another man in recovery named John.

John was a hellion prior to AA. In fact, he was the only person I have ever met who got a DUI while mistakenly driving on railroad tracks and then having the audacity to complain to the police officer that the streets in this neighborhood were the worst he had ever driven on. The officer saw no need to even do a sobriety test. He simply handcuffed him and took him to jail. Sometimes, being handcuffed can serve as a moment of clarity to an alcoholic, and in this case, it was John's moment. When we met at a meeting, he had two years and one month more sobriety than me. After seeing me for months at this meeting, he asked to speak to me afterward.

"Tom, would you be interested in working with me in my company?"

"What company is it?"

"I own an invisible fence company that buries wire around a property in order to keep a dog in the yard."

"John, I know nothing about invisible fences."

"Tom, you have been selling an invisible God for years—an invisible fence will be a piece of cake compared to that.

I loved him immediately. He bought me a pair of boots, a splicer, a roll of electrical tape, and I joined his company from that day forward. The two of us were the only employees, and for numerous reasons, his company continued to grow exponentially with the our team in service. Besides going to a meeting every day, I was now spending seven to nine hours six days a week with a fellow from the program. Obviously, God must have thought it best to inundate me with solid protective armor because my history in sobriety was sketchy at best.

Another recovery step was taken later when my sponsor suggested I take into my rental house anyone in the program who was experiencing a temporary-residence disorder. Now my life became totally immersed in the program. Whatever inconveniences all of this may have caused were totally negated by my gratitude for becoming a functional and sane human being.

CHAPTER 18

Step 4: Made a searching and fearless moral inventory of ourselves.
Step 5: Admitted to God, to ourselves, and to another human being the exact nature of our wrongs.

If you are Catholic and you have made occasional visits to the box, then these steps have been part of your practical knowledge for some time. The moral inventory is simply what we learned in second grade, which Catholics call an examination of conscience. What the fourth and fifth steps pinpoint and identify are the character defects that are present in our lives. Some of these defects may be debilitating, even though they were employed during our drinking and using history and they may have kept us alive until we hit bottom. In recovery, we have to get rid of them, but doing that without divine intervention has a terrible track record. Left to us, we tend to want to keep what we are accustomed with; change can be frightening. The AA program is adamant about seeking grace. I had partially worked these steps in treatment before, but now I had to apply the term "rigorous honesty" to this endeavor. I needed to confess everything.

Step 6: Were entirely ready to have God remove all these defects of character.
Step 7: Humbly asked Him to remove our shortcomings.

From my experience and also witnessing other people in the program, there are three words that may cause consternation in these steps. I initially balked at "entirely ready" until my sponsor asked me, "Were you entirely ready to drink and use?" I told him not really because I probably told myself I will not do that again a thousand times, even though I did it again every time. I showed some fleeting resolve that this behavior was unacceptable. He then asked me, "Are you entirely ready to stop drinking and using now?" I said emphatically yes. He then said, "Did you ask for divine assistance to do this?" I said yes. He then countered by asking, "It has worked so far, hasn't it?" I agreed.

So he said, "You now have a proven history of becoming entirely ready, and it is working for you a day at a time. You now have to take that same approach with character defects. Every morning, when you get up and identify yourself as an alcoholic and addict, you need to also include a character defect that you want to work on that day and then ask for assistance on sobriety and the defect. Remember, you can have a relapse on a defect and address it with step 10, but a relapse on sobriety is a completely different matter. Slowly, over time, the habituation with the defect will be replaced with the opposing virtuous habit of that defect." I told my sponsor, "Case closed."

The third word that can cause consternation is *God*. By product of my education, formal training, and life experience, I had no issues with the concept of God. My problem was I betrayed my relationship with God. Like Judas Iscariot, I sold God out for the sensual pleasures derived from mood-altering chemicals, and I never got paid in pieces of silver. In fact, it cost me big time. It didn't happen overnight, but it was an indiscriminate pattern of disrespect and detachment. And the behavior that ensued brought me into the realm of Dante's inferno.

Other people I have encountered in the rooms of AA have a slightly different problem. Just the mention of the word *God* recoils them and may even drive them from the rooms. They view the term as cultist or allege that this AA shit must be religious, and they really want no connection with that bullshit. Formed over the years by what they term as "horrendous personal experience with this crap," they made the decision to remove themselves completely from this arena. Where I presently live, St. Louis, I hear an awful lot of this talk. Irish Catholics who believe they had the grave misfortune of attending Catholic elementary schools bring up their nightmares quite often. What's interesting about the Irish is that they do not have a monopoly on the disease of alcoholism but they could make a strong case of having a majority interest. I say that statement as someone who is half-Irish, and I am damn proud of it. Unfortunately, all nationalities have their shortcomings. My other half is German, and one of its trademarks is something I have to battle once in a while. It's called emotional constipation.

The God issue is somewhat like entirely ready. When you go back to step 3, that asks us to turn our will and our life over to something we obviously have experience doing that also. When alcohol and drugs are ingested on a steady basis at some point, an invisible line is crossed. Where and when this happens is a completely individual experience. But when crossed, the progressive nature of the disease demands that person to surrender both their will and ultimately their life. So every alcoholic and addict who ends up coming into the rooms of AA has already been working a convoluted step 3. Whether they like it or not, alcohol and or drugs did become their higher power or their god of their understanding. If they have allowed this to happen to them and they have witnessed the monumental self-destruction of their lives, then all AA is asking them to do is replace their current higher power.

The beauty of the program is that it does not preach who their higher power should look like, act like, or be like. All of us are in some way are up for adoption, but we have the total freedom to choose what entity and family we want to dwell within. What a divine luxury this is for a whole host of previously orphaned vagabonds.

*****

"Peggy, you whisper. Did you chose to do this?"

"In a certain way I did, but it evolved slowly and was predicated by my relationship with Athanasia. She was so instrumental in both my rape and death, then she became my guiding light."

"So she led you like you are now leading me."

"Correct, Dorothy."

"What will be my ministry?"

"I do not know, but all I really do know is that it unravels while you complete the stages."

"When you say 'stages,' is there a set amount of them?"

"Not at all. The stages pertain to the luminosity you came into the afterlife with. Every soul has both light and darkness. How many stages is determined by the quality of your soul because the soul reflects the totality of how you have lived your life."

"Peggy, you had such a short life, and it ended so violently. Did you feel any remorse for this fact?"

"Tons of remorse at first, and it took more stages for me to go through to reconcile that fact. But Athanasia told me that my final emotional response after leaving my body was pity for the man who raped and murdered me. I saw him, and he was close to complete darkness. His soul only had a glint of life, and the evil one was trying to devour him. That, to me, was truly pitiful."

"So much of your ministry is to humans who are blanked in darkness? What does that say about me?"

"Oh, Dorothy! My mission for you was a personal request I made that Athanasia joyfully extended. Your luminosity was very present. Plus, I needed someone to help me with your son."

"As you know, I have a husband and thirteen other children still living. Some of them need to hear a whisper now and then."

"You technically are close to being able to provide those messages already."

"Thank God, Peggy. They need me."

"All humans need tutorial angels, Dorothy. The world presents so many unique challenges, and the free will extended by the Creator for people to choose becomes a burdensome chore at times."

"Peggy, I only wish angels could exert more influence to help people when their decisions demand a critical choice to be made.

The demons have the ability to raise their voices to someone they are attempting to influence. In fact, the decibel level they can rise to seems to drown out the angels' whisper. It doesn't seem fair."

"Dorothy, the Creator's unique gift to the entire universe is light—a light so pulsating, bright, and powerful that nothing in all the world can compare with it. This light is extended to all of creation and whatever or whomever it touches provides order out of chaos and a faith so illuminating that fear and death become completely extinguished. This is in direct contrast to darkness. Demons manipulate as they coax all life into submission and complete dependency. Their goal is to control, own, and to execute free will. In order to do that, they have to persuade souls by using ambiguity to lure anything or anyone into their grasp.

Evil's penultimate lie to all of creation is simply *it doesn't exist*. It's more subtle approach is masking a lie within a kernel of the Creators truth. If you notice deviancy always exudes a louder voice than virtue. The epitome of virtue has always been a declaration of humility, and that is best expressed by a whisper."

"Your soul was so young. How have you managed to attain such wisdom?"

"Athanasia gets all the credit for that. She is one incredible seraphim angel."

*****

It was time for me to return to the book of Genesis. God only knew I had to keep Fr. Sherman's and Rabbi Azerial's teachings close at hand. Genesis had become the blueprint for me to endure all that happened since I was fifteen years old, and there was a strong case to be made that it would remain this way for the rest of my days.

> So Joseph went in and told Pharaoh, "My father and my brothers, with their flocks and herds and all they possess, have come from the land of Canaan; they are now in the land of Goshen." And from among his brothers he took five men

and presented them to Pharaoh. Pharaoh said to his brothers, "What is your occupation?" And they said to Pharaoh, "Your servants are shepherds, as our fathers were." They said to Pharaoh, "We have come to sojourn in the land; for there is no pasture for your servants' flocks, for the famine is severe in the land of Canaan; and now, we pray you, let your servants dwell in the land of Goshen." Then Pharaoh said to Joseph, "Your father and your brothers have come to you. The land of Egypt is before you; settle your father and your brothers in the best of the land; let them dwell in the land of Goshen; and if you know any able men among them, put them in charge of my cattle." (Gen. 47:1–6)

Joseph who was sold into slavery by his brothers because of intense jealousy, and envy has now rescued them from famine and starvation. His father was told he had been eaten by a wild beast when, in fact, he was sold for twenty shekels of silver to the Ishmaelites, who were the family remnants of Ishmael, the son of Abraham. The brothers initially wanted to kill Joseph, but one of them called Reuben cried out, "Shed no blood; cast him into this pit here in the wilderness but lay no hand upon him." Reuben was an accomplice to the crime of delivering Joseph to slavery, but he had enough sense to intone that no blood should be shed. How many lives could all of civilization be spared if only Reuben's example was followed in the midst of the intense vices jealousy and envy invoke? Joseph's brothers needed to make an amends.

CHAPTER 19

Step 8: Made a list of all persons we had harmed, and became willing to make amends to them all.

Step 9: Made direct amends to such people wherever possible, except when to do so would injure them or others.

The most prostituted word in all vocabulary when making amends for alcoholics and addicts is the word *sorry*. It is so banal and inappropriate because it has been summoned so often to excuse behavior that gets repeated over and over again ad nauseam. The true definition of the word has been desecrated beyond repair.

Step 8 is so critical to recovery because it forces someone to acknowledge they have been a tornado in other people's lives, and now for the first time, they have to use a rear-view mirror to really see the destruction they have inflicted on others. The disease is certainly the cause of our malaise but all of us are directly responsible for the harm we have done.

A sponsor is mandatory in order to address step 9. Attempting to figure out when to begin working this step requires a qualified sponsor. Someone who has worked this step in their own recovery and also someone who has been in the program long enough to have heard horror stories from other people who made some disastrous mistakes while doing this step. The part about injuring others is definitely there for a good reason. All of us have the ability to learn from our own mistakes, but it requires further counsel to learn from other people's mistakes also.

The word *immediately* denotes a time frame, which may or may not be applicable to step 9. Careful consideration needs to be given to when this step is taken. Since everyone in the program comes into AA with varying degrees of previous dysfunction and damage, it is critical that recovery time be taken into consideration. Relapse is always a possibility. Unfortunately, if this step is repeated over and over again, it can lose all its spiritual significance, and the tornado effect will come into play for the people who are listening to our amends.

The term "a living amends" is a powerful adjunct to this step, but it has to be invoked with careful consideration. If it is used as an erroneous action to perpetrate procrastination, then it is wrong. What a living amends speaks to is one of the cardinal features of the entire program—it is attraction, not promotion. Often, people whom we have harmed and still remain in close proximity to them will take greater interest in our present behavior based on sobriety than on words based on contrition. Actions speak louder than words. But the step itself is grounded on the fact that we need it just as much or sometimes more than the person receiving our message. Since this step brings other people into the picture, it must be carefully administered with a lot of consultation and a lot of prayer.

One of the amends I made regarded a situation that had been gnawing at my soul for years. I pulled out of my wallet the name and phone number of Harry's oldest son. Harry was the recipient of one of my final ministerial duties in Omaha. He received last rites in Veteran's Hospital, where he was dying from a liver disease directly caused by alcoholism. I, on the other hand, being in the throes of alcoholism accidentally administered the sacrament with vodka instead of holy water. I dialed his son's phone number, praying to God he would answer and that the Holy Spirit would guide my words.

"Jeff...ah this is Tom. I was the priest who was at the Vets Hospital when your father, Harry, died. You are free to hang up this phone right now because what I did that early morning was unbelievably inconsiderate and was downright despicable. Your father did not deserve that treatment as he was dying. My behavior has been eating at my heart and soul for many years, and I needed to call you and apologize.

"I did not call you earlier because it was mandatory that I have a sustained period of sobriety before I would call. I now have five continuous years in the AA program, and my life has truly turned around. All those years have been in St. Louis and I plan on staying here indefinitely. Jeff, I truly apologize."

There was a period of silence.

"Tom, thank you. My family was hurt by what happened that night. Some family members, like my mother, got over it pretty quickly because my father inflicted so much pain and suffering on all of us. She made the comment that night after you left that it was a fitting way for old Harry to leave this world. I was probably the most upset, and it took awhile for me to get over it so I appreciate you calling me. Have you contacted anyone else?"

"No, Jeff. For whatever reason that night, I asked at the nurses' station for the name and phone number of the contact person on Harry's medical file. Your name was the only one on it. One more thing I need to add then, I will not bother you any longer. AA firmly believes it takes one alcoholic to reach out to another in order to help that other person into recovery.

"Now the alcoholic that reaches out is normally sober and in the program. Your father was sober because he had been in the hospital for some weeks, but obviously he never came into the program. *Still,* what happened that night ended up being the catalyst for my recovery. In a very extraneous way, Harry saved my life. In AA, terms his last act on this planet was a twelve-step visit to me. The twelfth step is when we help someone else. I will always remember Harry for this even though he did this unwittingly. Thank you, Jeff, for hearing me out."

"No, Tom, thank you for calling. I cannot tell you how much I appreciate what you just said. In fact, I'm crying. I will pass this on to my other family members."

"Good-bye, Jeff."

"Good-bye, Tom."

This was the best example I had of a direct amends even though it was over the phone. Most amends are to be done face-to-face, but this one required a phone call. My mother's amend was done long ago with my stab at a rudimentary poem. I was told later that if death precludes a personal amends, a letter to the deceased or a visit to the grave site are customary ways to work the step. All the steps have some degree of spiritual benefit when they are worked willingly and honestly. For me, they had another intricate gift—the snakes left for darker pastures.

CHAPTER 20

Step 10: Continued to take personal inventory and when we were wrong promptly admitted it.

Just because I am now sober and have worked the previous steps to the best of my ability, I am not a saint. This step provides all the ammunition a recovering alcoholic or addict needs to finally coexist and cope with the people of this world. When a character defect flares up or simply when a vice that has lingered reappears, this step provides a healthy response to bad behavior. It introduces us to the fact that we need to constantly monitor our interactions with society at large. In the past, when we were using improper language or being disrespectful with others, we may have simply blown it off or most likely believed the person deserved it. Being responsible for our actions is new territory for us, and this step requires we practice this principle on a daily basis. I have learned over time that a powerful tool to adopt is the use of a pause button. Simply pausing before saying something or sending something or doing something has the strength to reduce the number of times this step needs to be applied.

Step 11: Sought through prayer and meditation to improve our conscious contact with God as we understood Him, praying only for knowledge of His will for us and the power to carry that out.

It appears to me that there is a natural progression that occurs when spirituality is neglected by someone in recovery. Over time, calls to one's sponsor decreases, attending meetings drops, and self-identification that you are an alcoholic or addict becomes less frequent. What this produces is a natural recipe for relapse. Experts in the program have proclaimed quite often that relapse happens way before a drink or a drug gets ingested. The AA Big Book is totally clear on this point when it says that the best defense against a relapse is totally dependent on the quality of our spiritual condition.

For me, spirituality is an arduous discipline to not only acquire but to also maintain. First of all, I need to make time each day to do it, then I need to have a sanctuary where I can attempt to do it without interruption, and finally I need spiritual manuals that will assist me in getting started. Fortunately, there are many books available to assist anyone with this third need. They offer a daily reading, which plugs our brain into a topic of prayer for that day. Then I need to capture one thought or phrase from that reading, close the book, and begin repeating that short thought or phrase over and over again as I slowly remove all the clutter in my head, which impedes meditation. Eventually, I have the possibility of being relaxed and at peace. The phrase I chose is my mantra and changing it every day according to the reading of the day keeps my exercise with meditation vacillating and more spontaneous. Like any discipline, there will be good days and bad days. The challenge is not to become frustrated and give up if there are too many bad days in a row. Like I have found out over the years, this business is arduous.

I was fortunate to find a sanctuary in St. Louis very quickly. The Carmelite monastery became my new spiritual haven. Practicing the mantra I had chosen that day cleared my fractured brain and allowed me to sit in silence with my higher power. I found early on that minutes can be like hours with this discipline. Like so many alcoholics and addicts, we are addicted to monologues. A dialogue is somewhat foreign territory for us.

The grace of this step is that it says prayer *and* meditation. Foxhole prayers need to be replaced by authentic conversation with our God, and silent time needs to be given in order to receive some inkling of a response. Please do not expect that your higher power is going to have a resounding, loud conversation with you because if this does happen, you will shortly be bunking with black eye-patch Mary and James. For me, occasionally I may hear just the smallest trace of a whisper. Or more often, an intuitive thought may come to me, which defies my own originality. God speaks through many ways. Another authentic way this message may come is in AA meetings themselves. Because silence for periods of time has a way of increasing my listening skills, I may pick up a spiritual jewel of wisdom from someone at the meeting because I have honed this skill in my sanctuary.

The major payoff for prayer and meditation is the possibility that we can finally remove all the resentments we discovered in our step four inventory. The Big Book declares that these resentments are the most dangerous facets of our past. They have the power to cripple our recovery because they demand so much psychological negative energy for us to sustain them. The fallacy behind a potent resentment is that we want to get even with the son of a bitch any way possible, but we are the one losing sleep and burning negative energy while the person we hate is sleeping comfortably and probably not even wasting a mere thought about us. This truly begs the question of whether or not we have been restored to sanity. As hard as this may be, we need to take some time each day and petition God to remove our hate for this person. We have to quit drinking the emotional poison that malicious thoughts produce, and many times, a prayer offered to the person we hold the resentment against can prove to be the remedy for this malady.

I have also adopted once again another practice. Just as I go to ample meetings of AA, I also attend mass every day. Now this had been my practice for years, and I never suggest it to the men I sponsor or live within the sober house I run. This is truly my discipline because my renewed prayer life has recognized how powerful a gift this can be. Because I spent tons of hours, days, weeks, months, and years feeding my addictive life, I now have the freedom to spend a great deal of time and energy on my spiritual life. But I have become extremely picky about where I go to mass. Geographic boundaries mean nothing to me when I select a parish and a priest. I have reduced my options to three parishes in St. Louis after traveling to many possible locations, and Fr. Ted has become my penultimate choice as a spiritual adviser.

Fr. Ted is an incredibly instructed soul who has amassed a plethora of intellectual acumen and a faith life that demands attention. He is the epitome of a gentle shepherd who guides ones soul through the journey of navigating a transcendent God. Bishop Fulton Sheehan once stated in his writings: "If you want me to talk for an hour, I can do it now. But if you want a concise 10–15 minute presentation, I will need a lot of time to pour over copious notes."

My spiritual director abides by the copious format. What he has given me over the years is both immeasurable and priceless. All this has come about because I took the time and invested the energy to seek out this gift. Step 11 demanded that I do this, and I am glad as hell that I did.

CHAPTER 21

Step 12: Having had a spiritual awakening as the result of these steps, we tried to carry this message to alcoholics and practice these principles in all our affairs.

This is the last step, but it does not preclude working all the rest of them at different times throughout the rest of our lives. Because sober life has the capacity to throw curve balls at us, we need to revisit many of the steps quite often. But working through all of them in order places us in a position to garner a supernatural benefit.

The Big Book calls it a spiritual awakening. Obviously, every individual arrives at this benefit on different time tables and in various fashions. For some people, the removal of the obsession to drink or use is a spiritual experience of the highest order. For others, it may be a gradual development over time that God is doing for us what we could not do for ourselves. If every alcoholic and drug addict received a biblical burning bush experience, then fire departments all over the world would despise us.

These awakenings all seem to come in a multitude of ways. What is vitally important is they do happen if the person will simply do the steps with a qualified sponsor. In the Big Book, the clearest four words printed that epitomize a trait someone might come into recovery with are CONTEMPT PRIOR TO INVESTIGATION.

The book of Genesis, the Big Book of AA, the Twelve and Twelve, the Serenity Prayer, and the *Twenty-Four Hours a Day Daily Meditations* have now become my new lectionary and sacramentary. This program has finally completely transformed me and I am no longer a renegade priest or a lost sheep. This is totally due to the fact that God helped me to remove my contempt.

*****

"Peggy, Athanasia is called a seraphim angel. You are called a tutorial angel. What's the difference?"

"Dorothy, we are all part of the celestial host emanating from the Creator. But our ministries are divided into twelve disciplines. Each of these disciplines, in some fashion, are responding to creation. Since the human soul is created in the image of the Creator, the soul receives the penultimate attention."

"Peggy, I have noticed that you respond mainly with souls who are haunted by darkness. Was this your choice, or were you told to do this?"

"It was my choice. Free will applies to all creation. Angels, humans, and all natural phenomena are given the freedom to respond and to react. Just as there were angels who chose to defy the Creator and dwell in darkness, humans have the freedom to do the same. Nature itself responds and sometimes reacts to physical conditions in the universe. The Creator allows all natural and supernatural existence the freedom to proliferate."

"Don't you believe that it would have been simpler to just have all creation totally be in union with the Creator? Then disease, war, natural disasters, even evil, would never exist."

"Dorothy, you mean all creation fully residing in the beatific vision?"

"Yes."

"That is the goal, Dorothy, but life is both progressive and transcendent. There is an alpha and an omega. Transformation from the Creator and the journey to return to the Creator is the divine principle that rules all creation. All life has a primordial inkling of the destination, but free will is the challenge offered by the Creator to allow all life the freedom to reciprocate to the gift. The gift is simply to become resplendent, and being resplendent is the beatific vision."

"Peggy, back to my question about you being called to souls dominated by darkness. Why was that your choice because you obviously had so many other choices?"

"My rape and murder were the violent actions perpetrated by a soul immersed in darkness. Athanasia so miraculously lifted my soul into eternal life, and as I said before, my last cognitive emotion was pity for James. Now I have a ministry to whisper to souls who have deeply gone astray."

"But, Peggy, so many of these souls do not hear you at all."

"Dorothy, this is an eternal ministry. To use a phrase that is present in some form or another in all the spiritual books, I am whispering to the lost sheep and the return of that soul brings joyful salutation to the entire celestial court. As I used to tell your son when I was on earth, silly not to."

*****

I have now returned to the book of Genesis for the last time in this manuscript.

> And Joseph said to his brothers, "I am about to die; but God will visit you, and bring you out of this land to the land which he swore to Abraham, to Isaac, and to Jacob." Then Joseph took an oath of the sons of Israel, saying, "God will visit you, and you shall carry up my bones from here." So Joseph died, being a hundred and ten years old; and they embalmed him, and he was put in a coffin in Egypt. (Gen. 50:24–26)

Joseph died. The ages ascribed to persons in Genesis are somewhat a mystery because the writings are centuries before either the Julian or Gregorian calendars. Who the heck knows what constituted a year in that period of time? It could have been seasons or even full moons. Whatever it was really makes no difference because ultimately we all die sometime.

Going through the death of Peggy and all the other people whom I loved taught me lessons in grief that all people have to endure in their lifetime. Working the twelve steps of AA has brought me immense comfort with my own grief because it provides excellent coping skills to deal with life and death issues. If I had to identify one excellent response I had when dealing with another person in the program, it would have to be with Emerson. This was many years ago in treatment when we roomed together. The enormity of his medical condition and the fact that I loved him so deeply produced true empathy on a level I had not felt since being with George and Martha when I was fifteen years old. The difficulty was what, can a person say in response to Emerson's medical condition? By God's grace, I simply said to him, "AIDS today is what leprosy was in the time of Jesus, and we both know how Jesus handled it."

Many years after Emerson died, I found out through a reliable source that the cardinal of New York would privately volunteer at a AIDS clinic on his day off. I have no idea if he did this because of Emerson, but his spiritual stock rose to gargantuan levels in my book.

The self-inflicted use of alcohol and drugs has three destinations: institutionalization, imprisonment, and death. Because there is the possibility for anyone to receive recovery from this disease, then these three destinations are a self-inflected choice. We may not have chosen to have the propensity of having this disease, but we certainly have the option of how we chose to deal with it. It gets down to, do I want to be the problem, or do I want to be a part of the solution? Remaining in the disease for an entire lifetime has the possibility of incurring a tearless funeral.

The best example of this happened to two friends of mine when they were six and seven years old. These brothers were sitting on folding chairs in the parlor of their neighbors house in 1959. The neighbor was named Paddy, and he was laid up in a coffin like Joseph, but not in Egypt. Paddy was in Kansas City. As all of Paddy's drinking

FOUR DECADES IN GENESIS

buddies came through the front door and paid their respect at the casket, one of the men reached out and touched Paddy's cheek. With obvious shock. his hand recoiled and he looked toward Paddy's wife Mary and remarked, "Paddy's still warm." Mary, without missing a beat, responded, "Warm or cold, the son of a bitch is going in the ground tomorrow."

Long-term alcoholics have the propensity to turn relationships into hostage taking. Unfortunately, they tend to do this to the people they have loved the most in their life. When a person has endured living as a hostage for many years, the death of the alcoholic is viewed as a blessing because the deceased is now out of their torment and the survivors are no longer hostages. I am sure this scenario has been played out with married couples for centuries, especially back when divorce was a stigma rather than a lifesaving option.

I believe two of the most powerful words in the treatment of the disease of chemical dependency are *acceptance* and *we*. It is widely believed that acceptance is born by what is called a moment of clarity. The alcoholic views his or her life as utterly out of control and nothing they have tried so far has stopped their downward spiral in life. They desperately need help. This is merely the birth of acceptance, which means it requires a lot more time for it to develop. In my case, compliance was my entry into recovery. Fortunately, I remained sober long enough to reach acceptance. What I have discovered over the last five years is that most people go back out to drinking and using before they reach this stage.

We is critical for long-term sobriety. My sponsor advised me that I had to establish as many relationships as possible with other people in recovery. This meant not only talking to them at AA meetings but also socializing with them outside of meetings. The program says we have to radically change people, places, and things in recovery. My sponsor added we have to also alter our decision-making capability. If a compulsion to use occurs, it is mandatory to have a mental picture of many people in recovery blocking the image of our drug of choice. This can only happen if we have brought new people into our life of sobriety.

Without our drug of choice, which we used as our primary coping mechanism in addiction, normal daily life will undoubtedly throw many curveballs and change ups at us. This is a simple fact of human existence. Coping with these baffling experiences is critical to recovery. If we rely solely on what we have done in the past, then dreadful decisions are bound to occur. We need a filter to bounce off our own thinking with the potential wisdom of another person. That's why sponsorship and fellowship in the program are so vital. They can save us from numerous negative consequences following some very poor decisions.

One of the difficulties of having a sponsor is that you have to listen to their suggestions and recommendations, then you have to follow their advice. Since most alcoholics and addicts have a long track record of doing only what they want to do, it is totally new behavior to actually listen and obey what someone else is asking you to do. As my counselor, Maureen, told me in treatment, I was over-dosing every day on "vitamin I" so responding to anyone else telling me what to do was highly improbable. I was not teachable.

Learning to become teachable was the most arduous task I had to undertake in my five years of recovery. Without a competent sponsor, I truly believe I would not have stood even a remote chance of avoiding a relapse. Since sponsorship is not dealt with directly in the book of Alcoholics Anonymous, it has evolved over the decades. The blueprint that has been somewhat customary over the years for people in early recovery is to (1) contact your sponsor daily, (2) go to ninety AA meetings in ninety days, (3) begin working the twelve steps of AA with your sponsor, (4) refrain from any romantic relationships for the first year of recovery, and (5) start the discipline of spirituality on a daily basis by reading and reflecting on the prayer and medita-tion books that are available in the AA program. Obviously, this is just a blueprint, not a commandment, but it seems to be a suggestion that has provided sustained recovery for hundreds of thousands of alcoholics and addicts. In other words, it has worked.

My sponsor was quick to point out when he gave me this blue-print that I was not allowed to negotiate on any of these suggestions. He told me that if I had cancer, I would definitely undergo chemotherapy and radiation for whatever length of time the oncologist recommended. Or if I was in renal failure, I would submit myself to dialysis until a kidney transplant became available. The medical disease of chemical dependency offered a far less invasive treatment in order to place the disease in remission, so I was commanded not to whine or lament about the blueprint. The line he has used the last five years whenever I object to any of his suggestions is, "The Pharisees are murmuring."

Since some alcoholics and addicts discover in early recovery that they have a tremendous fear of being alone, the temptation to find a sexual partner appears to be an obvious coping measure. After all, when alcohol and drugs are removed from an addict in most cases, what is being removed is the most intimate relationship they have adopted in their life. Feeling totally alone makes complete sense.

The vice of concupiscence, which is best defined as sexual lust, can quickly enter, and the disease of chemical dependency has a definite side effect of removing just about every virtue a person used to have in their life. Vices typically replace virtues, and normally, honesty is the first one to check out. St. Thomas Aquinas wrote prodigiously on virtues and vices, and the best description I ever heard from a professor on concupiscence was "make all major decisions with the organs above your waist." Unfortunately, I violated this advice a couple of times in early recovery. What I learned was what most people in recovery eventually discover—the consequences of this violation are most of the time horrendous.

There is another saying in AA that does demand particular attention. Intimate relationships with others in the program sometimes bear witness to this adage, "The odds are good, but the goods are odd." This does not mean two people can never form a lasting, loving relationship after meeting in AA, but it does convey that it is necessary to be guarded and careful. The suggestion to wait at least a year is both prudent and cautious.

My sponsor has over thirty years in recovery, and it is by God's grace that he has guided me through my first five years. I followed the blueprint in early recovery, and I have continued to work with him with very few instances of "murmurs." Without his help, I sincerely doubt that I would be sober or alive today. He provided me with a micro glimpse of moving from crucifixion to resurrection. Good Friday and Easter Sunday now have a completely different perspective in my spiritual life.

*****

"Peggy, there's hope for Tom."

"Dorothy, the angels have a certain adage about souls, 'We have high hopes but low expectations.' Free will is a gift from the Creator, but it does make all souls a work in progress. The celestial court says the jury is still out."

"I have learned so much from you, Peggy, but it seems to produce so many new questions."

"It did the same for me too."

"Are there more stages to go through?"

"Dorothy, you just finished the first stage. Athanasia called this stage Genesis. Now we will enter the second stage. Athanasia will join us because this stage always requires three angels."

"Why three?"

"Because Creator, Redeemer, and Sanctifier are infused in all our ministry. We embody the entire realm of providence. Besides, stage 2 is supremely difficult. Athanasia referred to it as 'going into the desert.' It is here where we encounter and come to understand the evil one. Angels have free will also, so it is mandatory for us to witness the capricious and savage guile of evil."

"So we go in threes because there is strength in numbers?"

"Very good, Dorothy. That's part of it. The real importance of going in threes is the participation of Athanasia. She will display to you that the evil one has a potent ability to manipulate but the Creators power totally negates that potency."

"Stage 1 is called Genesis. What is stage 2 called?"

"It's called Exodus."

EPILOGUE

To all the souls who died in the four decades: May eternal rest grant on to them O Lord, and let perpetual light shine upon them. May their souls and all the souls of the faithfully departed rest in peace. Amen.

God is mysteriously transcendent, yet reachable through simple prayer.
Evil tempts us through lies masked in particles of truth.
Fictional novels are blends of factual experience and imagination.
Free will gives us the ability to combine them both.
Besides, it's silly not to.

A special thanks to Ned S., who tormented me to finish this novel. May he rest in peace.
A special thanks to Josh P., who inspired me. May he rest in peace.

ABOUT THE AUTHOR

Thomas Matt was ordained a Catholic priest on June 7, 1986, in Omaha, Nebraska. In 2001, he took a self-imposed medical leave of absence in St. Louis, Missouri, and left public ministry as he battled chemical dependency, bipolar disorder, hepatitis C, and a serious diagnosis of cancer. Residing in St. Louis, he was able to receive excellent medical care, and with the Creator's grace, he has fifteen years of sobriety, and all the other medical maladies are currently in remission. He is currently writing his second novel.

CPSIA information can be obtained
at www.ICGtesting.com
Printed in the USA
FSHW021326081119
63801FS